THE PRINCIPLES OF DIVING

MARK TERRELL

The Principles of
DIVING

South Brunswick
New York: A. S. Barnes and Co.

A. S. Barnes and Co., Inc.
Cranbury, New Jersey 08512

6633
Printed in the United States of America

Contents

Illustrations

Preface

This book has been written with both the technically minded and un-technical readers in mind, with the hope that the former may find as precise answers as may be to their questions and the latter may absorb the ideas and atmosphere that diving operations engender. The principles on which these operations are based are, Knowledge and Discipline, from which spring freedom of action. But there is also a less material and more philosophical statement that can be disregarded if the reader chooses. A thorough understanding of Man's relationship with the underwater environment shows both how well adapted he is to his existence in the air on land and how narrowly he has escaped the necessity to diversify into physiologically isolated species to adapt himself to change. His ability to use tools and techniques which can be readily adapted to new environments retains for him the immense benefits and opportunities that stem from being able to survive as a single biological family.

New facts are continuously pouring in and have already seriously delayed publication of this work. They will continue to pour, and nothing can be done to stop them. Therefore only principles have been expressed which may remain intact for a brief period yet.

No branch of knowledge or data has been withheld merely because misuse of it can be dangerous. The writer believes that ignorance is a far greater threat to adventurous and enquiring people than a little knowledge, for knowledge begets responsibility and diving is not an activity that can be enjoyed irresponsibly for long. Thus, for example, while the whole field of diving equipment is examined regenerative equipment is treated as fully as diving with standard apparatus.

Although other countries have pioneered diving as a sport and have enjoyed the great advantages of equable climates and clear, warm water, the author feels that this may have been to their disadvantage as they appear to have neglected their investigations into other forms of breathing apparatus and technique. In Britain we have a body of knowledge on the whole subject that is unrivalled abroad. This happy state of affairs is unlikely to last long now that the prizes to be won by the first to really conquer the shallow seas are becoming obvious. Already America has extended her territory by proclaiming the Shelf Doctrine in 1945, which lays claim to all the sea-bed out to the 100 fathom line round her coasts. We also see ourselves being gradually pushed off fishing grounds in the shallow seas because they are claimed as national territory.

To date much of the scientific research of diving has been done by, and on behalf of, the Royal Navy. This has insured that it has been conducted properly, thoroughly, and safely. As commercial activity increases and the division between military and commercial requirements exists, it is the author's contention that this research should now be continued by civilian concerns as well so that future discoveries can be published and used to everyone's advantage. At present the scanty knowledge, and therefore wild theories, that circulate amongst the public are due to military secrecy and the restrictions imposed on the publication of information which is inherent in any official research. This is not a criticism but an observation of necessary fact which makes it all the more desirable to have a parallel civilian organization which is bound only by the normal conventions of scientific rectitude.

Secrecy in the end stunts and kills the growth it was meant to protect because progress depends upon the effort of many independent but intercommunicating interests. When the intercommunication is cut advance comes to a halt.

To-day we see a vast array of technical skill, authority, and national funds ranged behind satellite programmes and schemes for outer space exploration. These programmes may be necessary from a military point of view but from that of an ordinary citizen the positive benefits that can possibly begin to accrue cannot compare with those that would be felt if we were able to move at will over the sea-bed of the shallow seas around our coast.

Any scheme to explore the possibilities of the continental shelf is not even contemplated although the cost would be small as compared with building and launching one satellite. Such a scheme is unfortunately not yet generally recognized as anything more than the dream of a few scientists supported by the enthusiasm of a larger number of amateur divers. That this is a mistaken view the author hopes to show later, for the sea-bed can, and should, be thoroughly explored now.

The sea offers us a cultivable area which is many times larger than the land on which we depend for so much of our food. In order to draw upon the full resources of the sea we must learn to feed, tend, capture, and selectively breed the individual animals living therein. At the moment our methods of harvesting in the sea have changed little from those used by our forefathers. New methods of husbandry will probably need the assistance of men actually working from the sea-bed.

In this book the author tries to indicate the way in which the problem could be solved by improving the technical resources of the diver.

Besides the food resources which could become available to the population of these overcrowded islands there is another kind of harvest offered by the sea. Many valuable cargoes lie untouched in the depths of the shallow seas. Untouched because the sea is a vast place and to find a wreck whose position is seldom known within a mile or so is, even to-day, a very expensive project. When the ship is found it must then be worked, and again the methods available to the salvage officer are those that have been in use for over fifty years. Both finding and working wrecks when starting from the sea-bed will be an easier, cheaper, and more reliable process than the hazardous operations subject to every whim of wind and wave that are considered economic to-day. It is not only the salvage officer who is harried by the raging of the sea, the wind, and the tide. The civil engineer is more frequently affected as public works are widespread and frequently occurring. Again, even in shallow water, the worker who can operate comparatively unaffected by the wildness of the elements should confer benefits that would ease the engineer's lot, and make the job cheaper.

With the appearance of successful nuclear powered submarines the advent of the submarine freighter, at least for liquid cargoes, may not be far distant. The navigation and control of such traffic would require a more complete organization of the sea lanes, of navigational beacons, and of lifesaving and salvage resources than were ever necessary with surface-borne traffic. To be efficient this will require men to penetrate into the depths as unencumbered by machinery as possible, and again this calls for diving of a type that is only in an embryonic stage.

The author would like to add here that it is largely due to the week-end or amateur diver that the technical advances into this field have been made. As in most fields of endeavour it is often the amateur who is responsible for the initial major discoveries and the original efforts of Commandant Cousteau and his band require no emphasis here.

The sea is an excellent training ground and both in and on it around our coasts it is the greatest fun to explore, offering everything that recreation should provide—effort, thrill, and achievement.

Lastly, in this book anyone who goes underwater will be termed 'a diver'. It may seem odd that attention should be drawn to this but there is in fact a frequent misconception prevalent, as much amongst the professionals as the layman, that a diver is one who wears a round copper helmet and heavy boots, who is connected to the surface by lines, and can communicate through a telephone, while the remainder are 'frogmen' or 'skin-divers'. The correct terminology for anyone who dives is 'a diver'. And a proper diver will use the best equipment for the job, although he may have a preference for one type, as he has for one type of job over another.

Finally, while it is hoped that this book may assist those who dive, and perhaps to encourage those pioneers who foresee the great possibilities in our national waters it may also give the chair-borne diver, the popular writer, and the reporter, some facts around which their imaginations can weave realistically.

I
The Sea as an Environment

At first sight it may seem improbable that man, a land-living, air-breathing animal, should go back into the sea and treat it as an environment in which to live even for short periods. Yet, as history shows, that is what we have been tempted to do from as long ago as we know.

The margins of the sea, where the tide covers and uncovers, have always been fruitful areas for the land scavenger. The beasts living there, visiting or simply escaping from their deeper enemies, themselves fall easy victims to their swifter and more versatile air-breathing adversaries. It then takes only a short time for the scavenger of the sea-shore to put to sea and become the fisherman. This may have happened to man when he was already using instruments so he has developed the instruments rather than adapt his physique, as the whales, seals, and others have had to in order to pursue their quarry further out. The result was that he then found it easier to remain in the air and develop a small piece of mobile land, the boat, to take him out on to the surface of the water. Now, with the compulsion to enter right into this new and hostile environment in his unadapted physical condition, he must again surround himself with a mobile, miniature, envelope of air in which he can survive.

The porpoise or the whale must return to the air to breath and therefore drown like any kitten if they are trapped below. Even the most perfectly adapted animal who lives in an environment to which he is in reality a stranger must carry with him the micro-climate of his proper world. The technical ability that we have to don micro-climates and extended sensory devices at will enables us to adapt ourselves to new surroundings very rapidly indeed. It is with the consideration of the differences between the air and water, that will dictate the design of equipment to enable us to live underwater, that this next chapter is concerned.

Contrary to many people's belief the actual pressure of water to which the body is subjected as the depth is increased, within the limits at present considered, is unimportant provided the few air spaces are maintained at the same pressure as the surrounding, or ambient, pressure. This is because the body is composed of liquids and solids which are virtually incompressible throughout the depths of the shallow seas. Some way below the edge of the continental shelves (600 feet) these conditions perhaps begin to change and it is likely that some effects, solely due to pressure, that attack muscle function will begin to be noticeable there.

The air spaces of the body are those in the chest, the ears, the sinuses, and the gut (see *figure 1*). In the normal healthy person they are inter-connected so that pressure in one, or a general increase in pressure from outside, is quickly transmitted (in the case of the ears and sinuses) through small passages into the main cavities. Lining these small passages and cavities are delicate membranes provided with a means of secreting a cleansing and lubricating fluid (mucus) and of keeping it flowing steadily towards the outside by the waving action of tiny hairs (cilii). Should any

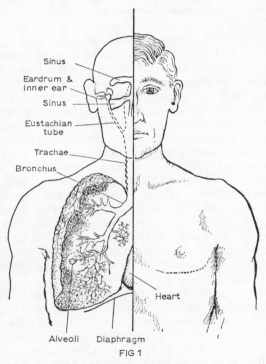

FIG 1

Air spaces of the body

of these small connecting passages to the ears or sinuses become blocked, for example with a cold, an increase in the ambient pressure is not accom-panied by a balancing increase in pressure in the blocked cavity. As the ambient pressure is transmitted directly to the blood the result is a differ-ence of pressure between the air in the blocked cavity and the blood in the capillaries of the lining membrane. If this difference of pressure in-creases the diver will experience considerable pain followed by a haemor-rhage into the affected cavity. In the ears it may also lead to bursting of the ear-drums either inwards, if the eustachian tube was blocked, or outwards if the ears were obstructed from the outside by a plug or tight-fitting cap, although it is more likely that the capillaries lining the passages will burst first and balance the pressure with blood. The eustachian tube is a small passage running from the back of the nose behind the jaw up to behind the ear-drum, and is a relic of the days when our ancestors had gills. This tube can be opened normally to equalize pressures by working the muscles of the throat as happens when swallowing, bending and raising the head, or working the muscles at the back and root of the tongue. This process is usually aided if a small pressure is held in the nose and throat by blowing against a nose clip. If the difference of ambient pressure and internal ear pressure is allowed to build up much increased difficulty may be found in 'clearing the ears' as the tube entrance then tends to remain closed by the difference of pressure.

Any attempt to clear ears or sinuses by forcing them is a dangerous practice and likely to produce more trouble than it cures. If the blockages are moved along by the pressure difference and if any haemorrhage takes place, the chances of spreading the initial infection is increased as well as causing damage to tissue that is delicate. Also it may well be found that if a cavity is forced into equalizing the pressure and the subject goes on submerging he may find it excessively painful to release the pressure again when surfacing if the blockage reasserts itself (as it often does) reinforced by products of haemorrhage.

The lungs comprise the largest air space of the whole body and unlike the others are variable in volume. These changes of volume and the residual volumes that cannot be changed have been given names that will be used throughout this book and will therefore be explained. Only four terms are considered to be necessary in practice and they are: Vital Capacity, Tidal Volume, Residual Volume, and Dead Space. The Vital Capacity is the maximum total volume of the whole lung and breathing tract. Tidal Volume is the volume of air that is inhaled in one breath, Residual Volume is the difference between Vital Capacity and the Maximum Tidal Volume, when a man exhales to a maximum and inhales as much as he possibly can. Dead Space represents the volume of the breathing tract. The air in this space is the first to be drawn into the alveoli and the last to leave, thus oxygen and CO_2 must diffuse rapidly across this volume which forms a barrier and the larger it is the longer the time taken to diffuse across it and the lower the rate of exchange of the two gases.

The effect of blocking the main air passages of the lungs during an ascent, by holding the breath, is a more dangerous practice as it can lead to a rapid death. This will not happen provided the diver is breathing steadily, or is carrying out the proper drill for 'free ascent' as detailed on page 117.

The dangers incurred in this case are those arising from having breathed in gas under a high ambient pressure, when the gas was considerably compressed, and, failing to release it, or trying to prevent its expansion as the diver surfaces and the ambient pressure decreases. If the pressure inside the lungs is built up to 2–3 lb. per square inch above the ambient pressure the lung wall may rupture or gas be forced into surrounding tissues, which is exceedingly serious. This involves the possibility of air bubbles being forced into the circulation or sucked in by the heart through the broken veins surrounding the lungs, and then pumped into the circulatory system where complete airlocks may be set up in vital places like the brain. This may give rise to a number of symptoms, some of them serious. (See TABLE VI.)

Except when diving deep without apparatus (see page 47) these are the sole effects of moderate pressures on the body and, in fact, are never experienced if care is taken to be in good physical condition before diving, and to follow the correct diving drill.

Apart from these more obvious mechanical effects of depth of water there are other more subtle ones which it is necessary for the diver and those connected with diving to know about as they affect the composition of the gas he breathes and provide the principal limitations on his freedom to ascend and descend as he likes.

In order to understand the significance of these effects and the measures taken to overcome or accommodate them it is first of all necessary to describe the normal breathing cycle at the surface in air.

TABLE I

Physical characteristics of the atmosphere at sea level

Gas	Chemical Symbol	Proportion by Volume	Partial Pressure (Atmosphere)
Oxygen	O_2	0·2	0·2
Nitrogen	N_2	0·79	0·79
Carbon Dioxide	CO_2	0·0003	0·0003
Water Vapour	$2H_2O$ (10°C)	0·0038	0·0038
Trace gases		0·0059	0·0059

The pressure at sea level is said to be 1 atmosphere absolute. This pressure is doubled by descending 33 feet into sea water and is stated to be 2 atmospheres absolute. The simplicity of this method of visualizing pressure will be appreciated when it is realized that when the temperature remains the same the volume is reduced as the pressure increases so that one cubic foot of air at the surface, that is at a pressure of 1 atmosphere, is compressed to half a cubic foot at 2 atmospheres, a quarter cubic foot at 4 atmospheres, and so on.

Partial pressure is another term that it is necessary to introduce at this point. It denotes the particular pressure of an individual gas in a mixture such as air. In this mixture at sea level it will be seen that the partial pressure of each of the gases is as shown in columns 3 and 4 of TABLE I. The table shows that what is meant is that if no other gas were present in a given volume except the gas under consideration, say the oxygen, then the pressure exerted by that gas alone is the same as the partial pressure that the gas exerts in the mixture, that is 0·2 of 1 atmosphere absolute.

Henceforth we will always refer to pressures that are expressed in atmospheres as absolute pressures. Thus the pressure at a depth of 33 feet is at 14·7 lb./sq. in. registered pressure on a pressure gauge but is an absolute pressure of 2 atmospheres, 66 feet is 3 atmospheres, and 99 feet is 4 atmospheres.

Oxygen, which is vital to the continuance of the diver's life, cannot be absorbed into his body in sufficient quantity unless its partial pressure is in excess of 0·14 atmospheres. Anything below this and he will begin to lose consciousness and, at about 0·1 atmospheres, will eventually die.

TABLE II

Limiting depths for breathing mixtures and partial pressures at crucial depths, and for the short periods allowed by the limited endurance of modern equipment

Breathed mixture Proportion by volume		1 atmosphere (surface)		2 atmospheres (33 feet)		4 atmospheres (99 feet)		Limiting depths Maximum Minimum	
O_2	N_2	ppO_2	ppN_2					feet	feet
1·0	0·0	1·0	0·0	2·0	0·0	4·0	0·0	33	
0·7	0·3	0·7	0·3	1·4	0·6	2·8	1·2	61·3	Well
0·6	0·4	0·6	0·4	1·2	0·8	2·4	1·6	78	above the
0·5	0·5	0·5	0·5	1·0	1·0	2·0	2·0	99	surface
0·4	0·6	0·4	0·6	0·8	1·2	1·6	2·4	132	
(Air) 0·2	0·8	0·2	0·8	0·4	1·6	0·8	3·2	297	0·0
0·1	0·9*	0·1	0·9	0·2	1·8	0·4	3·6	627	33

* Helium is usually used instead of nitrogen.

Study of the figures given above shows that the capacity of atmospheres with a different proportion of oxygen to support life will vary with the pressure, and it can be seen that the maintenance of the correct oxygen balance is vital to the diver's well-being. There are various methods of ensuring that this occurs. With open-circuit breathing apparatus the only problem is that which arises when the diver goes so deep that he may experience oxygen poisoning from the mixture of gases that he is breathing. For example, air will give rise to an increasing degree of oxygen poisoning as the depth and time increases. The effects of nitrogen narcosis will also be gradually becoming serious.

The problem of mental deterioration down to a depth of 100 feet has not so far been very serious as contemporary equipment imposes a time limit which is too short for the diver to be inconvenienced by the symptoms. However, as later designs of equipment and techniques already proposed will increase the technical ability to remain submerged for long periods the importance of these problems cannot be disregarded and will be briefly discussed when the roles of the remaining gases that are likely to be encountered in atmospheres used by divers are considered.

The major constituent of the air has been seen to be nitrogen and although this is almost a chemically inert gas, from a physiological point of

The Principles of Diving

view it is not unimportant to the diver. Where air or mixtures of air and oxygen are used for the diver's atmosphere nitrogen is the cause of what has been popularly termed 'the rapture of the deep' (*l'ivresse des grandes profondeurs*' from Cousteau) and 'the bends'. The proper names for these very different troubles being nitrogen narcosis and decompression sickness respectively.

Although the actual chemistry of the narcotic effects of the inert gases is not definitely known, and there are many hypotheses, two principal theories hold the field at the moment. The first is derived from the Meyer-Overton Law and may be referred to as the molecular weight theory as distinct from the carbon dioxide narcosis theory explained below. As TABLE III shows, the narcotic effect of each of the gases mentioned appears to be connected both with its relative solubility in oil and its greater molecular weight. This is not entirely consistent but seems to show that there is a relation between these facts that may be significant.

TABLE III

Narcotic effect of various gases

Gas	Molecular Symbol	Molecular Weight	Solubility ratio oil/water (volume). From Kety s.s.	Approximate Iso-Narcotic pressure (Atmospheres)
			Pharm. Rev. 1951	
Argon	A	40	5·3	6·28 } Observed
Nitrogen	N_2	28	5·2	7·9
Helium	H_e	4	1·7	55 } Estimated
Hydrogen	H_2	2	3·1	98

The second, put forward by some American and Continental workers, is that it is the carbon dioxide that is responsible for narcotic effects, although this is brought about by the gas under consideration inhibiting the diffusion of carbon dioxide out of the lungs to a greater or less extent depending upon its molecular weight, thus giving rise to high CO_2 partial pressures in the tissues. This high CO_2 tension is then said to give rise to narcotic symptoms when the blood is adequately saturated with oxygen, whereas when the blood is not so saturated the typical effects of asphyxia are shown, that is, heavy breathing, increased pulse rate, and panic. A very different set of symptoms to narcosis.

The arguments in favour of the molecular weight theory seem to me to be the more significant because it is difficult to demonstrate CO_2 narcosis in divers treated with oxygen and suffering from high tension of CO_2. Also, while it is possible to demonstrate increasing narcotic symptoms appearing when breathing a mixture of oxygen and nitrogen no such effect can be found when breathing oxygen and helium at pressures where the oxygen partial pressure and the total density of the mixture is the same as in the former mixture. It is well known that the CO_2 partial pressure does affect the narcotic symptoms and it is probable that not only is the CO_2

narcotic in the presence of complete oxygen saturation of the blood, but that it shares this narcotic property with the inert gases mentioned. Hydrogen is an exception to the oil/water solubility ratio, and has been found to give satisfactory results in deep dives (Sweden 1944, 492 feet). Helium is used by American and British deep divers (Britain 1956, 600 feet) and so far no narcotic effects have been observed in its use, but while it has the advantages of being non-explosive in the presence of oxygen it is very expensive outside the U.S.A. principally because of the cost of transport and the large amounts used in conventional apparatus.

When breathing air, as distinct from a mixture containing a lighter inert fraction than the nitrogen, there is mental deterioration at shallow depths and this has been inferred to be the effect of the nitrogen and a mild form of narcosis.

The diver is not normally aware of conditions being different until he gets to about 100 feet when a slight deliberation of thought and action becomes apparent. Some of this is also due to the increased density of the breathed gases which require a greater physical effort to breathe and seem to take on a slightly metallic taste. As the depth is increased the effects of narcosis become increasingly more apparent and assume many of the features of normal intoxication. Some people develop an increased sense of deliberate responsibility as they feel their normal senses becoming less accurate, while others give way to a happy irresponsibility that becomes rapidly more dangerous both to themselves and to their companions. The presence of CO_2 lowers the threshold of resistance to narcosis. At 240 feet it is usual to discontinue diving operations using air and instead change over to oxy-helium mixtures. If a subject suffering from nitrogen narcosis is given an oxy-helium mixture to breathe instead he rapidly regains his normal composure besides enjoying the relief that the cooler and less dense atmosphere immediately affords.

One interesting feature of pressure effects which may be inferred to be due to the nitrogen is the effect that it has on the voice and the muscles concerned with noise production. It is a commonly observed fact in de-compression chambers that when a man is subjected to a pressure corresponding to 100 feet in water his voice becomes high-pitched—and the hilarity amongst a group of trainees subjected to this treatment for the first time may be evidence, both of the narcotic effect of the nitrogen in the air and this effect on the voice. It is also impossible to produce a whistle below about 90 feet. Yet all three types of musical instrument, string, wind, and reed, preserve their pitch and tone unaffected under these conditions. The introduction of helium of course changes the voice as it changes the resonant properties of the vocal spaces. The effects of nitrogen under pressure and helium or hydrogen at all times on the voice will become of increasing importance as communication between divers, or the diver and the surface, is carried out by telephone as a matter of course rather than a special operation or an extra facility.

By far the most serious effect of nitrogen is its solubility in the body tissues as the pressure on the body is increased and then, unless the diver scrupulously observes the rules laid down in decompression tables, to come out of solution in the form of bubbles when the pressure is decreased, giving rise to decompression sickness. The other names for this being Bends and Caisson disease. This is such an important factor in diving that the subject will be treated at length in the separate section below where the other major 'carrier' gases, in this respect helium and hydrogen, will be discussed as well.

*   *   *   *   *

It is a common experience that when a bottle of champagne is opened there is at first a 'pop', followed shortly afterwards by an increasing number of small bubbles rising to the surface. If the bottle is shaken, either while the bubbles are rising or even after the liquid has been allowed to become flat, more bubbles will be formed. These bubbles originate in the gas given off during the process of fermentation and, as the pressure in the bottle increases, more of the gas is being forced into solution in the champagne. When the pressure is suddenly dropped, by removing the cork, the amount of gas that can now be held in solution has also decreased, and the excess gas accordingly bubbles out. It is very much the same process that has happened to a diver suffering from decompression sickness. When he was submerged under pressure all the gases he was breathing dissolved into his blood to a greater extent than occurred at the surface. If the pressure is released too suddenly these gases form bubbles in the tissues before the blood stream has time to carry away the excess and get rid of it through the lungs. Fortunately oxygen not only diffuses through the tissues quickly but is constantly consumed by them and as care is taken to keep the partial pressure low because of the danger of poisoning so it seldom constitutes a problem in the decompression sickness from which divers may suffer. However, in deep dives it may convert an incipient 'bend' or 'silent' bubble into an actual one. Several serious physiological results follow from bubbles if they are allowed to form. The milder effects give rise to pains in the joints but those occurring in the more slowly saturated tissue, such as nerve fibres, are far more important as they may cause paralysis. If a large number of bubbles are formed because of a gross neglect of the proper decompression precautions, then blood vessels may become blocked, delicate tissues damaged, and the victim suffer a variety of symptoms of more or less severity. In order to avoid this the diver must ascend slowly. The deeper he went and the longer the time that he spent working down there, so the ascent must be slower and more careful. But a man who has been working hard in cold water is likely to be chilled by the end of his dive so that the long ascent is viewed no longer as a lifesaving necessity but as a calculated torment of cold, boredom, and exhaustion. It is therefore desirable to reduce the time as much as possible and many efforts to find an acceptable theory from which tables for ascent can be constructed have been made with varying success.

In 1908 Haldane first produced a table which required the diver to stop at every 10 feet of the ascent and wait at that depth for a period shown in his table instead of the previous practice of ascending slowly and steadily the whole way. Haldane's theory was based on the assumptions that the tissues to be taken into account had certain rates at which they became saturated and that each tissue could be characterized by a 'half-time' of saturation, while the partial pressure of nitrogen that the tissues could tolerate in solution at any depth without forming bubbles was 1·6 times the ambient pressure at that depth (1·7 for helium). This theory and the tables constructed from it were a vast improvement on the previous information available and enabled divers to work safely over a wide range of times and depths.

However, it was not entirely satisfactory as his investigation had been carried out using fully saturated tissue. But gases dissolving into tissue do not do so in a wholly homogeneous way. The average state of saturation is exactly as stated, but this is an average figure for the whole tissue and expresses the middle value between positions where more gas or less gas is present. But it is at the points where greater concentrations of the inert gas exist that bubbles will form even though the average value is still below the safe maximum concentration.

Thus the simple 1·6:1 ratio has been adjusted by all the navies of the world with the result that while the decompression times involving lower concentrations of nitrogen are shorter, those for the longer and deeper dives are longer. The problems of most rapid methods of decompression from great depths and long periods have still not been solved, although Hannes Keller has made the great advances in this field in the past few years being able to work at 750 feet at the time of writing and having dived to 1,000 feet.

However, it is unlikely that the emphasis will be laid on rapid decompression from great depths in the future but more on completely safe decompression from fully saturated states, while the shallow diving decompression is unlikely to be significantly shortened. The shallow diving decompression tables must also take account of the fact that tissue tolerance to excess N_2 pressure is not a static value but one which varies not only between individuals but also in the individual and will be found to depend upon the condition of every part of the body at the time of the dive. Thus, as we shall see later with other gas poisonings, the effect of carbon dioxide on this threshold is significant.

The physiological difficulties and dangers associated with the diver's ascent from any considerable depth are thus all accentuated by the need to relieve the pressure on him as soon as possible. There is, however, a limit at each depth for the amount of gas that can be dissolved in the body, and when once this limit has been reached the time required for it to diffuse out again when the pressure is relieved will be the same. Thus the time spent under pressure beyond that required to saturate the body is time gained as far as decompression is concerned, as the time spent in decompression will remain the same thereafter. Whether any deterioration takes place due to living in a high pressure atmosphere, analogous to the deterioration experienced by mountaineers living above 20,000 feet, is not known for certain, but probably depends entirely upon the constitution of the type of atmosphere chosen for the depth. As work on the narcotic effect of nitrogen shows, a high partial pressure of this gas present produces a loss of efficiency. This would certainly develop under the postulated conditions but with the use of gases having a smaller, or even negligible, narcotic effect it should be possible to live in a high-pressure environment for protracted periods. The importance of this would then be that the diver could become largely independent of surface aids with their attendant risks and could decompress at leisure under ideal conditions with no urge to hurry the decompression procedure thereby incurring the possibility of a bend.

So far we have dealt only with the problem raised by dissolved nitrogen but because of the narcotic effects that this gas has when breathed under pressure it is often desirable to use either helium or hydrogen in its place. These gases are both relatively inert as far as the body chemistry is concerned and can be breathed safely without similar symptoms at the moderate depths being considered for flexible suit diving to date. However, the rate at which they will diffuse through tissue differs from that of nitrogen. Fortunately these differences are known and the tables for nitrogen can also be used for a similar concentration of helium or hydrogen provided the correcting factors are applied. Both diffuse more quickly but dissolve to a different degree in the tissues so that although the decompression time is shorter than when nitrogen is used for the shorter dives it is longer for the longer dives. A further advantage of these lighter gases is that they give far less resistance to breathing through the tubes and orifices of apparatus than the denser gases, and below 100 feet the increased resistance of the latter is becoming a serious limiting factor to the physical effort the diver can produce.

The last gas to be considered, and the most important, is carbon dioxide (CO_2). This is the result of breathing in oxygen and combining it with food products in the tissues. There it combines releasing energy available for the bodily processes and muscular activity. The CO_2, together with water, are waste products and the former is dissolved in the tissues as carbonic acid. It is eliminated by becoming loosely combined with the haemoglobin of the blood when this is deficient in oxygen, and being transported to the lungs where oxygen displaces it and it is breathed out as CO_2.

It is the CO_2 tension which provides the prime stimulant in the breathing cycle, although a low oxygen concentration and decreased lung volume do have an effect.

If CO_2 is allowed to build up in the breathing apparatus so that the concentration reaches 0·01 atmosphere then the first symptoms of carbon dioxide poisoning will begin to appear. These vary but generally will be found to include an increasing feeling of apprehension, and a desire to breathe more deeply and rapidly. If the concentration continues to rise it will be found that at about 0·056 atmosphere the symptoms will have become far worse and the diver may start to show distress. Breathing becomes very heavy, nausea, headache, and panic may be experienced and, although it is unlikely that any one victim will experience more than one or two of these symptoms, it will be appreciated that the effect of this waste product, if it is allowed to accumulate in even small amounts, can be dramatic. When the partial pressure of the CO_2 in the breathed mixture is the same as that in the alveoli, where it is normally kept within $\pm$ 0·001 of an atmosphere, then in order to diffuse out, the alveolar, and consequently tissue, pressure must rise. This causes real distress and between 0·06 and 0·09 atmosphere of CO_2 the victim will become uncontrollable and will eventually collapse and die. Besides the poisonous quality of the gas itself it also serves to lower the threshold of resistance to all the other poisonings, although it does serve as a warning before the onset of anoxia which can otherwise take the diver unawares and render him unconscious without being able to do anything to prevent it. Otherwise, susceptibility to oxygen poisoning, narcosis, and decompression sickness, is increased.

Breathing resistance is the last of the factors affecting the respiratory cycle that we will consider will be met while treating the sea as an environment.

The method employed by all air-breathing animals of circulating air over the receptive surfaces is some kind of pump system and in vertebrates the rib cage and diaphragm work together as a bellows to suck the lungs open and then allow them to collapse under the influence of the elasticity of the stretched muscles. This involves a flow of air through restricted passages. Frictional resistance to flow is set up and depends upon the density, viscosity, and velocity of the air. This increases with the rate at which the gas is required to flow. Thus the harder you want to work and puff the more resistance your breathing mechanism has to overcome. In addition there is the elastic resistance of the tissues themselves to consider which increases with the depth and rate of breathing.

When air is compressed its density, and therefore it resistance to being breathed, increases so that at a pressure equivalent to 100 feet depth breathing is becoming a conscious act and requires twice the effort of breathing at the surface. In addition to his normal air passages the diver has to force the gases through more pipes, valves, and obstructions to the free flow of the atmosphere in the breathing apparatus. It can be seen that with the increase in resistance as the depth is increased the diver may come to a point when the whole of his effort is being devoted to breathing unless his apparatus is very carefully designed.

Although a man can breathe against 9 inches water gauge pressure ($\frac{3}{8}$ lb. p.s.i.) yet this is very hard and exhausting work and prevents him doing anything else.

Apparatus should be designed so that the unavoidable resistance occurs if possible on the inhaling rather than the exhaling side as the lungs are built to overcome a greater resistance to inhaling than exhaling, and it is therefore less exhausting if the design of the breathing apparatus follows the physical design.

Whenever resistance to breathing occurs it results in a build-up of carbon dioxide in the small passages (alveoli) of the lungs which in turn gives rise to the desire and attempt to breathe more deeply and faster, thus increasing the resistance still more. Although this can become an unstable situation it is seldom allowed to develop as the immediate reaction is to cease some other activity and thus reduce the rate of evolution of carbon dioxide.

The peak inspiratory flow at which a diver may breathe when working hard will lie between 300–600 litres/minute, and at this rate the breathing resistance should not be more than $1-1\frac{1}{2}$ inches water gauge ($\frac{2}{48}-\frac{3}{48}$ p.s.i.) at the maximum designed depth for the apparatus. Anything more than this and he will have to limit his activity in order to get enough to breathe.

The Senses (see *figures 2 (a) (b) (c)*).
The faculties that we are principally concerned with underwater are sight, hearing, touch, speech, orientation, and maintenance of body temperature. The senses of taste and smell are entirely relative to the breathing environment as they are physically enclosed by it and can therefore be ignored here. Each of these faculties will be dealt with in turn although most of them are in some way interconnected.

Sight is dependent upon the presence of light and its accuracy and discrimination are dependent upon the properties of a lens and upon central nervous associations which have to be learnt by every individual.

Light of certain wavelengths will penetrate clear water to a maximum distance of 1,000 feet from the source, but vision is seldom possible in British waters over 50 feet and more usually varies between 6 inches and 10 feet, the principal obstruction to vision being the scattering or random reflection of light from particles in suspension which gives the effect of a dense fog. But the naked eye immersed in water will fail to 'see', that is to discriminate, with any accuracy at all, beyond a few feet in the clearest water, because its construction for use in air prevents it from focussing in water.

The water is so nearly the same density as the cornea (lens of the eye) that the light rays are hardly refracted, or bent, at all and as a result fail to come to a point and focus on the retina as they would on land when passing from the air through the far greater density of the cornea. Thus everyone with unaided eyes will be hopelessly short-sighted underwater (*figure 2 (a)*).

The minimum necessary aid to clear vision is a layer of air maintained in position over each eye and an optically plane water surface normal to the line of vision. This is usually accomplished by means of a visor or mask with one plane transparent surface and an air pocket between it and the eyes. This will not, however, give an undistorted view as the images at the edge of a wide window will be fainter and distorted differently to those seen in the centre which in themselves are distorted by the light passing from water through glass to air. The effect of the central distortion is to

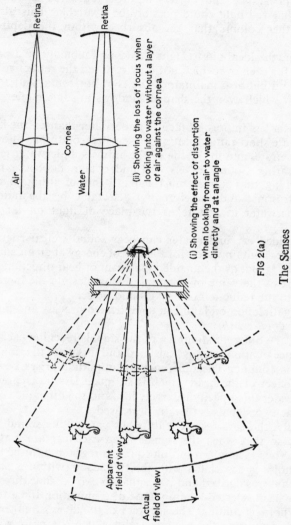

Retina

Air

Cornea

Water

Retina

(ii) Showing the loss of focus when looking into water without a layer of air against the cornea

(i) Showing the effect of distortion when looking from air to water directly and at an angle

Apparent field of view

Actual field of view

FIG 2(a)

The Senses

increase the apparent size of the object by 4/3, or to make it appear ¾ of its real distance away.

Although red light disappears very rapidly yet the eye accommodates for its disappearance and objects may be registered as red far below the depth that red light could possibly be available. This also happens with the other colours that get absorbed within the depth range of divers.

However, the ideal aid to sight would undoubtedly be a properly designed lens for each eye which not only restored the refractive conditions found on land but also maintained the 160° horizontal and 100° vertical field of view which even the shaped windows in some modern visors fail to do.

Vision is a less important faculty underwater than on the land, except as an accurate short-range locating sense when conditions allow sufficient light to penetrate, and in the life of the animals underwater takes second place to hearing. Sound travels well underwater, far better than in air, and everything that moves must make a 'noise' although much of it will be infrasonic and therefore not detectable by the human senses. Sound underwater in fact takes the place of light on land for these animals.

The unaided ear underwater can hear sound well particularly if the aural passages contain water, for the loss of energy at an air surface is very great ($\times$ 10^{-4}), but as the unaided man cannot hear direction underwater a great part of the value of this sense is lost despite the increased sensitivity due to the reduction of background noise.

Hearing direction on land is a complicated process and takes place in three parts (*figure 2 (b)*).

Firstly, the different strengths of the signals reaching each ear, that is the difference of amplitude, is registered and this gives the side from which the noise is coming. The difference of amplitude arises because of the screening effect of the head which is so much less transparent to sound in air. In water this opacity is largely lost and the difference of amplitude between the two signals is thereby decreased.

Secondly, the ears receive a different part of the sound wave at the same time so that when the signals from each ear are matched in the central nervous system a resulting sound is registered in the system. This resulting noise is associated with the frequency (within a narrow band) from which it was derived and is peculiar to two possible directions on the side of the head selected by amplitude discrimination to be the side from which the noise is coming. The accuracy of the diver's frequency discrimination will determine the accuracy with which the noise source can be located, and obviously a loud continuous noise with a wavelength approximately twice the distance between the outside of the ears will be the easiest to find direction from for sources between 45° and 90° to the side. The frequency then being approximately 3 kcs in water, that is 3½ octaves above middle C.

The final pin-pointing of direction is done by a slight movement of the head which will immediately enable the second method of phase discrimination to eliminate the wrong choice. Brief experiments with tone-deaf people indicate that the inability to discriminate frequencies may confine them to discriminating by amplitude alone, which is greatly impaired underwater.

In water the unaided diver is at first able to get an idea of where a noise is originating, and his first guess is the most accurate that he will make,

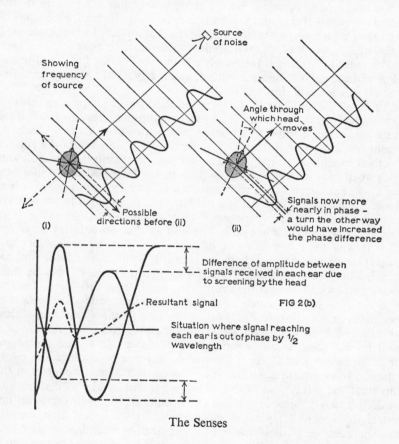

The Senses

because having failed to get an idea of direction by trying the second method, as soon as he turns his head to bring into play the third method of detection as shown above he becomes hopelessly confused. Had the 'resultant noise' in the central nervous system not been linked to a definite frequency band then he would happily point out a direction, although wrong. But, in fact, he merely becomes muddled until the sound may be thought to be coming from anywhere. As soon as the 'directional patterns' related to frequency can be restored so once again his directional faculties are restored. This can be shown by simply extending the ear-base length until it bears the same relation to the unaided length as the speed of sound in water does to that in air. This ratio is 4·8:1. A further improvement is to restore the screening properties of the head by means of insulating material.

Sounds, or vibrations, with a frequency below the audible limit in humans are a source of location and direction-finding that are widely used by fish and enable them to 'hear' the slow wriggling of a worm or the gliding approach of a predator long before he could be seen. Emissions of very high frequencies, up to 200 kcs. (× 10 that audible by man), are used by the whales, porpoises, and dolphins, to detect their prey.

The sense of hearing is intimately associated with the faculty of orientation as the same organs are involved, and the effect of a strange environment on this sense is similar.

Although the majority of divers spend their time only passing through the main body of the sea on their way to the bottom or back to the surface yet the mid-water is important even to such a transitory visitor. When the bottom has disappeared from view or been lost to touch and the surface is not yet in sight the unaided diver has lost practically all the horizons which keep him mentally stable and maintain his physical equilibrium. This may be sufficiently disturbing in even a short time as to provoke him into acting dangerously or feeling ill. The visual and aural horizons have been impaired or lost and nowhere is there a sense of weight as the diver is very nearly neutrally buoyant. The risk of disorientation, that is not knowing which is up or down or sideways, may then become a very real threat. Generally it is possible to see that it is lighter towards the surface; some bubbles, or the inherent 'inertial navigation system', may be sufficiently developed to avoid the symptoms, but if these safeguards are lost the diver may develop acute apprehension, nausea, and dizziness. It is only necessary to restore one horizon to banish the symptoms almost immediately. Even a finger resting on something solid will suffice, or a small bubble seen to be ascending past the face glass. The symptoms appear to be confined to those few people who are psychologically easily disturbed by complete isolation. It is outside the conscious control of the individual and if it is present should be recognized by him so that he does not deliberately subject himself to the conditions that will excite an uncontrollable and possibly dangerous reaction. This disorientation can also have the effect in shallow water of concentrating attention so much on the visual horizon that it becomes all-important, and when the seaweed is being pulled back and forth over its rocky bed by the action of the waves above the impression of a surging sea-bed is created and acute nausea may develop.

The sensation of touch is probably the least affected of all the senses, and, as mentioned above, plays an important part in the diver's powers of orientation. But the sharpness of the faculty is decidedly dulled underwater and it no longer serves as efficiently to keep the diver from harm as it does on land.

Feel is a combination of sensations resulting from different stimuli. First there is the stimulation resulting from pressure (*figure 2 (c)*). The pressure exerted by the reaction of a large object with generous surfaces is felt not only at the area of contact but also throughout a considerable part of the body structure, at joints and by tension on muscles and neighbouring stretches of skin. But it is important to the safety of the body that a small object, such as the point of a pin, should be detected the moment it comes into contact and begins to exert pressure on the skin. This is accomplished in the natural state by the surface of the epidermis having a firm, slightly scaly texture with a certain degree of mechanical rigidity so that the load exerted by the point of the pin is distributed over a larger area of the skin than that covered by the point alone. This ensures that the maximum number of nerve endings affected by pressure are stimulated while those close to the point are more deformed, and therefore stimulated most violently. The proportion of pressure at the locality to the small load transmitted to the supporting structures being a warning of impending

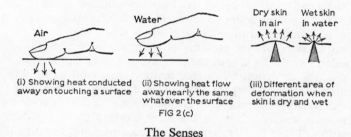

Air

Water

Dry skin in air   Wet skin in water

(i) Showing heat conducted away on touching a surface

(ii) Showing heat flow away nearly the same whatever the surface

(iii) Different area of deformation when skin is dry and wet

FIG 2 (c)

The Senses

sharpness if damage is allowed to occur. This is an essential protective mechanism and enables the limb or part of the body affected to be withdrawn before damage occurs. If the pin should puncture the skin pain is felt because not only the nerve endings, which are discharged by damage, but also others which react to the presence of histamine produced by cell damage which remains in the wound, are stimulated while the fact of the man being psychologically free from stress in his normal environment adds to the general feeling described as pain which serves to engender a more or less violent escape reaction.

If the skin is immersed in water, and in particular salt water, the action of these protective devices is weakened. The skin surface becomes softened by water so that it loses its mechanical rigidity and, if the surface is punctured, the water washes away the offending fluids produced by the damaged cells, while the psychological stress of being immersed in physically strange surroundings dulls the sense of pain considerably. Thus a very weakened sense of danger and escape is engendered and the protective devices of the body impaired. This becomes particularly marked in cold water and is a constant source of annoyance to divers working in such places as wrecks or barnacle-covered structures. But the function of touch is not only to protect the body from immediate harm, it also serves as the instructor for the other senses of location and as our principal informant about texture.

This information is in the main derived from the measurement of heat as a value relative to the body temperature and the rate of change of heat values at the nerve endings. In fact it may all be regarded as a measure of rate of change of heat observed from points at different distances from the stimulation. On land, as air is a poor conductor of heat, the rate at which heat is conducted away from say a finger where it touches an object is dependent upon the heat-conducting properties of the material and the fact that the initial temperature of the finger is different to that of the air or the object. Thus a wooden handle, a poor conductor of heat, feels warmer than a steel bar, a good conductor. Also wherever water is present there will be a localized low temperature area caused by evaporation, and a wet object holds a wealth of meaning for us evoked simply by its temperature qualities.

A further stimulation arises from the smoothness or roughness of an object. This is simply a development of the faculty of rate of change of pressure discrimination spread over a large area.

It will be seen that the presence of water again impairs, if it does not wholly destroy, the faculty of temperature discrimination, while it interferes with the detection of surface texture by reason of its lubricating properties. Water is a comparatively good conductor of heat and when it surrounds objects which have no regulatory mechanism or source of heat of their own, reduces them to the same temperature. Also there is no evaporation. These two facts make it exceedingly difficult to make the fine discrimination of texture that is possible on land by feel alone and there is little to be done to aid the diver in this respect.

It has been mentioned that water is a good conductor of heat and when a man forsakes an environment where he is surrounded by a poor heat conductor for one in which the heat is conducted away easily he must expect to lose his body heat more rapidly. In fact, water conducts heat away × 24·5 more readily than air.

As a result the body cannot keep pace with the heat losses, despite extra clothing. The layer of air which surrounds a swimmer is seldom more than $\frac{1}{4}$–$\frac{3}{8}$ inches thick, whereas on land under better heat-retaining conditions it may be as much as 3 inches. The diver dressed in heavy standard gear is in this respect better off as he enjoys not only the large air space in the helmet but can also ensure that a greater thickness of clothing, and therefore air envelope, surrounds him. It can be seen that the efficiency of heat-insulating materials around a swimmer should be a prime concern if he is to remain immersed for long periods while retaining full control of his senses and remaining efficient.

Water being a dense fluid exerts considerable resistance to movement and this dictates the forms that mobile creatures shall take. Thus, although he has no need to support his own weight, an effort that costs him the expenditure of the greater part of his energy on land, the diver must study the new environment carefully if he is to become mobile in it. Having little weight, and as the speed of any falling is limited by the water resistance, walking as we understand it on land is not possible. Instead the diver must lean forward as though getting down on hands and knees and push with his feet, thus progressing with his face only a couple of feet from the ground. It can be seen that the swimmer, with his smaller cross section, possibilities of better streamlining, and a method of efficient propulsion, will be able to progress more easily, particularly if he is unhindered by long lengths of air and life-lines to the surface.

Propulsion through water without contact with the ground requires, as in air, that a certain weight of water shall be pushed backwards in order to accelerate or propel the body forwards against frictional forces, and the amount that has to be pushed backwards is dependent upon the resistance, or drag, of the body in water. Unlike an aeroplane that is heavier than air the diver does not also have to propel a mass of water downwards to keep himself up. As the diver has an available thrust of 12–18 lb. when using fins it can be seen that this is a small fraction of his strength. It suffices to give him a speed of 4 knots when unencumbered on the surface and an average speed of 1 knot when wearing equipment and submerged.

In conclusion this examination of the physiological factors which will determine how a man can go under the sea, for how long he can remain there, and how deep he can penetrate, shows that unaided his ability to penetrate either deep or for long is very restricted and his powers to do anything when he is submerged are also almost nothing. Perhaps the height of perfection is reached by the pearl divers of the South Seas, or the Japanese pearl fisherwomen.

The aim of the designer of diving apparatus should always be twofold. Firstly, that as every piece of equipment can fail it should only be used where necessary and should be as simple as possible in order to reduce the probability of failure. Secondly, that the essential characteristics of an air environment should be provided. These are (a) that oxygen should be available at the correct partial pressure, (b) that the carbon dioxide concentration shall be kept below 0·01 atmosphere absolute, (c) that the resistance to breathing shall not exceed 2 inches W.G. pressure at any rate of breathing, (d) that the heat losses from the diver shall not exceed those experienced in air, (e) that the senses of sight, hearing, and touch shall be sufficiently augmented to remain efficient in the new environment, and (f) that the diver shall not have to use more energy in propulsion than is absolutely necessary. Finally that as all mechanical equipment will eventually fail at one time or another an independent system of breathing sufficient to get the diver safely back to his base must be included in the apparatus.

Each type of diving apparatus must be designed to operate efficiently in its own field, for no type can be a truly universal outfit. Generally the equipment may be divided into those types which enable a man to be mobile and those which enable him to work for long hours within a small compass, while the design will be concerned also with the depth to which each may be expected to be used.

Shallow diving in which no decompression is required, however long the dive, is between 0 and 40 feet.

Shallow decompression diving lies between 40 and 240 feet, for these are the limits between which decompression first becomes a consideration and the maximum practicable depth to which a mixture containing nitrogen can be safely used. Equipment specially designed for deep diving is necessary from 240 feet downwards as decompression is then an urgent consideration, different inert gases must form the bulk of the breathed atmosphere, and special consideration must be given to the flow of gases through the breathing system and the disposal of CO_2.

To date only equipment suitable for static and mobile diving to 240 feet has been designed; although adaptations have been made to serve for the occasional descents below 300 feet they are not suitable for continuous hard work at those depths.

The greater part of the equipment used by professional divers can be used for shallow decompression diving, and that for recreation can be used for shallow diving as the proportion of diving below 40 feet as compared with that above this depth, is minute.

The reasons for choosing these particular depths as the dividing lines are briefly recapitulated below.

Firstly, as was seen above there is considerable evidence to show that direct ascents from 40 feet can be made even when saturated with the nitrogen concentration of air without running a risk of bends. Thus, as the surface is close and always safely available, and as wave action at 40 feet can still be fierce in heavy weather, diving to this depth is an essentially surface-based operation. The division of work into static and mobile categories is simply a convenience because it is usual to employ different techniques for the different types of work even though very similar equipment may be used.

The depth range 40–200 feet is that wherein an ascent routine is necessary but where air, or a mixture of air and oxygen, can still be used safely provided the descent is not prolonged. It is also the depth where the diver may require to operate from the surface or from the sea-bed. Both these techniques require a very different approach as the former is essentially the end of the shallow-diving range, and the latter is the shallow end of the deep-diving range.

The deep-diving problems have barely been explored as we have not yet learnt how to penetrate with facility to great depths. Usually the expense of such operations is so large, as the surface resources are required to be extensive and the time available in which the weather is suitable is so short, that the prize must be immense. Such prizes are rare, and as salvage is the only commercial activity that can expect large prizes and so gamble large resources this has been the only activity in which deep diving has generally been done commercially. At the present time observation chambers, explosives, and very powerful grabs have superseded even the deep diver. But as explained later on this situation is likely to change quickly in the near future when a new and unrecognizably different deep diver will probably emerge to explore and exploit the shallow seas to the edge of the ocean abysses.

2
Safety and Communications

Safety Regulations.

A great deal has been written and argued over regulations that should govern the conduct of diving operations. Most clubs, and all navies, have books filled with little else. Each time a diving accident occurs there is a tendency to create yet another complex of restrictions to prevent that particular sequence of events recurring.

However, just as no body of law can be framed to cover all the exigencies of life on land so are the operations under the sea too complicated and varied and only the most general principles can be considered to have the force of law, leaving each operation to be planned according to the circumstances as regards the detail.

It was shown in Chapter 1 how the diver is surrounded by a medium essentially inimical to his form of life so that he must always carry with him a small part of his own environment which by its nature will only give him a comparatively short endurance before he must return to a base to replenish supplies and recuperate physically. In addition, as he is dependent upon mechanical apparatus to maintain his essential environment, and as all mechanical contrivances can become defective, so he must be able to retire to a place of safety reasonably easily.

After due consideration I conclude that if every diving operation is planned so that the simple law stated below is observed then no serious accident should occur. Thus:

'No diver shall be allowed beyond the reach of immediate effective assistance.'

The definitions of 'immediate' and 'effective' are of course vital to the meaning of the phrase.

In this context the word 'immediate' would be understood to mean within the time between a man losing control of the maintenance of his artificial environment and his death as the result. This will obviously vary with different types of apparatus and the reasonably foreseeable defects that can occur in it but should not exceed 20 seconds after the loss of any reserves of breathing gas in the apparatus.

Examples of an interpretation of the word 'immediate' are given for guidance below, but, as they are hypothetical, although drawn from actual experience, they cannot be taken as invariable. Each diving operation will have to be interpreted by the person in charge bearing in mind the physical condition and experience of his divers, type and state of the equipment being used, and other circumstances such as wind, sea, water traffic, etc.

(i) When diving without apparatus the swimmer can be brought back to the surface within 30 seconds of diving and forced breathing begun.

(ii) When wearing standard equipment a new air supply can be substituted without moving the diver within 3 minutes of the failure of his air supply. Although it has happened that a connection carrying the air supply and non-return valve on the diver's helmet has broken away, thus rendering him liable to drowning, this is so unlikely to happen if the tending and maintenance are good and a telephone is fitted that it is discounted as a reasonably foreseeable accident beyond providing the telephone and life-line (usually both included in a breast-rope).

(iii) When wearing self-contained apparatus the diver can breathe from the air or a new source of breathing gas within 20 seconds of the total failure of his breathing apparatus.

'Effective' assistance in the strict sense would rule out any possibility of there being an accident, by definition, for the assistance could not have been effective if an accident occurred, and therefore it begs the question. A practical interpretation of the phrase, however, has useful meaning. Examples of what we would consider to be 'effective' assistance are as follows:

(i) One diver down with the surface party and equipment sufficiently strong to haul up the diver and all possible obstructions to the surface within the time defined by 'immediate'. The surface party being in constant communications with the diver.

(ii) Two divers swimming linked together so that they cannot lose contact with each other and each trained, competent, and practised in 'lifesaving' the other. The diving being done in conditions where access to the base or lifesaving the companion is reasonably certain for both divers within the time defined by the word 'immediate'.

(iii) One diver diving amongst obstructions under bad conditions using apparatus with good communications and sufficient reserve and emergency supplies to extend the time defined by the word 'immediate' so that a second diver could render the requisite assistance in the event of any reasonably foreseeable accident.

Where resources of men and materials are limited the question of the minimum number required to form a diving party inevitably arises. Those with small resources vigorously defend the precautions that they are able to take as adequate, while those not so restricted roundly condemn the risk that appears to be taken and which they have no need to incur. A compromise between the two positions is generally feasible although the varied circumstances mentioned before and the individuals concerned will determine whether a risk exists and is justified. For most diving in poor conditions where obstructions exist, there is no visibility, and tidal or weather conditions are severe, one diver down and one attendant or two divers and one attendant are considered to constitute the minimum number provided that all are fully experienced in the physiological disabilities that may be experienced, and have dived as a team frequently before.

A single diver, however competent, can only be effectively assisted if he can be hauled to the surface plus all likely obstructions, and where this cannot be done then the distance away and the time taken for a second diver to arrive and render effective assistance must be taken into account and related to the definition of 'immediate' as applied to the particular apparatus being used and the foreseeable defects that could occur to it.

Thus the interpretation of this law in each operation must be a matter to be decided by the person responsible for the operation and cannot be laid down beforehand, although many valiant attempts to do so have been made before with the result that work has been unnecessarily hampered and other risks engendered. For example it has occurred that a post mortem showed that the victim of an accident had vomited a meal taken shortly before diving. A ban on feeding before diving to ensure that there could be no food in the stomachs of subsequent divers led to an initial stage where there was increased risk of fainting because of the disturbance of a habit and consequent hunger. Later the diminution in work led to resumption of large feeding via the snacks which had to be introduced. Whereas, had the law stated above been observed no accident of that nature could have ended fatally in the first place.

However, certain guiding principles can be formulated but with the proviso that they may not always be relevant to the particular situation.

Whenever diving is taking place there must be one responsible person who at all times during it is able to be in a position to direct the conduct of the operation. Obviously he cannot be the diver in a party with only one diver and where two divers are swimming alone one must be the 'senior' one until such time as he may be the one of the pair requiring assistance. Then his partner must assume responsibility for the rest of the operation. In the event of there being more than one pair of swimmers in the water then the person in charge of the operation should not be amongst the divers but a member of the personnel remaining on the surface. Thus normally whoever is in charge will be on the surface or at the base throughout the operation, and in this position he is best able to co-ordinate the surface resources and facilities both to assist the diver in all his requests as well as being in a position to take the most effective action in the event of an accident.

Although it is not necessary that the person in charge should be a diver himself, this is a most desirable qualification. But it is of far greater importance that he should be someone well informed upon diving matters and with sufficient strength of personality to ensure his orders being carried out promptly under all circumstances. This is of course particularly important in those circumstances where there is no apparent institutional authority to impose disciplined conduct on the party.

Thus in this context signals sent by the diver are requests, not orders, although they are usually treated as orders unless there is good reason not to. For example the diver may request to come up at a time when it might be hazardous for him to do so because of the movement of the diving boat, and in this instance his request would be refused by an order to stay down. Naturally he would be permitted to ascend as soon as possible when it was safe to do so and of course the emergency signal to come up sent from the diver would be treated as an overriding order.

An important factor in the safety of the diver lies in everyone in the diving party, the divers, the attendants, and those handling boats or working with the diving party with cranes or similar operations, being fully informed about the purpose, the plan, and the progress of the work. The diver should always ensure that the surface party are kept informed about his intended movements as he should bear in mind that they will react immediately if there is unexpected action on his part on the assumption that the unexpected is dangerous until proved otherwise. Frequently the diver finds that the circumstances underwater are quite different to what was thought on the surface and that the plan of action must be changed. His correct course is then to signal, communicate by telephone or, if necessary, surface, to explain the situation and remove causes of anxiety or uncertainty from those tending him. The same holds good when two divers are swimming together. Unless each is fully informed of the feelings, reactions, and intentions of the other surprise may lead to disaster.

An illustration of the possible dangers in this situation is given in this instance where two divers were exploring a cave, one of them leading and paying out a guide-line as they went. They were linked with a 'buddy line' and were swimming through clear dark water by torchlight. At the end of the guide-line they stopped and were immediately enveloped in a cloud of fine silt that completely removed the visibility. The second diver dropped his spare guide-line by mistake and after threshing round and searching still could not find it. The first, not realizing what had happened and unable to feel the second diver on the buddy line with one hand as he had come very close but was invisible, though audible, thought that his partner was lost and in trouble. For a few seconds there was considerable risk of dangerous confusion before they both started back to the base. Thus an initial lack of foresight on the part of both divers followed by the lack of communication between them might have led to a disastrous situation.

Generally, when a diver is swimming he should never dive alone unless he is wearing a life-line to the surface where it is constantly tended by an attendant, or has some other means of maintaining constant direct contact with other divers on the surface or at the base. When he is wearing boots and walking there is of course no other method of ensuring the diver's safety than by means of a life-line.

In order to economize in manpower it is sometimes necessary from a military point of view to equip divers with self-contained apparatus and walking on the bottom with life-lines secured to small floats or blobs, sufficiently buoyant to bear the weight of the diver. The attendant, person in charge, and stand-by diver then cruise about in a boat in the vicinity of as many as four divers and may communicate with them in a number of different ways. The diving law advocated here cannot be observed under these circumstances, and this form of attending is strongly condemned for use in any but extraordinary circumstances even if lifebelts are being worn. Should any drastic defect occur to the equipment, or if the diver himself suffers any sudden physiological disturbance, he cannot signal properly and it is impossible for him to be sure of hauling himself up the blob-line, hanging on the to blob, and enabling himself to breathe fresh air. Even under the best conditions of weather he should be equipped with an easily inflated lifejacket which will support his head well clear of the water and will lift him from the bottom. This necessitates a relief valve being fitted to the lifejacket to release the expanding gas near the surface. When life-lines are being worn by divers there are certain rules that should always be observed. Firstly, the lines must be strong enough to take the greatest weight that they may be called upon to carry. In the case of a standard diver with a flooded suit this means that the greatest load will be the weight of the diver, his equipment, and the amount of water that can get into the suit, an approximate total load of 550 lb. The line should also be thick enough for the attendants to be able to get a sufficient grip to haul that load comfortably.

The life-line must be properly secured round the diver. In most standard diving outfits the breast-rope is the life-line and is secured in a special way to the helmet, but with other types of equipment it is necessary to make the securing to the diver. Frequently when the diving is taking place in shallow water and no telephone is being used the air pipe will be used as the life-line. When this happens the greatest care must be paid to the safe condition of the pipe-line and the circumstances in which diving is allowed to continue. The life-line may best be secured by a bowline round the diver's waist made sufficiently tight so that he cannot slip out of it if he turns upside down. The life-line must always be kept in hand by an attendant and when the diver is entering or leaving the water he should be alert for signals or unusual movements. It is essential that the life-line is never abandoned for a moment or made fast round a rail or stanchion. If an accident happens it may happen at just the moment the life-line is unattended and when the attendant returns it will already be too late. Considerable assistance can be given the diver as he enters or leaves the water by intelligent use of the life-line. It can be used to steady the diver, prevent him sinking too far on first jumping in, help him to the shot-rope or the ladder, or assist him against the tide.

The attendant should always keep his imagination alert as though he were doing the dive, thinking what each movement of the line means and how it is translated into action at the diver's end. By doing this the diver's progress can be intelligently followed, many of his signals anticipated or amplified in meaning, and the course of the operation made smoother. The unintelligent or inattentive attendant is a danger, nuisance, and a load on everyone's mind. The end of the life-line should be secured to the diving boat or platform so that it cannot be lost over the side and the attendant should adopt a position so that he is unlikely to overbalance or otherwise lose contact with the diver for even a few moments. It is essential to the success of this type of diving that both diver and attendant are fully conversant with the same code of signals, and a suggested code is contained at the end of this chapter which is sufficiently flexible to pass any kind of operating instruction.

While the attendant is tending the diver the life-line must be held lightly but firmly so that although it is tight enough to feel the diver moving yet it is neither hampering his movements nor unduly affecting his trim, or weight in the water. To tend properly takes considerable practice and the best results are undoubtedly obtained if each diver and attendant work as a pair for a long time so that they learn each other's individual habits which will give them so much additional information, particularly about how the diver is feeling, whether he is cold, angry, absorbed, pleased, or fed-up. Good tending becomes more difficult the longer and thicker the life-line and the deeper the dive, together with strength of tide, wind, and sea. When conditions become sufficiently bad to make signalling with a life-line difficult, even when in telephone communication, consideration should be given to abandoning that method of diving and substituting another.

The life-line may very well be the diver's only indication of direction when the water is black and the attendant can be of considerable assistance to the diver by taking the line away in a definite (and previously agreed) direction from the shot-line until the diver is on the bottom. He then knows by the direction the line is taking which is forward or aft of the diving boat if one is being used. This practice also prevents the diver turning round the shot-rope with the lay of the rope on descending or ascending as he is otherwise likely to do thereby twisting up his life-line and the shot-line.

Similar attending rules should be observed by swimmers operating together and linked by a light line. The length of this line must be determined according to the circumstances, but when it is not being used as a snag-line for searching but only for connecting the two divers then the best length is between 6 and 10 feet. The end should be made fast to the swimmers' opposite wrists so that they cannot slip off. A bowline or timber hitch will ensure that the line remains easily accessible and safely secured. Some practice is needed for swimmers to operate satisfactorily using a 'buddy line', as the Americans call it, as without a little disciplined swimming the line becomes tangled up with obstructions on the bottom, with the breathing apparatus, or with the swimmer's fins. When once they have acquired the knack of using it, however, they are then able to operate much more efficiently as a two-man team than as two single swimmers even in black water, quite apart from the safety that is ensured.

So that the diving law can be observed by two swimmers operating together it is necessary that they should each be trained and practised in lifesaving each other. Also they must realize that each is personally responsible for the safety of the other and that this is his prime duty. In training and practising lifesaving the same equipment should be worn as will be used when diving. After deciding the actual routine that is to be followed in the lifesaving drill this should be thoroughly rehearsed on land, then tried in very shallow water where both divers are well within their depths, and finally in deeper waters.

Despite attention to detailed planning and discipline on the part of all concerned it is inevitable that the occasional fatal accident will occur. Other accidents will also be experienced from time to time through error of judgment, failure of equipment, and a combination of similar unfortunate circumstances, and these facts must be accepted while every effort should be made to reduce the number of such incidents and to do this the most necessary information required is the cause of failure, and this cannot be ascertained until the equipment and the body are recovered. Thus, it is not only the normal humane considerations that should inspire the search for and recovery of the victim of any accident, it is also the protection of other divers through improved knowledge that should drive the searchers on until all hope of finding the victim has disappeared.

Communications.
The essence of good safety arrangements is good communication. If the diver cannot signal that all is not well then nothing will be done to assist him, while even worse may occur through the chaos engendered by hastily invented signals that are unknown to all those taking part in the operation. The meanings of signals should be as instinctively understood as words of command.

There are many different diving codes evolved throughout the world to suit different circumstances, but the one advocated here has been adapted from the single life-line code established by the Royal Navy. This code has been more widely and thoroughly tested than any other under all conditions of diving, and has given most satisfactory service. In addition, as a large proportion of the professional divers from the United Kingdom learnt their diving in the Royal Navy, so they are most likely to find this code most suitable for their work, while the amateur divers have here a code that will amply fulfil their possible needs.

In the signal code set out below there are two principal types of signal, one is a 'pull' which is relatively long and firm, and the second 'bells', which are short sharp pulls grouped in pairs and given as though striking a ship's bell. The two types of signal are incorporated to give variation to meanings but pulls never follow bells in case a pull should get confused with the odd bell of a group. As single pulls and bells are indistinguishable at the end of any length of life-line in a tideway, or other than perfect conditions, no distinction is made, and in fact the single pull (or bell) is referred to as a 'tug' in the code. The procedure for sending the signals is as follows:

Whichever party is initiating a signal first gives a tug to attract attention. The recipient answers the tug with a tug. If the intention was merely to ask, 'Are you all right?', then of course the answering tug will be understood as 'Yes', because no further exchange follows. However, if the tug was the prelude to the signal, when an answering tug is received then the signal is sent, care being taken to be sure that under the prevailing conditions of tide, weather, amount of line out, and the circumstances of the dive, that the signal will be received clearly. The recipient will answer the signal when understood, by repeating the signal. If this repetition is not received then after a short pause the signal will be sent again until it is understood and acknowledged. If a signal is repeated back which does not correspond to the signal sent then the signal 'Stop', or 'Attention', that is, one tug, is given and answered and the original signal sent again until it is correctly repeated.

In the case of the emergency signal this procedure is not observed. As it is always the diver who will send it, he is hauled up as fast as possible immediately it is received without reference to any other authority. In the case of swimmers the lifesaving drill is immediately put into operation.

There is always considerable discussion about the shape that the emergency signal should take. The ideal signal must satisfy three requirements, which are:

(i) It must be completely distinct from all other signals so that it cannot be confused with any other.

(ii) It must not form part of any working signal.

(iii) It must not be so long or complicated that the diver is unlikely to be able to send it when possibly only half-conscious and panicking.

The emergency signal given here forms part of the ascent series of signals which bring the immediate phase of the operation to a close anyway, and are always closely attended to. Secondly, 'four-and-four' is easily remembered. For example, it was used and remembered so effectively by one diver during the second dive of his life when his equipment completely and suddenly failed that he was hauled through a distance of 40 feet in a few seconds by his equally novice comrades, and suffered no ill-effects, whereas he could have been burnt badly and drowned had they delayed.

When using the working signals the procedure for drawing attention is not used after the first time as it would waste time, be impracticable, and is anyway unnecessary, as the working instructions are being awaited.

The code is flexible and can be adapted for many different situations. For example, operations involving towed divers may require increase and decrease speed signals, hoist and lower, and go right or left. This would then require that the two signals for 'Come in to your shot', and 'Go out' (2 bells and 5 bells respectively), should be adapted to speed signals meaning faster and slower.

Whenever adaptations are made, the nearest possible meaning that is already established and most easily associated should be carefully selected, and the possibility of unforeseen events should be borne in mind so that the adaptations do not in any way mask a signal that has a special meaning that could be vital to the safety of the diver or the efficiency of the operation. Thus as a general rule the only signals that should be used for adaptations are the working signals, leaving the personal signals or those to do with the welfare of the diver strictly for that purpose. Whatever code or adaptations of a code have been decided they must be thoroughly understood and practised by both diver and attendant, or by both swimmers, and anyone else connected with the diver's safety or work.

PERSONAL SIGNALS:

Signal		Attendant to Diver, or Senior Swimmer to Swimmer	Diver to Attendant, or Swimmer to Senior Swimmer
—	1 Tug	Attention—are you all right?	Attention—stop—am attending.
− − −	3 Pulls	Descend until stopped.	I want to descend.
− − − −	4 Pulls	Ascend until stopped.	I want to ascend.
− − − − · ·	4 Pulls and 2 Bells	Ascend quickly, or hurry up.	Help me to ascend.
− − − − · · · ·	4 Pulls and 4 Bells		Emergency—pull me up immediately.
· · · · · · · ·	2 Bells repeated		Am fouled and need assistance.
· · · · · · · · ·	3 Bells repeated		Am fouled but can clear myself.

Swimmers only:		
− −	2 Tugs	Take over senior swimmer.

WORKING SIGNALS:

Signal		Attendant to Diver, or Senior Swimmer to Swimmer	Diver to Attendant, or Swimmer to Senior Swimmer
—	1 Tug	Attention—stop.	Attention—stop.
− −	2 Pulls	(Not swimmers). Numeral signal. Begins and ends all signals that are to be used as numerals. These should always be sent as bells and never as pulls, e.g.: − − Am about to send a numeral signal. · · · · · · · · · Gap for repeat reply, then · · · · · Gap for repeat reply, then − − Number 95 ended by numeral signal. Used also as a spare signal.	Numeral signal.
· ·	2 Bells	Go to the end of your distance-line.	Hoist.
· · ·	3 Bells	Go right facing the shot.	Lower.
· · · ·	4 Bells	Go left facing the shot.	You are holding my life-line too tight/slack (it is obvious which).
· · · · ·	5 Bells	Come in to your shot.	Have found the object of the search, or, have done the job.

This code can be used either in conjunction with a line, sound, gestures, or tugging on equipment.

Sound carries well underwater, and despite the loss in transmission to the ear-drum, can be heard well enough for a hammer, or heavy spanner, banged against a steel ladder, pipe, ship's side, or other metallic sounding board, to be used to control divers over a radius of several hundred yards from the diving boat or base.

When the visibility is good so that the divers can gesture to each other this code will give more complete and certain information than hand signals which can mean different things in different organizations. When the visibility is bad, buddy lines should be in use, but as part of the other swimmer's dress may be nearest to hand then the pulls and bells can be transmitted direct by pulling or tapping out the signal.

When using a telephone which only allows one-way speech at a time it is necessary to follow a strict procedure so that signals are not interrupted and succeeded by chaos.

All conversations should begin with the caller stating whom he is calling and then who he is, thus, 'Diver 1—Surface.' The attendant then waits for the reply which will mean that the diver is listening, thus, 'Surface —Diver 1.' The message is then sent and when finished is concluded by the word 'over'. This means that the message is finished but that the communication system is still being used. The word 'out' will seldom be relevant in diving operations except when there are long periods of silence punctuated by occasional messages. The word 'out' should then be used to indicate that that group of messages is ended. Otherwise it would only be used, if at all, when the diver had surfaced and was opened up to the air by having his front glass removed or his face-mask off.

Obviously when there is only one diver and a surface attendant the procedure can be considerably shortened, and in fact, provided some warning call is sent to indicate that the caller requires attention, then the messages will be transmitted efficiently. One of the principal reasons for insisting on a certain minimum of procedure even when only one diver and attendant are concerned is to ensure that the equipment is working satisfactorily.

When simultaneous three-way telephones are used it is more important that the divers and attendants should indicate who they are, and whom they are addressing, whereas this is unnecessary when only a diver and attendant, or two swimmers, are communicating.

Polite expressions are not only unnecessary but may crowd out other information, and, if the reception is not exceedingly good, may even cause confusion. The acoustic properties and transmission characteristics of divers' telephone gear is seldom first-class either in volume or clarity, and as this is often further impaired by high background noise and changing resonant frequencies so the importance of keeping the messages short, simple, and clearly spoken, becomes obvious.

When helium or other gases are being breathed which differ from air in density the diver's voice will change drastically so that he becomes

difficult and often impossible to understand over a telephone, particularly
as no one has yet spent a sufficient time in such atmospheres to become
accustomed to the change in speech.

Through-the-water communication systems call for a high standard of
communication discipline. Thus, all calls should start with the attention
signal, and the caller stating whom he is calling followed by who he is.
For example, 'Hello Diver One—this is Diver Two'. This call will be
repeated until the recipient gets the message or is able to reply, when he
should do so in the form, 'Hello, Diver Two—this is Diver One'. If only
two divers, or only one diver and the attendant, are communicating by
this method, then the calling procedure can be shortened as before. The
sending of the message and the indication that the message is complete
is, however, more important so that the proper uses of 'over' and 'out'
must be more carefully adhered to. 'Over' being used to mean that that
particular transmission is complete, and 'out' to indicate that the group
of messages is complete and no further communication will be expected
until another initiating call is made.

In certain kinds of diving activity, particularly those in which Sub-
Aqua Clubs and swimmers are involved, there will be a number of occasions when the divers are on the surface and communication with the
attendant is necessary. The occasions for this type of communication
should be avoided where possible as it is extremely difficult to ensure that
in poor conditions such as a choppy sea, bright sun on the sea, and a
distant diver up-sun from the attendant, the signals will either be seen
or understood. However, such a code should exist although only to convey
the most basic information, and accordingly the British Sub-Aqua Club's
recommendations are accepted and two surface signals are mentioned.

Any arms being waved mean that the diver is in trouble and requires
IMMEDIATE ASSISTANCE. A single arm raised and kept raised until
answered by the attendant means that the diver is all right. The diver must
not dive or continue with any other activity until this signal is answered
by the attendant also raising his arm and keeping it raised for a short
period.

It is obvious that where groups of divers are swimming this is an unsatisfactory procedure as there is no telling which of several pairs of divers
the attendant may be answering if they happen to surface at the same time
but spread out unless the attendant always points to the diver with whom
he is communicating.

Signals between swimmers underwater should always be according to
the signal code as there is no room for doubt with it, and it can be transmitted by line, sound, gesture, or tugs on equipment.

Another method of signalling to divers underwater over a greater
distance than blows with a hammer will carry is sometimes used but is
not recommended. This employs a detonator on the end of a short length
of safety fuse and is always used as a surfacing signal. It is, however, almost
impossible to observe the rule of immediate effective assistance if this
system of signalling is necessary unless a number of pairs of swimmers

are being used at widely separated positions. In this event it would certainly be safer to provide more safety boats to attend adjacent pairs, or even a through-the-water electronic acoustic system.

The single life-line code was originally derived from the Standard Diver's double line code, where both the air-line and the breast-rope were used for sending signals. Generally speaking the signals sent on the air-line concerned the air supply, while those on the breast-rope were working signals.

A code often used is given below:

DOUBLE LINE SIGNALS:

Generally only used when shallow diving using Surface Air Supply—0 to 50 ft.

Breast-rope	Diver to Attendant	Attendant to Diver
1 Pull	I am all right.	Are you all right?
2 Pulls	Send me a slate.	Am sending a slate/wire as previously arranged.
3 Pulls	Send me a rope.	You have come up too far, go down slowly till we stop you.
4 Pulls	I am coming up.	Come up.
4 Pulls and 2 Bells	I want to come up, pull up.	Come up, hurry up.
1 Bell	Hold on.	
2 Bells	Pull up.	
3 Bells	Lower.	
4 Bells	You are holding my line too tightly.	
5 Bells	Have found/started/completed work.	

Air-line	Diver to Attendant	Attendant to Diver
1 Pull	Less air (ease pump).	Search (or remain) where you are.
2 Pulls	More air—(faster on pump).	Go to the end of your distance line.
3 Pulls	Take up slack pipe and breast-rope.	Go to the right.
4 Pulls	Emergency, pull up.	Go to the left.
5 Pulls		Come in to your shot rope.

However, with the increasing use of light-weight surface supplied demand apparatus, where the air supply line is also the life-line, this code will be of less use than the single line code mentioned before, and it is given here merely as a matter of interest.

Whenever diving operations are taking place and water-borne traffic is a possibility, the proper flag signals should be shown by the diving boat

by day, and the requisite lights by night, as laid down in the International
Code of Signals (*figure 3*).

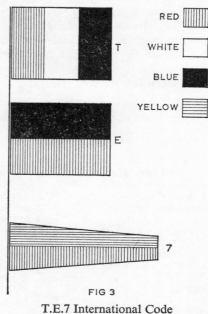

FIG 3

T.E.7 International Code

*   *   *   *   *

This concludes the chapter on general safety and communications.
Essentially safety depends upon good communication coupled with
efficient action as mentioned before and repeated.

3

Diving Without Apparatus

So much is heard of diving with the aid of breathing apparatus that it is not generally realized that a considerable range of activities are open to those equipped with no more apparatus than a pair of fins, a mask, and a snorkel tube. A practised swimmer can then descend to a hundred feet and carry out a dive lasting one and a half minutes even though he could only hold his breath for 30 seconds if he stayed on or near the surface. However, this form of sporting diving requires a far higher standard of physical fitness than diving with breathing apparatus, and those who intend to indulge in it should have a thorough medical examination of ears, nose, throat and sinuses, as well as the whole respiratory and cardiac system. The examination should include an analysis of lung volumes as the ratio of lung capacity to residual volume determines the maximum depth to which the individual can go without crushing the chest or running the risk of haemorrhage in the lungs. (See APPENDIX 2.)

The majority of people are just buoyant in sea water by a matter of 2–3 pounds. Approximately one in twenty are negatively buoyant, which means that if they relax but hold a medium breath in salt water they will sink from the surface. At a depth of approximately 12 feet from the surface nearly everyone will sink, having taken a full breath of air at the surface, due to the pressure of the water on the chest wall and diaphragm compressing the air within to $\frac{11}{15}$ of its initial volume.

As the swimmer sinks so the air in the lungs is being compressed and the smaller air volume is being accommodated without any pressure gradient being allowed to build up by the slow collapse of the chest wall and lift of the diaphragm. There comes a point when the air has been compressed to a small volume and the chest wall cannot collapse any further. This will occur when the ratio of

$$\frac{\text{Total lung capacity}}{\text{Residual volume}} = \text{The absolute pressure in atmospheres at the depth.}$$

For example, if the maximum lung capacity of an individual is 6·0 litres, and his residual volume is 1·5 litres, then the maximum depth to which he can go on one full breath taken at the surface is:

$$\frac{6\cdot0}{1\cdot5} = 4 \text{ atmospheres} = 99 \text{ feet}$$

The result of greatly exceeding this limit would be fatal as it would cause haemorrhage into the lungs and heart failure.

There are three factors making people breathe which, taken separately, are:

(a) A build-up of alveolar CO_2 tension to 0·07 atmospheres.

(b) A drop in alveolar O_2 tension to 0·08 atmospheres.

(c) A decrease of lung volume close to its residual volume.

Each factor is variable in different individuals and each is varied if either of the other two occur with it. For example, it has been found that if the alveolar oxygen tension drops to 0·066 atmospheres, at the same time as the alveolar CO_2 tension rises to 0·066 atmospheres, then the individual will not be able to hold his breath beyond this breaking point any longer and will be forced to breathe.

It has been found after experiment that a dive from the surface to 90 feet is accompanied by an interesting economy of the breathing gases which allows the diver to remain submerged for one and a half minutes, whereas had he stayed on the surface he would have been restricted to only 30 seconds.

As the diver descends the gases in the lungs are compressed and the partial pressures increase. The production of CO_2 is at the same rate as it would be for the same muscular exertion on the surface. But there is a certain capacity to store CO_2 in the tissues. During the descent the O_2 partial pressure is steadily increasing, and at a depth of 100 feet can still be as high as 0·337 atmospheres, assuming a rate of descent of 1 foot per second. The ascent must be made fairly rapidly after one and a half minutes as the CO_2 tension will have risen to nearly 0·079 atmospheres, and as the lung volume is small there is a strong inducement to breathe. As the ascent continues the lung volume increases again and the partial pressure of the CO_2 drops. As the CO_2 'reservoir' is comparatively large this takes an appreciable time to diffuse out. The nitrogen will, however, comprise a greater proportion of the gas in the lungs due to the oxygen being used up. This proportion has been found to rise from 0·79 of the inspired gas to 0·89 of the exhaled gas. When near the surface the drop in alveolar O_2 tension will become important as it will be in the region of only 0·0658 atmospheres.

Although no measurements are available concerning the use of a face-mask as a reservoir of gas at the expense of the ratio lung capacity/residual volume, yet there is no doubt that in practice the proper use of this space is important and helpful.

During the descent the volume of the mask is kept constant by blowing out through the nose and during the ascent the expanding gas is breathed back into the lungs through the nose, thus providing a small volume of gas with a higher O_2 partial pressure and lower CO_2 partial pressure at the time when this aid is most required, in the last 15 feet of the ascent.

The swimmer who intends practising free diving of this type must become practised in keeping his ears 'cleared'. In other words he must be able to open the Eustachian tube so that the rapidly increasing pressure as he descends will be equalized on both sides of the ear-drum. Also the passages to his sinuses must be free, for having no large reserve of gas or time he cannot linger during a dive, particularly on the way up, if he is in pain through a blocked sinus.

Many people find that a nose clip is always necessary for them to be able to equalize the pressure on their ear-drums, in which case they should make certain that the clip is not so tight that they cannot blow past it and so keep the pressure in the mask equalized. If this is not done there is considerable strain on the eyes for they are the softest tissue in the face and tend to get sucked into the mask by the difference between the low pressure (surface value) in the air of the mask and the higher pressure of the water acting on the blood at the depth. This may give rise to bloodshot and uncomfortable eyes for some days after the dive. Whenever possible the nose clip should be dispensed with and the nose either blocked off slightly by pressing the lower rim of the mask against it with the thumb and forefinger, or by holding the whole mask on to the face and blowing into it. Furthermore, a nose clip has the disadvantage of preventing the air breathed into the mask to equalize the pressure from being reinhaled on the ascent, thus losing a considerable proportion of the available respiratory resources.

The knack of opening the Eustachian tube is not easy for everyone and may require practice. The aim is to work the muscles of the jaw and top of the neck as well as distending the entry to the tube. This is best done by holding a small pressure in the nose and mouth by blocking both off and blowing gently and swallowing. This should be accompanied by a clicking, and a change in pitch of noises, in both ears. If there is a slight blockage in one ear or the tube is slow in opening there may be a series of smaller clicks, or snaps, before the tube is properly open. A cold, or other infection of the mouth or nasal passages, may well result in an accumulation of catarrh carrying infectious material, and the result of attempts to dive or clear the ears under these circumstances may be that this matter is carried into the narrow passages of the sinuses or ears and lodged there to create further centres of infection, quite apart from the probable effect of creating an immediate mechanical block to the system. If the dive is continued and the pressure increased so that the blood pressure in the affected part results in a haemorrhage then the blockage may be reinforced and as some leakage into the space past it may have taken place, pain will be felt as the pressure is reduced during the ascent.

Ear plugs should never be used where there is any possibility of going underwater. The effect of wearing them is to drive them into the outer ear and burst the ear-drum from within, or fill the ear with blood from the delicate capillaries lining the system. If the swimmer's ears must be protected from the water he should wear a hood with a good neck seal and plenty of space for air so that it can be compressed easily and the pressure balanced between inside and outside the hood. Ear-cups which form a water-tight seal around each ear can be worn for the limited depths likely to be reached by the swimmer, but care should be taken to be sure that they are very flexible, have ample volume to accommodate the required decrease in gas volume inside, and will not resist deformation to the full extent as pressure from outside is applied.

In order to make the maximum use of the available oxygen in the lungs and to keep the production of CO_2 low it is important to keep warm and to move as gently and efficiently as possible.

Warmth can best be secured by putting on extra clothing. Even a sweater and closely fitting trousers make an appreciable difference both to the time the swimmer can remain in the water, and the length of time that he can hold his breath. It has been found that if the water temperature is less than 85°F. the average male will lose more heat into the water than he can replace, and will eventually get cold. On the other hand some courageous American experiments have shown that a fit man can stand immersion in water at 42°F. for 50 minutes without harm beyond considerable pain on cooling down and warming up.

Therefore, while for practical purposes it can be assumed that the water is always cold enough to justify protective clothing, the decision whether or not to wear it and what type will depend upon the water temperature, the time the swimmer expects to stay in, and his financial resources.

Undoubtedly the most efficient insulating dress is a suit that keeps the body dry and allows space for a layer of CO_2 retaining clothing to be worn. As air conducts heat away very much more slowly than most other practicable fluids (see TABLE V) it is the principal constituent to be incorporated in any insulating layer apart from foam material which uses CO_2 as the insulating gas. Less heat is conducted away by the air if the size of convection currents can be reduced. Thus a closely woven material of fibres composed of air cells is the best fabric for the purpose discovered so far. The smaller the bodies of air that are trapped in the fabric the less heat will be conducted away by convection currents because the dimensions of each body prevent large differences of temperature or differences of gas velocity from building up. The disadvantage of such a fabric is that it wets easily and the water then becomes the insulating medium. A substance which overcomes this defect for only a slight loss in insulating efficiency is foamed neoprene in which the CO_2 filled closed cells are impermeable to water. This elastic material has been found very suitable both for underclothing below 'dry' suits, and as a 'wet' suit in its own right. In this application water is not excluded from penetrating to the body, but as the suit is a very neat fit all round there is no great mass of water into which heat can be lost rapidly while all round the insulating layer of CO_2 is preventing the loss of body heat. This type of suit has been used with success in low temperatures and even a poorly fitting suit will allow a swimmer to operate in water of 42°F. for twenty minutes without great discomfort. Being windproof they also keep the wearer warm when emerging from the water. The success of such suits depends upon a close fit and adequate thickness combined with suppleness of material. The problem of the mobility of the air in a suit worn over woollen clothing does not arise with foam material as the gas is locked up in the small cells and cannot migrate from one end of the suit to the other when diving and surfacing. Close fit and flexibility are necessary to avoid pumping warm water out and sucking cold water in, like a cooling water system, when bending the body or limbs.

The thickness of material in general use at present does not exceed $\frac{1}{4}$ inch and any increase has been found to restrict the diver's movements considerably. It is therefore a consideration whether movement or warmth is the most important factor for any particular operation. Under a dry suit a single $\frac{1}{4}$ inch foam suit is suitable for temperatures down to 45°F. and depths to 30 feet. For dives in colder water and greater depths the question of clothing will be taken up again later.

Clothing that merely serves to retain a comparatively static layer of water round the body is of limited use because the heat conductivity of the water is so high that the body cannot replace the loss without cooling itself, although it is more effective than the naked skin.

Different physiques do display different heat-loss characteristics and there is no doubt that the man with a thick layer of subcutaneous fat is better insulated than the man without such protection. But to make use of this advantage the body must be trained to be accustomed to cold. In effect, this means that the heat-regulating reactions of the circulatory system in the skin are exercised and come into operation the moment the environment becomes cold without the delay that occurs in the unpractised body.

Improving the heat-insulating layer around the body by means of an air envelope involves increasing the buoyancy of the swimmer, who in order to dive must counteract this effect by adding weight. This should be done by wearing a belt carrying lead (as the densest practicable material) in the form of separate blocks secured to it, or weights in pockets, and must be easily released in an emergency while remaining tightly secured round the waist normally. Wearing the belt round the waist is both convenient and correct from the point of view of the normal position of the

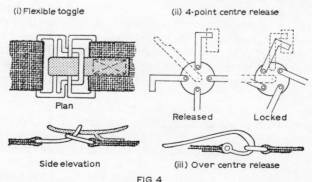

(i) Flexible toggle   (ii) 4-point centre release

Plan

Released   Locked

Side elevation   (iii) Over centre release

FIG 4

Quick Releases

diver's centres of gravity and buoyancy, which are both in approximately the same position, although of course variable within limits, depending upon posture.

The amount of weight required to counteract the increased positive buoyancy will depend upon the swimmer's natural buoyancy and upon the amount of clothing he has on and therefore the amount of air trapped around him. The additional weight required will be approximately 14 lb. for every $\frac{1}{8}$ inch thickness of suit, not taking into account the actual weight of the clothing required to achieve this thickness.

There are numbers of different types of release mechanism, but whatever type is used must be simple, impossible to clog with sand or clay, and easily operated by hands that are clumsy with fright and cold. Examples of quick releases in general use are shown above (see *figure 4*).

At the beginning of the chapter it was stated that the only equipment really required to 'dive without apparatus' was a mask, pair of fins, and snorkel tube, while considerable space has been given to consideration of suits. Although the suit is not absolutely necessary for short swims it is eminently desirable in British waters at all seasons for the average person who wants to dive for periods up to half an hour, and some protection is vital for everyone who wishes to remain in for longer. Properly protected, a swimmer can remain as comfortable in British waters in winter as he will be in the Mediterranean in summer with only a small loss of the freedom of movement which nakedness bestows.

Having considered the vital principle of warmth we will examine the principles upon which the essential equipment should be judged and used.

Firstly, the mask. Without a flat transparent shield of some sort, retaining air in front of the eyes, the diver will be grossly short-sighted underwater. Because of the diver's binocular vision this barely affects his ability to judge distance and he will find that although an object can only be seen as an exceedingly blurred mass yet it can be grasped with accuracy. The short-sightedness arises because the refractive indices of water and the cornea of the eye are very similar so that light entering the eye through water is hardly bent at all as it would be in air, and as a consequence cannot be brought to a focus on the retina however much the cornea is squeezed into a 'sharper' or more nearly spherical shape (see *figure 2(a)*).

The most practicable way to achieve clear vision underwater is to wear a mask, constructed of rubber or other elastic material, which has a window of perspex or shatter-proof glass fixed into the front. The soft material forms a seal round the forehead, temples, cheeks, and either under the chin or the nose.

The masks that seal under the nose are usually considered to be the safest for swimmers to use as the mouth is then left clear for breathing from a snorkel tube. Otherwise, with the full face-mask, the swimmer's breathing and vision are dependent upon the water-tight integrity of the mask, while additional mechanisms in the form of valves are required in order to prevent water entering the mask through the breathing tubes. Furthermore, as the valves are made to work by gravity and buoyancy so, when the diver

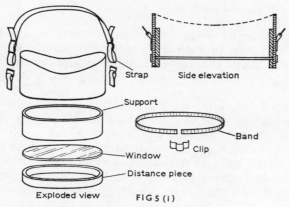

Strap

Side elevation

Support

Band

Window

Clip

Distance piece

Exploded view   FIG 5 (i)

Construction of simple face mask

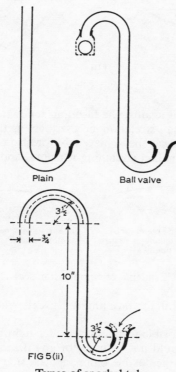

Plain   Ball valve

$3\frac{1}{2}''$

$\frac{3}{4}''$

10"

$3\frac{1}{2}''$

FIG 5 (ii)

Types of snorkel tube

turns upside down and his head is necessarily underwater, the valves open and the mask floods up.

Some masks are so designed that the nose can be gripped between the thumb and forefinger in order to clear the ears, thereby eliminating the requirement for a nose clip. However, the penalty for this facility is slightly more restricted vision than is available through the wide-vision curved windows.

Methods of sealing the mask on the face are generally restricted to making the edge of the mask very thin and pliable while being shaped to a general face formula. Inevitably there are a few individuals who do not fit the formula sufficiently accurately to achieve a water-tight seal and their only course is either to make their own mask up, as in the *figure 5 (i)*, or to get a mask which employs a method that seals by compression rather than tension. Such is the water seal (see *figure 6*) in which a flexible tube

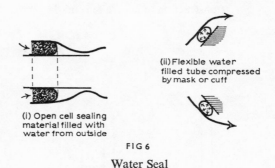

(i) Open cell sealing material filled with water from outside

(ii) Flexible water filled tube compressed by mask or cuff

FIG 6

Water Seal

full of water is pressed against the face and tends to fill up any concave irregularities rather than stretching across them as the usual tension seal does. A similar result can be achieved by pressing any elastic material against the face rather than stretching it round, and *figure 7* shows how

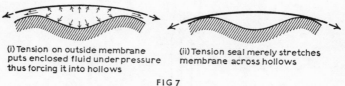

(i) Tension on outside membrane puts enclosed fluid under pressure thus forcing it into hollows

(ii) Tension seal merely stretches membrane across hollows

FIG 7

Principle of compression seal

this has been done both for face and wrist seals where concavities cause the most trouble.

Sometimes it is possible to purchase water-tight goggles with separate eye glasses. These should not be used for any descent underwater unless they are fitted with large flexible bulbs on each side so that the air inside can be compressed as the pressure increases, without putting any strain on the eyes. Otherwise the eyes will become bloodshot and damage from haemorrhage may result. An additional disadvantage is that unless the plane of each glass is parallel two visual images will be seen which destroys visual judgment of distance as well as straining the eyes.

The test for fitting a mask is to push it gently against the face without breathing. If it holds for a few moments by reason of the small difference of pressure created between inside and out then the mask is probably suitable for that face. If it cannot be made to cling without a strong pressure first, then after some time in the water it will probably become acutely uncomfortable at the points it bears hardest.

If the swimmer requires to wear spectacles underwater these can be secured to the front glass of the mask by suction pads so that they are always in the right position when the mask is put on. Those masks with compression seals will frequently allow spectacles with thin flat ear supports to be worn without letting water in.

The snorkel tube is best kept as simple as possible. Usually it is constructed of some light-weight metal alloy or of plastic, has one 180° bend in it with a mouthpiece on the short end, and may carry some simple ball valve (see *figure 5 (ii)*). Although this apparatus has the merit of cheapness and general availability it is not the most efficient.

As usual when designing even simple apparatus, a compromise between conflicting requirements must be made. In this case it is between making the bore of the tube large enough to reduce the resistance to breathing at high flow rates and reducing the volume of the tube to restrict the dead air space. The length cannot be less than a total of about $16\frac{1}{2}$ inches so the compromise is in diameter. Thus, while a tube of $\frac{1}{2}$ inch diameter will add approximately one extra breath per minute to the total in order to ventilate this dead space, that of $\frac{3}{4}$ inch will incur only an extra half breath. The difference that this amount of dead space makes to breath holding time is to reduce it by approximately five seconds, while the difference in tube diameter only makes a difference of about a second. The difference in resistance due to the increased diameter as compared with the smaller tube will be to reduce the pressure or suction from a maximum resistance of 6 inches W.G. to 4 inches W.G. The diameter of a tube to require only 1 inch W.G. of pressure difference would be 1·8 inches. This is obviously impracticable and anyway the dead space is becoming so large that it would be necessary for the breathing circuit to be arranged to be one way only, the exhaust being through a valve straight into the water at the surface.

Most designs of mouthpiece allow the air through a slot 1 inch across and $\frac{3}{8}$ inch width, which is not only a smaller cross-sectional area than the tube but, because of its shape, a more restrictive one to high gas flows. In order to allow the mouth to be opened wide while retaining a water-tight seal with the lips the mouthpiece must be elastic and the flanges on the lip seal and tooth studs much larger than is normally fitted.

A valve on the top of the snorkel tube is not only unnecessary but may serve as an additional restriction to flow, and therefore an additional factor detracting from the swimmer's efficiency and increasing the rate at which he will become exhausted, for any increase in breathing resistance tires the swimmer without his being as conscious of the drain on his resources as he would of other muscular effort. On the other hand, a straight and naked tube 12 inches long is not sufficient as it collects spray and allows the water from waves washing over the swimmer's head to drain into the tube. A second 180° curve, while adding very slightly to the resistance of the tube, will act as an efficient air-lock, as soon as the swimmer has learnt the knack, and prevents the entry of all water when on the surface. When once the swimmer dives the tube will fill with water anyway, unless a valve is fitted that depends neither on buoyancy nor gravity for operation. All the valves in general use operate upon one of these two principles.

The design of swim fins has been exhaustively examined during the past two decades and the most practicable for general swimming have been found to be those that are made from a mixture of hard and soft rubber, are easily removed from the feet, have a very low aspect ratio, and are angled downwards.

The most efficient fins are those that have the blade set at an angle to the foot because the line of the sole of the foot of the average person is at about 30° to the axis of the body and while a blade set at this angle will deliver a reasonable thrust on one stroke it will subtract from that thrust on return. A slightly flexible blade set in the line of the body will, however, generate an even train of waves behind the swimmer, and will avoid cavitation. Depending upon the effort the swimmer is prepared to put into the stroke so the fin should be more or less flexible for maximum efficiency. An illustration from nature shows this fact. The fast, open water, or pelagic, fish and swimming mammals have hard, high aspect ratio tails (the main swimming organ), while the slow bottom feeders, or rock dwellers, have low aspect ratio flexible tails. Man in the water can only be considered a slow creature and will have use only for the low aspect ratio 'tail'. However, as there are various ranges of speed even in the slow category so these considerations will determine the required stiffness of his fins. The best type of fin for all swimmers is one long in the blade and angled, while those who may wish to swim long distances or fast should choose the stiffest available; those who merely wish to swim slowly within a small radius will be best equipped with soft fins. Care should be taken to ensure that the width of the foot entry is sufficient because, as the feet grow tired or cold, a restrictive foot entry can give rise to cramp and other discomforts. Further attention should be paid to the arch of the flipper that will rest on the upper part of the foot. This part takes considerable pressure in swimming and unless it is soft and well rounded will quickly chafe the naked skin. To avoid it socks or shoes are sometimes worn, but unless they are part of a suit they will incur more drag in the water and thus necessitate more effort.

Enough has now been said as an introduction to the equipment, and we will now proceed to the methods of diving.

When going out for the first time it is as well to conduct all the experiments in clear, calm, shallow water. Inevitably the first few attempts will lead to a tube full of water, the inability to breathe, and possibly difficulty in managing to swim with the flippers. To have all this happen in deep water can be alarming and genuinely dangerous. Having chosen a spot that is well within the swimmer's depth, has clear water, and is not isolated from sympathetic and attentive help, the equipment should be donned. Enter the water with care as it is very easy to fall or slip when encumbered with flippers and restricted vision. The flippers offer least resistance to walking in water if the wearer walks backwards.

Having reached a depth about waist deep the swimmer should then lie quietly and gently on his front to get used to the idea of breathing through his mouth with his face underwater, and able to watch the scenery below. Once he feels happy in this state he should then roll gently from one side to the other and then move his head up and down to establish the limits of movement before the top of the snorkel tube dips into the water. At first the movement will probably be misjudged and the first indication is a surprising breath of water instead of air, causing the experimentalist to try to leap to his feet. As this is difficult to do in a hurry with fins on, a wild splashing will ensue followed by coughing and spluttering as the incident passes. Eventually the slight increase in resistance as water laps up to the tube entry, coupled with the development of a surprising ability to sort out the water from the air, will warn the swimmer to take action in time. This will consist of a swift blowing out to clear the tube, and alteration in its position so that it is clear of the water for the next breath. It will be found easiest to accomplish this drill if the breath is sucked in from the tube into the mouth under the tongue. If any water does come in the tongue quickly blocks the tube like a valve flap and the small amount of water can be swallowed. Eventually he will be able to breathe without noticeable effort even in a choppy sea.

The next act will be to attempt to propel himself by means of the flippers. The legs should be kept straight and the toes pointed even when wearing angled fins. The legs are then moved as when walking, but quite slowly. There will be a tendency to roll, which can be corrected by the hands which otherwise should lie flat along the sides of the body, and the knees will tend to flex. Flexing of the knees is inevitable to some extent but should be resisted. Thereafter it is only practice that can improve the swimmer's ability with flippers, but provided he pays attention to keeping the legs straight, the toes pointed, and the whole action from breaking the surface, there should be no difficulty. In fact the swimmer may eventually get so practised that without fins he is practically helpless in the water.

The most important things to remember when diving without apparatus are that in order to get the next breath the swimmer must return to the surface, which requires time, that the snorkel tube will be full of water and must be cleared by a powerful blow, and that the more effort that is made the more rapidly is CO_2 evolved in the tissues and oxygen absorbed, so the more quickly the breathing impulse will become irresistible.

There is a temptation for people who are about to hold their breath for a considerable time to breathe deeply a number of times before doing so. This is called hyperventilation and has the effect of eliminating a certain proportion of the CO_2 from the body and thus lowering the CO_2 tension in the body. It does not increase the amount of oxygen in the body as no significant oxygen store exists, and under normal conditions the haemoglobin is already 97 per cent saturated with oxygen after passing through the lungs.

The effect of 'washing out' this CO_2 from the body can be exceedingly dangerous and has led to accidents that the swimmer himself is powerless to avert. The nervous mechanism responsible for initiating the breathing rhythm is primarily dependent upon the stimulus provided by a rising CO_2 tension in the blood. If this tension is artificially lowered well below the normal there will be insufficient stimulus to breathe from the lowered oxygen tension and the swimmer loses consciousness suddenly through lack of oxygen in the blood supplied to his brain, in other words, through anoxia. Although there is generally warning of anoxic conditions available to the diver, other stimuli may be so powerful as to swamp detection of them. Also the indications are that this warning is in some way related to the presence of CO_2 in the tissues and because this state of anoxia has arisen through lack of CO_2 to stimulate breathing the warning may be even less apparent than is the case under other conditions.

Anoxia may be recognized in the few seconds available before unconsciousness supervenes by a feeling of anxiety and greying of vision. As the vision greys and gets darker so it may also become 'tubular', that is as though the world were being regarded through a tube with dark walls and the tube getting longer and longer. A feeling of unreality and distance will also be apparent as the senses of feeling and hearing are overtaken.

The danger of anoxia to the swimmer during a dive is that even if he does feel the symptoms approaching and takes immediate action, the mere effect of surfacing drops the partial pressure of oxygen in the blood and ensures that he will be unconscious when he reaches the surface. As the circulation rate also drops after an initial slight increase at the onset of the anoxia symptoms, the CO_2 tension may not increase sufficiently to restart the breathing rhythm, and the victim will eventually die of anoxia. Even if he recovers from it there is every chance of permanent damage to nervous and brain tissue after a severe anoxic experience.

Therefore while a few deep breaths are helpful and not dangerous the technique for holding the breath a long time should emphasize the importance of rest and relaxation before each dive so that both breathing and pulse rates are normal, the conservation of warmth, and the avoidance of all movement that is not absolutely essential.

It is said that some professional divers exhale before plunging into the depths. If this is so then they are sacrificing the advantage of carrying an oxygen store and a larger space for the CO_2 to diffuse into, so that the breathing impulse will occur sooner than if they had inhaled. Furthermore, the depth they can go to will be more limited as the ratio of the volume of air in the lungs to the residual volume is decreased. It is only the aquatic mammals who have become adapted to tolerate high CO_2 tension, store oxygen in their muscles, and reduce their pulse rate on diving, who can and do exhale on submerging. These adaptations enable them to descend to great depths and for long periods compared to Man.

In order to submerge, the swimmer takes a deep breath, put his head and shoulders underwater, bends at the hips and then raises his legs and flippers in the air. This can be done slowly and with little effort but results in the body being driven underwater by the weight of the legs and the momentum gained can be maintained by one sweep backwards with the hands and arms, like a penguin or cormorant. Once the chest is at a depth of about 12 feet the downward movement will continue as the naked body is now negatively buoyant. Throughout the operation the diver should pay constant attention to clearing his ears, for if it is done repeatedly the opening of the Eustachian tube is unlikely to become shut off like a flap valve by the pressure difference between the inner ear and the nasal passages. Thus the descent is made vertically downwards in order to save effort and conserve the respiratory economy.

Besides clearing the ears during the descent it will also be necessary to blow gently into the mask to relieve the sucking feeling against the eyes.

When the diver feels it necessary to ascend this should again be accomplished with as little effort as possible being expended. If the bottom is close enough to push off from it should be used, otherwise slow but powerful strokes swimming with the fins will quickly send the diver up. As he ascends so the air in the mask will expand and should be breathed in before it can escape. This will relieve the urge to breathe by working the diaphragm and throat muscles (thus half satisfying the urge to execute the breathing behaviour pattern) and providing a little more volume of gas in which to dilute CO_2 as well as a small supply of air relatively rich in oxygen. This may seem only a marginal device for aiding the diver's breathing economy but it does make a great difference in practice and increases the time that a swimmer can remain submerged.

On breaking surface the first action is to exhale forcefully, expelling the water from the snorkel tube, and then inhale deeply while lying still or only swimming gently on the water.

If a suit of any kind is going to be worn it is as well for the swimmer to become practised with the mask, breathing tube, and fins, in a swimming bath, unencumbered by the protective clothing. This clothing raises problems of its own and these additional considerations will interfere with the swimmer acquiring confidence and competence in manœuvring himself accurately under strange conditions.

As mentioned above, a considerable volume of air will be trapped by clothing worn under a dry suit as this is the object of the practice. If this layer of air amounts to as much as $\frac{1}{8}$ inch thick, it will require a counteracting weight of approximately 14 lb. of lead in order to restore the swimmer to his naked buoyancy state. In fact this will not be achieved with normal clothing as a considerable proportion of the trapped air is mobile and will concentrate itself in the shallowest part of the suit (or highest when on the surface) instead of remaining evenly distributed as it would with a closed-cell foam suit. Thus more than a certain amount of clothing will lead to the swimmer becoming unbalanced and finding it very difficult to submerge as his feet fill with air like balloons and tend to keep him on the surface. Once submerged and wearing clothing with a $\frac{1}{8}$ inch layer of air he will then become less and less buoyant until at 33 feet he will be at least 14 lb. negatively buoyant and may require all the power he can develop with his fins to leave the bottom at all. In fact, he may easily find himself forced to jettison the weight belt in order to surface. A practised swimmer with a good pair of fins can develop up to 18 lb. thrust and to retain some margin of safety should ensure that he leaves the surface against slightly more than his natural buoyancy when wearing clothing.

When finding the weight required to be worn with a suit and clothing it is as well to enter shallow water for the experiment so that the embarrassing effects of misjudgment may be avoided and the swimmer can sink to the bottom without harm. All the easily mobile air should be vented from the suit either through the valve at the back of the hood, the neck seal, or by holding a cuff open with the finger of the opposite hand and keeping both hands above the head as the rest of the body is submerged. When the trim is right the swimmer should just float in an upright position with his mouth level with the water. In this condition he will be neutrally buoyant when submerged at a depth of approximately 9 feet.

Having achieved a certain mastery of the equipment the swimmer is now able to continue gathering his own experience without instruction. However, it may be as well to make a brief mention of the types of conditions he is likely to meet with that might present a problem at first as well as mentioning the activities open to him.

The places around any sea coast that are most likely to attract the swimmer equipped to dive are almost invariably rocky and are probably subject to breaking seas. This is no obstacle provided the swimmer does the right things. When entering the water obviously he does so in a comparatively sheltered spot which is also deep. He should not let the water swirl him around willy nilly, but hold on to rocky points and crannies, only letting it take him in the direction he wishes to go. Swimming against a sea rushing amongst the rocks is on the whole a waste of effort and useless, and progress should be confined to holding on and waiting for the right current before letting go and travelling to the next hold fast. The aim should be to get out beyond the breaking seas and white water as quickly as possible, otherwise the attention is fully occupied avoiding obstacles or hanging on. A breaking sea can be dived through in the normal way and the additional thrust available from the flippers will be found to be an immense advantage.

When returning from the sea to land the breaking sea should always be studied for a while from seaward and beyond the line where it is breaking. The line of approach should be selected that leads through the least broken water into a quieter inlet, if such is available, or to a slope where the water washes smoothly up and then pours away. If the landing place is a beach then the line of approach should avoid the places where waves are curling right over and collapsing with a flurry of foam almost on the beach, and should rather be selected to lead where there is a gentler break or terraced effect. Having selected the line of approach the swimmer should advance slowly and carefully. There is no need to keep a watch backwards as the increasingly sharp crests of the waves will tell him how close he is to the breaking line, while he will hear an unusually large break behind him and can submerge to dodge it if necessary. When the landing place is close and the wash of the sea almost taking the swimmer up to it he should stop and await until he feels a big sea starting to run under him, then, swimming forward to the slope, he should let the sea carry him up it while he assists by swimming, and running over the rock lightly with his hands. As soon as the wash begins to slacken he should hang on tightly, let the sea drain away, and as soon as it is clear clamber up a few more feet before taking his flippers off. All the time the aim must be to get the sea to do the work and devote all the effort into guiding and directing its effect upon the body. Treated this way, and never fought against, the sea can be used and will hold no fear for the swimmer, but if attempts are made to fight against it it will nearly always win, both because the power of moving water is far greater than a man's strength, and because the fear of losing the fight for life engenders panic that is almost impossible to subdue when once it has gained control.

If the swimmer finds himself in a tideway that is swifter than he had thought likely before beginning the trip, and which has started to run, perhaps after he has been in the water for some time, and has been so absorbed that he has rather lost track of his position, the same rule of not fighting the sea holds good, it will lead to exhaustion and panic that can only have dangerous effects.

Most tides run parallel to the coast and when sweeping round a headland into a bay will decrease in speed on passing the headland. Steady swimming with flippers will give an average speed of 1 knot or more which can be kept up for some hours, and if the swimmer heads directly in for the coast and keeps swimming doggedly he will succeed in making a landfall even though the average tide speed around the British Isles is 2 knots, rising to 3 knots or more in a few places. When faced with a long swim in flippers it is best to remove the mask and snorkel and roll over on the back. This is more comfortable for long periods and easier to maintain a set course. Do not abandon the mask and snorkel as they may well become useful if any sea or wind gets up, or on landing. On this sort of occasion the swimmer dressed in a suit has no worries as he is protected from the only really exhausting and demoralizing effect that the sea can exert, namely the cold. Weights should not be abandoned, provided the swimmer has no difficulty in keeping afloat. There will be none if he is properly trimmed, and the weights will assist the swimming action by keeping the flippers properly submerged while their lack of streamline, or drag effect, will not be appreciable at the low speeds the swimmer can achieve.

After a long swim and frequent diving in cold water it is likely that the swimmer's skin temperature will have been lowered considerably, so much so that all he can do is shake uncontrollably, looking blue, and feeling impatient. Even when clothed in warm, dry clothes again this shivering may continue for some time up to an hour later, and if he has been very cold he may even experience a shiver throughout the rest of the day. This is because while the air is a good insulator of heat it also gives up what little heat it has slowly. Water not only has a high latent heat (i.e. has a large heat storage), but gives it up comparatively readily (i.e. conducts heat well compared with air). Thus a hot bath will restore the heat lost by the body more rapidly and more completely, and diminish the continued feeling of cold throughout the rest of the day.

Diving without breathing apparatus can be carried on in all climates and seas but is obviously most suited to those areas with clear water and depths under 60 feet. Within these limits the swimmer can take photographs, catch fish, and carry out simple searches for lost objects. Small jobs can be carried out and many a yacht has had a fouled propeller, choked inlet, or entangled anchor, cleared by a swimmer.

4

Diving Using Surface Air Supply

The time-honoured methods of diving which were first developed for commercial purposes some eighty years ago are still widely employed to-day and it has not been until recently that there have been any significant improvements to change the technique beyond substituting an engine-driven compressor for the man-powered one. While these improvements have appeared and the old style Standard Diver will be gradually supplanted by the more lightly equipped and efficient modern diver as the older men retire from active work, yet this heavy equipment is still in use and demands examination.

The principle of the Standard Diving Equipment is that of the diving bell. The diver's head and shoulders are encased in an open-bottomed bucket. This bucket, or helmet (see *figure 8*), is supplied with air at a slightly higher pressure than the water at the level of the bottom edge, and in sufficient quantity to keep the partial pressure of the CO_2 produced by the diver when working, below 0·03 of 1 atmosphere by diffusion and exhaust. A suit is secured to the lower edge of the corselet into which the diver fits with as much clothing as he likes to wear, and the only part of his body exposed to the water may be the hands. In cold water diving gloves are fitted to the suit so that the diver is totally enclosed in a thick envelope of air maintained around his body by the resilience of woollens to crushing under a head of water pressure of 12 to 60 inches depending upon his stance, and round his head and chest by the level of the air under higher pressure than the water level at the bottom of the corselet.

British Standard Diving Equipment has been evolved primarily for naval use and has then been used commercially by divers whose training has been largely drawn from the Navy. Thus the design of the equipment has followed the tradition that the officer in charge on the surface, being responsible for the diver's welfare, is also responsible for the amount of air that he gets. As a result, in the British equipment the diver can only control the escape of gas from the suit. In Continental and American designs he can also control his own air supply.

Because of the large volume of air carried in the suit and helmet it is necessary for the diver to be heavily weighted in order to counteract this buoyancy so that the weight in air of standard diver's equipment will be of the order of 187 lb., while, even with this weight, he may be buoyant in water and cannot have negative buoyancy of more than about 30 lb. without the addition of weights not normally supplied for the equipment.

Air is usually supplied to the diver nowadays from a low pressure air cylinder having a capacity of at least 10 cubic feet at a pressure of 100 lb./sq. in., and itself supplied with air from a low pressure compressor. Hand pumps are still in operation in a few places, but they are only suitable for shallow diving to depths less than 60 feet and require a crew of four men to keep one diver working. The air is supplied to the diver at a pressure of 1 lb./sq. in. higher than the depth he is working at in the British Equipment, whereas in the equipment that allows him to control his own gas supply it will be supplied to him at approximately 100 lb./sq. in. or 7 kg./sq. cm.

This is a convenient point to discuss the principles which govern the design of equipment in which the problem of diluting and exhausting CO_2 is the main feature. Some proportion of this mixture is rebreathed by the diver and some is exhausted through a valve into the water to waste.

Once the system is in a steady state the amount of CO_2 which the diver evolves must leave the helmet to waste, and the proportion of CO_2 to the remainder of the gases in the exhaust must be the same as that of the mixture in the helmet. Only a certain partial pressure of CO_2 is tolerable in the alveoli and it is obvious that the atmosphere external to the diver, but in the helmet, must contain less than this partial pressure of CO_2 in order to drain it away from the lungs and maintain the system in a steady state. The problem is how much free air is required to dilute this CO_2 and carry it away to waste?

The maximum proportion that the CO_2 can bear to the rest of the mixture at the surface pressure of 1 atmosphere, is for example, decided to be 0.03. At this point the average diver is beginning to notice the increase in his breathing and pulse, or respiratory rate. It is desirable to maintain this proportion of CO_2, which we will call P, below 0.01 at the surface. The amount of CO_2 that a diver produces is variable within limits that are well known. These limits have been shown in TABLE II. The amount of CO_2 produced compared with the amount of oxygen consumed is also variable, depending upon diet, state of health, and type of work. It is usually close to 0.9 of the oxygen consumed and is known as the respiratory quotient. The remaining quantities to be taken into consideration are shown below.

At the surface $\dfrac{E}{F - C + E} = P$ where
- F = Flow per min. litres.
- E = CO_2 produced per min. litres.
- C = O_2 consumed per min. litres.
- P = Proportion of CO_2 in exhaust mixture volume.
- D = Absolute pressure in atmosphere.

$$\therefore F = \frac{E}{P} + C - E \qquad \text{Volumes at S.T.P.}$$

But as the depth increases so the tolerable volumetric proportion of the CO_2 decreases and when this formula is adjusted for change of depth,

$$F = \frac{ED}{P} + C - E$$

This is the formula from which the volume of free air required by a Standard Diver can be calculated and by which the values in TABLE VI are derived.

If there is any dead space in the breathing system such as the tube of a 'pendulum' breathing closed circuit apparatus, or the volume of a full face-mask with no mouthpiece, then this will require a greater flow of gas to maintain the CO_2 at a given level for any given work rate.

The formula for calculating the effect of a dead space at any depth is given by

$$F_T = \frac{D(0 \cdot 056\,V + E)}{P} + C - E$$

where V = Respiratory rate per minute × dead space volume, litres
F_T = Tidal volume per minute, litres.

It is obvious from this formula that the effect of any dead space, in addition to the anatomical dead space of the lungs and air passages, is significant, particularly if the respiratory rate is high and the breathing shallow. Thus as there is dead space in the breathing circuit anatomically if not by reason of the equipment, breathing should be controlled to be as slow and deep as possible.

This explains why it is necessary that the diver should breath deeply and slowly so that he needs to ventilate the dead space as little as possible. This is not only true of any dead space added by the equipment but the natural dead space of his own breathing passages.

The Standard Diver's air-line is a flexible pipe about 2 inches outside diameter and just over $\frac{1}{2}$ inch bore supplied in lengths of 60 feet. A length of buoyant air hose followed by non-buoyant line is used next to the diver if he is working in deep water so that he will not be troubled by the buoyancy of the air-line pulling him off the bottom. In shallow depths only the buoyant hose is used as it will then keep clear of debris and obstacles that are more likely to be on the bottom than in mid-water.

Wherever hose of varying ages or condition is used, the oldest or most worn lengths should be put nearest to the diver where the least difference of pressure between the inside and outside will occur. It is sound practice that no hose more than three years old be used.

The air flowing into the helmet must also be allowed to escape if the diver's trim is to remain constant, and this is achieved by means of an adjustable spring-loaded non-return valve situated on the right-hand side of the helmet. The adjustment can be made from outside by the diver himself, and fine control of this valve is the secret of the diver's skill in moving about on the bottom. If the valve lifts too easily, air will escape until the outside water level is above the man's diaphragm level and he will find increasing difficulty in breathing. As the corselet comes down over the upper part of the chest, coupled with the strength of his rib muscles, he will never be prevented from drawing breath altogether. He may also become heavier in the water by about 20 lb. If the valve is shut off too much the volume of air will increase and the diver become more buoyant until he finally leaves the bottom and floats to the surface out of control. After the diver has risen a few feet the excess pressure in the suit is sufficient to fill his suit out so that he is helpless and unable to bend arms or legs. Spreadeagled like this he lies on the surface until the air has escaped through the exhaust valve. The great dangers of this mishap are that the suit may burst, releasing the air suddenly so that he drops and is drowned by the water rushing in and compressing the air to a level above his nose as he sinks to the end of the breast-rope. His rapid ascent will have beaten the attendant so that a considerable amount of line is still out when he starts to sink and the time taken to get this slack in and haul him back to the surface may be a couple of minutes. The second danger is that in the uncontrolled and rapid ascent in a helpless condition he can damage himself against obstructions or become fouled up. In extreme cases divers have been found in a 'blown up' condition, upside down, with the lines tangled on an obstruction far below them. This requires very careful handling if the diver is not to suffer a severe squeeze as he sinks to the bottom to free the lines, or a burst suit if the lines are freed and he is allowed to shoot to the surface. There is also the danger that if the dive has been at a depth and for a time which makes decompression necessary then he is exposed to the risk of decompression sickness of more or less severity. If the suit is intact and the lines free he can descend quickly to begin the correct decompression routine but if damage has occurred then good drill will be necessary either to put the diver into a new suit and put him down again or get him into a chamber, all within five minutes.

Other valves on the helmet are a 'knock' valve which allows more air to escape than the regulator explained above. It is used when changing position or ascending, when a comparatively large volume of gas must be allowed to escape to preserve trim. This valve is fitted in the helmet so that it can be knocked open by moving the head inside the helmet, either to one side or forwards. As it is important that the diver shall be able to use this valve, particularly when ascending, and as a man may find the helmet rising off his shoulders and above his head as the gas in the suit expands, so a crutch strap from the corselet is fitted to prevent this happening and should always be used. It is vital to ensure that it is used in any deep diving as the diver may otherwise get out of control and be exposed to all the dangers of 'blowing up' from a great depth.

A non-return valve is fitted on the air supply line where it enters the helmet so that in the event of a loss of pressure or broken air-line near the surface the air at a higher pressure in the suit, helmet, and diver's lungs, is not expelled up the air-line towards the lower pressure further up. If this did happen the diver would suffer the same effect as if he had fallen in shallow water and incurred a 'squeeze'. In Continental and American equipment the air supply valve is situated either on the left-hand side of the helmet, or at the waist. A 'spit' cock is also fitted to enable the diver to let water in to clear the windows of the helmet. This he can only do by bending right down so that the water at the level of the spit cock is at a higher pressure than the air inside.

The breast-rope which is the life-line often carries a telephone cable inside it. This line is secured to the back of the helmet on the right-hand side and leads under the diver's right arm where it is secured to the corselet with a stout line before leaving him for the surface.

The diving suit is a heavy rubberized twill cut to approximately the diver's dimensions but leaving plenty of room for woollen clothing and the larger man. The suit is secured to the corselet by studs through a stout rubber collar and the whole clamped tight with wing nuts. Thick rubber cuffs at the end of the sleeves allow the hands to project through into the water while making a water-tight seal on the wrists. These are usually made large enough to go over the largest hands when well lubricated with soft soap (hydrocarbon greases are never used on rubber equipment) and as a result do not make a water-tight seal on any but the thicker wrists.

For diving in cold water it is usual to fit tough, fabric-lined, rubber gloves to the sleeves instead of cuffs. Although this makes the diver more liable to flood the suit through cutting the gloves on sharp obstructions this is preferable to his being unable to feel anything after a few minutes in the water, being in agony as the circulation is re-established on return to the surface, and eventually suffering damage to his hands after prolonged exposure to these conditions. Besides which he is more liable to injury and less useful if he cannot feel anything with his hands when working in the dark.

As mentioned before, in order to counteract the large volume of air trapped in this equipment considerable weight has to be added to enable the diver to sink at all and normally two 30 lb. lead weights are slung, one on the front and one on the back of the corselet. The boots each weigh 20 lb., both to help increase the diver's weight and to ensure that he remains head uppermost. A broad two-edged knife in a brass scabbard may complete the diver's equipment. This knife is shaped like a small Roman sword, and is used with a hacking motion.

It can be seen from *plate 5* that the accent on the gear is robustness, weight, and simplicity of construction. The improved performance of modern materials has not been exploited in most constructions and the sole advantage that it has had over the light-weight gear for some years has been the warmth that is possible for the diver to enjoy in cold water during long periods underwater. Now, with the improved types and methods of clothing even this advantage is disappearing.

Before starting operations with Standard Equipment it is most necessary to ensure that the facilities for dressing, entering, and leaving the water are adequate, bearing in mind that the diver out of the water weighs anything up to 400 lb., and if his suit is flooded may weigh 550 lb. Thus the ladder must be strong, easily gripped, and without rough, sharp edges, or splinters. It should project out of the water and above the platform by 3 feet, and below the surface by 3–4 feet. It should also slope down at an angle of 20° from the vertical so that the diver can stand and lean on it in comfort. To ensure that it will retain this angle of slope when the diver's weight comes on it it should be fitted as in *figure 8* (*i*) (*ii*) (*iii*) (*iv*) (*v*). The width is also important and should not be less than 2 feet.

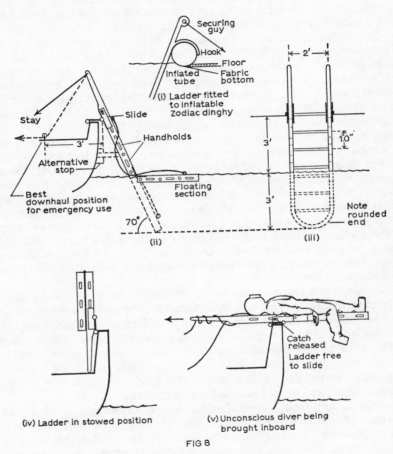

FIG 8

Diving Ladders

When diving in rough weather from a ship or boat a considerable improvement in the range of weather in which a standard diver can operate is achieved by the use of a ladder whose lower half is hinged and floats on the surface. As the diver's weight comes on the bottom of the ladder then it swings down until it is in line with the remainder of the ladder. This type of ladder does not endanger the diver as he surfaces while the ship is rolling heavily, but it gives him a solid support deep into the water as he grips hold of it.

The diving platform, whether it is a boat, a catamaran, or a dock wall, should be close to the water and on the same level as the ladder. There should be plenty of space for the compressor, for dressing, and for tending. If possible the diver should be able to dress and undress under shelter within a few feet of the ladder, and the compressor, likewise, should be under cover provided that the air intake and exhaust are widely separated and no possibility of contamination of the air for the diver is possible. This is particularly important when it is realized that a trace of exhaust gas at normal temperature and pressure may only be unpleasant, but as the pressure increases in the diver's breathing system, and the volume remains constant, so the partial pressure of this gas in increasing and may be increased sufficiently to cause an accident. The most likely exhaust gas to cause trouble is carbon monoxide (CO) which has an affinity for haemoglobin 257 times greater than oxygen. As a result a proportion by volume of only $\frac{0 \cdot 2}{257} = 0 \cdot 000778$ in the air supply will have the same effect as reducing the oxygen in the inspired air by half. The effect of a given proportion by volume of carbon monoxide will be independent of depth.

A thoroughly reliable supply of air at a sufficient pressure for the maximum depth to which the diver could go during the particular operation must be ensured both for the diver doing the job and the stand-by diver who may be required in an emergency, even if he is not actually present on the site. Air supplies may be got from hand pumps, engine-driven compressors, or banks of high-pressure compressed-air cylinders, but whatever method is used it is the responsibility of the man in charge of the diving to be sure that with regard to the possible difficulties the diver may encounter, emergencies, decompression routines, or the necessity for a stand-by diver, that there is an ample supply of air, and, if possible, an alternative method of supplying it in the event of a breakdown or exhaustion of the main supply. The quantity of air usually considered sufficient for one diver working moderately at different depths is shown in TABLE IV.

Other points to look for are that there is a stoutly constructed seat for the diver so sit on while being dressed, or undressed, or waiting, that there is a bench, and a suitable place for tools and diving gear to be properly stowed. Space must be available for the air-line and breast-rope to be coiled down properly, and some convenient place should be chosen to site the telephone amplifier.

The number of men required in a Standard Diving Crew will depend upon the type of job, and the position it is in, but above all upon the experience of the diver and his attendant. Many jobs can be done with only one experienced diver and attendant while Naval regulations insist on a minimum of 5 for a normal dive and 17 for a deep dive, but the decision must finally rest upon the person responsible for the diving operation.

The routine adopted for dressing the diver will depend upon the type

TABLE IV

Air Supply required per minute at S.T.P. for Standard Divers
at various work rates and partial pressures of CO_2

Partial Pressure of CO_2 in Exhaust (Atmospheres)		0·01		0·02		0·03	
Pressure (Atmospheres)	Depth (Feet)	Litres	Feet³	Litres	Feet³	Litres	Feet³
1	0	24·25	0·9	14·25	0·5	8·0	0·3 Rest
		91	3·2	45·5	1·6	30	1·1 Light Work
		192	6·8	96	3·4	64	2·3 Hard Work
2	33	48·25	1·7	24·25	0·9	16	0·6 Rest
		182	6·4	91	3·2	61	2·2 Light Work
		384	13·6	192	6·8	128	4·5 Hard Work
3	66	72·25	2·6	36·25	1·3	24	0·9 Rest
		273	9·6	136·5	4·8	91	3·2 Light Work
		576	20·4	288	10·2	192	6·8 Hard Work
4	99	96·25	3·4	48·25	1·7	33	1·2 Rest
		364	12·9	182	6·4	121	4·3 Light Work
		768	27·2	384	13·6	257	9·1 Hard Work
5	132	120·25	4·3	60·25	2·1	40	1·4 Rest
		455	16·1	227·5	8·0	152	5·4 Light Work
		960	34·0	480	17·0	320	11·3 Hard Work
6	165	144·5	5·1	72·25	2·6	48	1·7 Rest
		546	19·3	273	9·6	182	6·4 Light Work
		1152	40·7	576	20·4	384	13·6 Hard Work
7	198	170·25	6·0	85·25	3·0	57	2·0 Rest
		637	22·5	318·5	11·3	212	7·5 Light Work
		1384	48·8	692	24·4	461	16·3 Hard Work

of equipment being used in detail, but follows the general pattern whereby
the diver, having dressed in woollens and put the main diving suit on, sits
on the stool or bench and is assisted by the attendant with his boots first,
followed by the corselet, clamps, and helmet. The weights are usually left
until the last moment and may either be put on when the diver is on the
ladder, or just before he goes to the ladder. In this instance the front glass
will have been left off until he is on the ladder (see *plate 5*).

Before the helmet is put on the diver the air-line and breast-rope will
have been secured to it. When no breast-rope is used, the air-line is used
as a life-line instead.

Whenever the diver moves off the stool with boots on he should be
accompanied by the attendant who should have a line secured to the
diver and have it in hand. This is a simple precaution easily allowed to be

relaxed, but if the diver does slip over the side it is almost certain that he will be quickly drowned. When going to the ladder he should be assisted and all obstacles removed from his path while the attendant should keep his life-line or breast-rope reasonably tight to check any incipient fall or slip. Once on the ladder the life-line should be hitched to it while the front glass or helmet is secured and made water-tight.

Before the diver is finally buttoned up the air supply must be turned on and the diver's assent that it is satisfactory obtained. Likewise when a telephone is fitted communication must be established satisfactorily before closing up the helmet or front glass.

Because of the burden of the helmet and weights the diver should not be kept waiting about before going underwater. Thus all briefing should be done before dressing and everyone concerned with the operation should understand both the object of the operation, the intended method of execution, and any special signals that may have been improvised.

The novice who first dresses in Standard Equipment will be appalled at the unaccustomed burden on his shoulders and his encumbered feet. However, this feeling passes with practice and it will not be long before he is able to swing each leg in turn over on to the ladder with ease.

When the diver is closed up and breathing comfortably he will descend the ladder until his shoulders are awash, having allowed some of the air to escape from the suit through the regulatory valve at the side of the helmet. Only enough will be allowed to escape to prevent his being so buoyant that he would have difficulty in pulling himself down the shot-rope. If too much is allowed to escape then his rate of descent will be cut down as he waits for the volume of air to build up in the suit sufficiently for him to breathe comfortably again. With the system whereby the diver controls his own air supply this problem does not arise and he can achieve a good trim on the ladder.

Part of the routine for rigging the platform for diving will have been to provide a sinker, or shot, made fast to a rope, or shot-rope, to act as a guide-line for the diver to and from the bottom as well as a point of reference for him. The size of the shot that will be required will depend upon the tidal or current conditions, the type of bottom, the depth, and the hoisting and lowering facilities on the diving platform. When there is little or no current a half-hundredweight sinker will provide a perfectly adequate shot. If, however, a tidal stream is expected then the size will have to be increased in order to prevent both the diver and the shot being washed to the surface downstream by the force of the water acting on them like a child being pushed upwards on a swing. In deep water and a fast tide even a 5 cwt. sinker may be carried off the bottom. This is particularly important to bear in mind if decompression is likely to be necessary as it may be in depths over 40 feet, depending upon the time that the diver has been down. The shot-rope must be of a sufficient thickness for the diver to get a comfortable hold on even when his hands are numb with cold. It should never be less than a 2 inch rope.

The shot-rope should be lowered as close to the job as possible for the Standard Diver has comparatively little mobility down below and any walking away from the shot that has to be done increases the length of air hose and life-line that have to be paid out. As these are both a substantial size their resistance to water flow is considerable and they are therefore further encumbrance to the diver. The Standard Diving Equipment is essentially for static working conditions, and although experienced divers can move about with considerable facility it still requires a great deal more effort and skill than lighter equipment.

Essentially the skill of the Standard Diver is measured by the skill with which he can control his trim, that is his positive or negative buoyancy and the position of his centre of buoyancy.

When the shot is on the bottom the shot-rope should be well secured so as to be up and down from the shot, and the diving ladder should be situated close to it. It will be necessary to adjust the shot-rope for the movement of a floating platform if there is a tide, and a watch should be maintained to ensure that while the shot is kept on the bottom the shot-rope is kept taut.

When the diver is ready on the ladder and has vented what air he wants to he will close the exhaust valve and then signal to the attendant to be hauled over to the shot-rope if he cannot reach it from the ladder. Having reached it he should then signal, generally by a wave of the hand, answered by a tug from the attendant, and will descend as fast as his ears and volume of air in the suit allow. If he is descending in black water on to unknown obstacles he will of course proceed with caution. Meanwhile the attendant should leave the position where the shot-rope is secured and take the breast-rope a_d air-line away to one side (as previously agreed with the diver). This will serve to prevent the diver going round the shot-rope and getting tangled with it, for he will tend to turn with the lay of the rope, as well as giving him an idea of direction on the bottom, for when there is no visibility the diver will quickly lose all sense of direction without the aid of tangible marks.

If the job is situated away from the shot the diver will first have to find it and one method of doing this will be by using a distance-line, one end of which is secured to the shot and the other end taken by the diver as he circles round searching. When the job has been found it can always be found again without waste of time if the diver secures his end of the distance-line to it. The line should always be made up and secured in a definite way so that there is no difficulty in handling it even in cold, dark water. Long thin lines tend to get tangled easily and the length should be adjusted to the job. One method of making up the line is shown in the diagrams (see *figure 9*).

As the diver arrives on the bottom so he should signal to the attendant with one tug. The attendant then knows what the diver is about to do in the absence of a telephone. Before moving off the exhaust valve should be adjusted to allow only a sufficient volume of air in the suit to give the diver comfortable breathing and the weight that he wants on the bottom. On soft mud and no tide or current he will want to be very light so that he

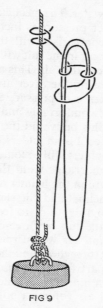

FIG 9

Distance line made up

skates easily over the surface on his stomach without ploughing into it. If it is hard sand or gravel with some tide then the opposite will be true although he will still be proceeding almost horizontally, as in *plates 7 and 8*, for it is practically impossible to walk upright underwater.

In shallow water, any change of posture which results in any part of the body being higher than before will necessitate releasing some air. For example, a diver in 33 feet of water (at the bottom) who stands up from a prone position will have gained 3½ lb. of buoyancy, and although some of this extra buoyancy will be quickly lost through an increase of flow through the exhaust valve, yet a small amount will remain for some time until the air pressure differences in the suit return to normal, or the diver opens his knock valve briefly to release the excess air. The capacity of typical exhaust and knock valves are as follows:

at 18″ W.G. flow = 7 c.f.m.
at 12″ W.G. flow = 3 „

Constant alert attendance on the diver is of particular importance when diving in shallow water with the British design of equipment and particularly if there are considerable differences of depth in the area, such as exist between deck level and the sea-bed round a wreck, or on the steeply stepped sides of flooded dry docks. If the diver loses his hold or balance and falls without being checked by the attendant he will suffer what is termed a 'squeeze', which can cause serious injury and even death if it happens in a few feet of water. The mechanics of the accident are that as the diver falls so the water pressure is increasing rapidly. In shallow water this increase is large in comparison with the absolute pressure so that the reduction in volume of the air in the suit will also be large in proportion to the volume of air in it before the fall. This air can only shrink into the helmet, but the water is pressing the diver and the suit into the helmet as well for as long as a difference of pressure exists. The less serious case will merely be exceedingly uncomfortable and the diver will feel the suit being tightly clamped round his body and the 'weight' of the helmet and corselet bearing down hard on his shoulders. As the fall becomes more serious the weight on the shoulders will become more intense, the eyes will become bloodshot, and haemorrhage from the more delicate tissues exposed to the lower air pressure in the helmet may occur. In bad cases the diver is pushed up into the helmet and corselet.

A fall from the surface to a depth of 10 feet will result in a reduction of the volume of the air in the suit by three-quarters of its value on the surface. If the diver is in trim this would raise the water level from his diaphragm approximately 4–6 inches, and he would have difficulty in breathing properly, quite apart from the discomfort of the helmet and corselet bearing heavily upon him. If the same fall occurred from 100 feet to 110 feet the reduction of air volume would be to twelve-thirteenths, instead of three-quarters as above, and the rise in water level between 1 and $1\frac{1}{2}$ inches.

The attendant must keep the breast-rope and air-line firmly in hand, but without hindering the diver, and be ready to check a fall at any time. The diver on his part must be careful not to get himself into the situation where the attendant cannot help him. For example, he should never pass under the keel of a ship to the other side. If he loses his hold the attendant can do little to prevent him swinging down and out to a greater depth and inevitably being squeezed.

This is also the principal danger in the diver losing control and floating to the surface, or 'blowing up' as mentioned before.

When the job has been completed, or the diver wishes to come up, the proper signals should be exchanged with the surface so that the attendant is informed. If the diver is then told to come up he will make up the distance-line if it is no longer required. When ready to ascend he will signal the fact and will then be told to do so. He should then close his exhaust valve to make himself a little lighter, give a tug on the breast-rope to signal that he is leaving the bottom, and once the ascent has begun open the exhaust valve so that as the air expands during the ascent it can escape through the exhaust valve. The diver may have to release more air with the knock valve so that he retains control of the ascent. If there is any fear of losing control he must check his progress by holding on to the shot-rope, signal the fact that he has stopped by one tug on the breast-rope, and adjust his trim. When ready to start off again he will give the signal asking to come up on the breast-rope.

If decompression is necessary (see TABLES I and II), or the depth of water is over 40 feet, both the breast-rope and the shot-rope should be marked off in tens of feet as necessary according to the decompression tables. These markings should be from the position where the breast-rope is at the diver's chest, in 10-foot intervals. If a current is running which sweeps the diver and shot-rope out at an angle so that the markings do not correspond to the diver's actual depth then regulation of his depth should be done according to the reading of the pressure gauge on his air supply. This is a direct measure of the depth of the water level at his chest and is the position for which the decompression tables are calculated. This can only be done with the apparatus whose air supply is controlled from the surface.

As the diver ascends he will be checked at the correct depth for decompression. If he actually stops above or below the position he must be told to come up or go down as necessary until he is within $\pm$ 1 foot of the correct place. The time for the stop must then be taken from when he is in this position. The time for which he must stop at each depth is laid down in the tables and must be strictly adhered to as there is only a very small safety margin, determined empirically, for each decompression procedure, and any departure from the table incurs the risk of the diver having decompression sickness, or a 'bend'. The diver should try to arrive at each stop, and travel between stops, as quickly and accurately as possible.

Apart from the difficulties of handling a heavily encumbered man on the deck and ladder of a moving platform there is an additional reason for cancelling diving with Standard Equipment during rough weather in depths of water where decompression may be required. If the diving is being done from a boat or small vessel there is a considerable pumping action caused by the shape of the craft as it pitches and rolls in the sea, which is effective to a depth of at least 10 feet. The effect of this pumping action is to make the diver's position at the last and most important stop of all, that at 10 feet, almost impossible to hold either accurately or without great effort, which is inimical to safe decompression.

When the diver arrives on the surface at the shot-rope it may be necessary for him to turn around it to take out any turns with it and his own lines. This he should have been able to do during the ascent even in black water unless the tide or current was preventing him. Having become disentangled from the shot-rope he is pulled to the ladder and climbs up it until he can rest comfortably and the attendant can undo and remove the front glass. In rough weather he should come right inboard before doing this. After ascertaining that the diver is well other information can be exchanged.

Some consideration must now be paid to procedures that are adopted to cope with accidents and emergencies, but before being able to decide upon the effectiveness of any line of action all the peculiarities of the equipment must be understood.

Firstly, the Standard Diver is surrounded by a volume which is sufficient in itself to accommodate a substantial amount of CO_2 without the partial pressure rising above 0·06 atmospheres. Generally it is taken that a man can survive three minutes, without any additional air supply to wash out the accumulating CO_2, and this allows time for the diver to take emergency action. It also gives a stand-by, or assistant diver, time to fit a new air supply to the first diver's helmet in place of the old one, while the non-return valve in the helmet prevents the escape of air from the suit.

Secondly, even if the suit is punctured, although the diver will get very wet and cold he will be in no danger provided the helmet and corselet are kept upright so that they work efficiently as a diving bell.

Finally, it is possible, though exceedingly risky, for the diver to remove his front glass provided he remains facing vertically downwards so that the air pressure at the lowest point of the aperture is higher than the water pressure.

It is unlikely that the Standard Diver will become unconscious on the bottom unless he is grossly unfit and has failed to get sufficient air into the helmet to reduce the CO_2 partial pressure, or is suffering from some other physical upset. If the circumstances under which the diving is taking place are good then it is unlikely that a stand-by diver is available and the only recourse when signals are not answered is to pull the diver up slowly. If he is pulled up too fast the expanding air will have no opportunity to escape and the diver will 'blow up', and possibly damage himself against the bottom of the boat, the ladder, or any other obstructions that may be on the water.

Once on the surface the diver must be pulled to the ladder as quickly as possible and as far up it as the strength of the attendants allows in the first pull. The breast-rope is then secured round the ladder and the diver's front glass taken off. He should regain consciousness quickly unless the accident has been caused by carbon-monoxide poisoning. In this event he must be supplied with oxygen if it is available, or at least uncontaminated fresh air. When his breathing has been attended to it is then time to start relieving him of the weights and hauling him inboard. A type of ladder is shown in *figure 8* which can be hauled past the horizontal and the diver slid on to the deck. If this type of ladder is fitted then the diver should be brought to it with his back against it.

It has been known for the helmet to be punctured, or the air hose connection to be torn out, leaving a large hole in the helmet. Under these conditions the diver may have time to give the emergency surfacing signal and whenever this signal is given he should be hauled up rapidly without regard to the danger of blowing up. If he surfaces at some distance from the diving platform there will be considerable difficulty in getting him to the ladder in time before he sinks again. But while he is in imminent danger of drowning he will not suffer from a 'squeeze' as there will be no air in the suit to be reduced in volume. When he is got to the ladder with his back to it he must be removed from the suit as quickly as possible, particularly if he has stopped breathing. This cannot be ascertained for certain before access has been gained to him, but it can be inferred if the helmet is full of water. In this event the suit should be cut open at the corselet but not all the way round, the sleeves must be slit open and the diver extracted from the helmet and pulled up until the legs can be slit and the boots cut off. If the diver has drowned and breathed water into his lungs the rescuers will have approximately 20 seconds in which to expel the water and start artificial respiration before his heart fails, and should this happen there is little chance of recovery with the resources available on a diving operation (see page 125 on drowning).

The most likely emergency to occur is that the diver becomes fouled by wires or obstructions underwater and is unable to free himself. If the job is one in which the diver could become fouled then a second set of equipment and a stand-by diver must be available. How quickly they must be available must again be a decision for the person responsible for the conduct of the operation, but, while it is unlikely that the diver's air supply will fail at the same moment as he gets in difficulty it has happened and it should not be forgotten that the chances of failure while he is still fouled must be considered.

There may be several reasons why a diver who is caught up may be unable to signal the fact. For example, he may be trapped through sand collapsing over him, because the lines are snagged round an obstruction out of his reach, or because he is floating upside down in mid-water with the lines fouled on obstructions on the bottom. In each case he is helpless unless a telephone is fitted.

Good attending may well result in such accidents being prevented provided the diver also has his wits about him and both ends are concentrating on the task in hand.

The stand-by diver proceeds down the first diver's breast-rope, using it as his shot-line. This will take him straight to the man in difficulty and from there he must decide the method of rescue, as each accident will be different. The method of rescue may require painstaking digging or jetting with a hose, changing an air supply line, or merely disentangling fouled hose.

If a stand-by diver is required he will of course need his own attendants in addition to the attendants for the trapped diver, and the air supply system must have sufficient capacity to keep two divers operating together at the maximum depth they could attain in that position and without unduly taxing the machinery.

While this account of the more usual forms of accident and emergency may paint an unduly dark picture in the mind of the reader of the dangers of this form of diving yet in fact serious accidents rarely occur and this type of equipment has proved safe and reliable. It is only through knowledge of the various accidents that can occur and the action to be taken in the unfortunate event of one doing so that its effects can be mitigated or avoided.

The principal differences between the Standard Diving Equipment and the more modern surface supplied gear lie in eliminating the large volume of air around the diver and in supplying him with air as he inhales it, and exhausting it to waste on exhalation.

The advantages of this system are that the amount of weight required by the diver is only that required to overcome the buoyancy of the man and the essential air in his clothes; the air he breathes always has a negligible proportion of CO_2 in it, and the consumption of air is less for a given rate of work. In addition one less line is required, for the air-line is usually used as the life-line and the support for the telephone cables, and it is of small diameter. It is very strong as it works at a higher pressure than the standard apparatus and its strength to withstand this pressure renders it adequate for the loads imposed when used as a life-line.

The surface demand apparatus consists of a demand valve supplied with air at a pressure that is usually at 50 p.s.i. above ambient pressure although some high pressure equipment is available that works at pressures between 450 to 3,000 p.s.i. The lower pressure apparatus is more usually met as this air pressure is generally available for driving compressed air tools, while it can also be easily obtained from a high pressure cylinder by leading it through an oxygen pressure reducing valve as used with oxygen cylinders for oxy-acetylene flame work.

Demand valves are so constructed that as soon as the diver begins to draw in air when inhaling the slight drop in pressure is transmitted to a diaphragm which moves and opens a valve admitting a supply of air from the cylinders into the breathing system. As soon as the diver has inhaled a lungful and stops inhaling there is no longer enough pressure to hold the diaphragm, and thus the valve, open, and it closes shutting off the supply of air. By this method the diver only uses the volume of air required to fill his lungs during each breath and at all other times the flow of gas is shut off. When the diver exhales the exhaust gas escapes through a second tube to an exhaust valve close to the supply except in those types where the demand valve is fitted to the mask and there are no tubes. The exhaust valve is then part of the mask. This is a great saving of gas as compared with that required by the Standard Diver who must have it flowing through and ventilating the helmet all the time and enjoys the great advantage that it does not incur any CO_2 problem (provided the dead space is small). The air is drawn into the lungs, charged with CO_2, and blown to waste so that none remains to affect the next inhalation.

To ensure complete ventilation like this, however, it is necessary to breathe through a mouthpiece so that the flow is directed in one direction only. With no mouthpiece there is bound to be a small additional dead air space, however cleverly designed the mask is, which will affect the breathing rate and thus limit the diver's efforts to some small extent.

Some demand valves work directly off a high pressure supply of gas without a valve to reduce the pressure interposed and these are termed 'single stage' demand valves. Others using a reducer to reduce this high pressure to a low pressure, similar to that obtained from the oxygen pressure reducing valve mentioned before, are called 'two stage'. Each type has its own advantages (see *figs. 10 (i) (ii)*).

The single stage valve is generally simpler in operation and by eliminating the additional complication of a reducer reduces the chance of

mechanical failure. It also has a very simple built-in by-pass system.
Usually it is easy to reach the diaphragm with a finger as most designs
have a hole cut in the valve casing to enable the diver to do this. De-
pressing the diaphragm displaces the valve off its seat and there is then
no obstruction or filters between the bottle and the diver's breathing.
Although the rush of high pressure air may be considerable it is never
sufficient to embarrass the diver and the excess escapes round the edges
of the mask. Furthermore the demand valve thus by-passed will allow the

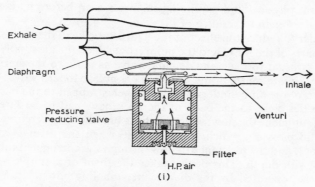

Two-stage demand valve

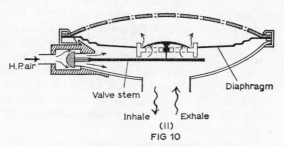

FIG 10

Single-stage demand valve

remaining gas in cylinders to be used when the supply is from these instead
of from the surface. In the event of mechanical failure it is the more likely
to 'fail to safe'. A disadvantage of this valve when it is used with the high
pressure system or cylinders is that unless it is very carefully designed, the
breathing effort required to operate it is higher because of the absence of
a reducer, and it requires a higher low pressure to drive it than the two-
stage valve. The lowest pressure that demand valves work at is approximately 15 atmospheres, because at that pressure the flow through the
small supply orifice is inadequate to match the breathing rate. This consideration is absent when low pressure surface supply demand valves are
used.

The prime disadvantage of the two-stage valve is the presence of a reducer which, being a mechanical contrivance, can and sometimes does fail. When this occurs the diver is in a serious position as few equipments are fitted with a by-pass valve for such an emergency.

Positioning the demand valve on the diver is as important as the design of the valve itself. The whole effort of the designer being to reduce the resistance to breathing and to allow the diver to inhale air as fast and frequently as he may desire without restriction. This is a most important feature to ensure, for if the man is not able to breathe freely he will be under great physical and psychological stress even before he is subjected to other stresses in the course of his dive.

In order to reduce the effect of the hydrostatic head that exists between various parts of the lungs and the point from which the air supply is finally drawn it is usual to place the demand valve as close to the sternal notch (the approximate centre of the lungs) as possible. Modern valves mounted on the top of the air cylinders which are then strapped to the back so that the valve lies close to the back of the neck have had to be fitted with a device to augment the flow when the diver breathes to overcome both the hydrostatic pressure, which is appreciable when the diver is swimming on his front, and the resistance to flow through the corrugated tubes which increases with depth. This device takes the form of a simple venturi jet which, once operated by the diver's first inhaling effort, draws the gas through from the demand valve against both resistance and pressure (see *figure 10 (i)*). Demand valves mounted at the mask or the mouthpiece appear to give the best results with the simplest apparatus, but incur the penalty of greatly increased noise. The slight annoyance of exhaust bubbles obscuring vision in certain attitudes can be reduced by the pepper-pot type of exhaust valve to break up the bubbles into very small noiseless ones. This improvement, coupled with a silenced intake sufficient to enable satisfactory telephone communication to be maintained with the demand valve so close to the microphone, would make this type of equipment quite the safest and most efficient for hard and varied work at all depths for which the system was suitable.

Although the surface supplied demand valve affords great savings of gas over the Standard Diving gear, and has banished the problem of CO_2 elimination from the breathing system, yet it still requires a large quantity of gas as compared with the more efficient system of closed-circuit operation.

While a trained diver in good conditions may need only 25 litres per minute of air at any depth it is usual to assume that the average diver will require approximately 35 litres per minute. This is a very arbitrary figure which will be varied both by the breathing characteristics of the individual diver and by the circumstances of the dive as they bear on that diver. This volume is required at any depth in order to ventilate the lungs and eliminate the CO_2 from the respiratory system, and it can be seen that as the depth increases so does the mass of gas (or volume of free gas at N.T.P.) blown away, until at 100 feet four times the amount of air is being used to what was required at the surface. In addition, as the depth increases so will the breathing rate increase in order to provide sufficient ventilation to get rid of the CO_2 which is being increasingly impeded from diffusing through the denser body of gas in the lungs. Thus, for dives to 100 feet with a surface supply the capacity to be allowed for the supply should be at least 5 cubic feet of free air per minute per diver at the pressure required to work the particular apparatus plus 50 p.s.i. As the compressors are also complicated mechanical contrivances which can fail the supply should be drawn from cylinders of a sufficient size to allow time for the stand-by diver and the working diver to ascend whilst observing whatever decompression routine may be necessary, after the failure of the compressor.

The air-line is generally a rubber-covered fabric hose in 50 or 60-foot lengths coupled together as required, and similar to that used with oxy-acetylene cutting gear. The essential features of the line are that it shall be flexible, will not kink, is resistant to abrasion, and capable of taking a pull of at least 300 lb.

A harness consisting of a belt carrying weight or battery pockets, and the straps to position the demand valve (unless this is carried on the mask), comprises the remainder of the apparatus. On this harness, although it is seldom fitted, a reserve should be carried consisting of an emergency cylinder and by-pass valve to supply the diver with sufficient gas to get clear from any obstructions and ascend to the surface in the event of damage to the air-line or failure of the air supply. Thus for depths down to 60 feet a gas supply of 375 litres (13.4 cu. ft.) should suffice for five minutes. This emergency supply should by-pass all the usual valves and depend upon hand control by the diver.

The mask worn with this equipment should cover the whole face. If a telephone is to be used then the mouthpiece must be dispensed with, unless the mask has a soft front so that the mouthpiece can be replaced easily after talking. The danger of the separate mouthpiece and mask for working is that if an accident should occur so that the diver loses his mouthpiece then at one blow he may be in a very serious predicament. This will be particularly evident if the man is unconscious as he will immediately start to drown. If he can still breathe, even though unconscious, he is at least safe for a time and will suffer from anoxia which, although dangerous and ultimately fatal, does give more time for effective aid to be rendered than if his lungs were flooded. A more usual inconvenience is that after long periods in cold water the lip muscles become tired and the water-tight seal over the mouthpiece deteriorates so that water is breathed in as well as air.

It is obvious that sealing a full face-mask is vital if the mask is without a mouthpiece because the diver's vision and breathing depend upon its water-tight integrity. Consideration of the way in which this integrity is achieved falls into two parts, firstly the way in which the mask is secured to the head, and secondly the way in which water is excluded. Sometimes the two functions are contained in one unit so that the mask is attached to a hood which covers the head and may be secured to the neck of a suit, a neck seal, or be an integral part of a suit with a back or middle entry. If the hood is connected and open to the remainder of the suit it is then necessary to seal the air supply in and restrict it to the diver's face, otherwise, when he turns upside down the air will rush into his back, or feet, the suit will inflate with the diver's head downwards and unable to breathe.

Where the mask is a separate unit from the rest of the diver's clothing care must be taken to ensure that it is properly secured by at least four stout straps and buckles to a pad bearing on the back of the head, and that the face seal is thoroughly reliable and will remain water-tight even although displaced to one side, up, or down, by an inadvertent blow on any obstruction. This can only be achieved by a compression seal of the type illustrated in *figure 7*. In addition this seal should be fitted with thin membranes of rubber, or other elastic material, on each side to prevent egress of air other than through the exhaust valve, and ingress of water. Only when these membranes are fitted can the mask be thoroughly purged of all traces of water, which otherwise cause a spray to be kicked up by the inhaled gas.

If a hood is worn that has the mask incorporated in it, but the breathing supply is provided through a mouthpiece also included in the hood, some difficulty may be experienced by the diver, particularly if the heels and arms of the suit are fitted with exhaust valves, as in the Constant Voulme Suit, for when he turns upside down his lungs, and in particular his lips forming the seal round the mouthpiece, are at a differential pressure compared with his feet, equivalent to the vertical distance between them. This means that there will be a strain on his lips tending to make him exhale which may be difficult to resist. In addition, unless the visor has a face seal the air in the face piece will be expelled towards his highest point, in this event his feet, and the mask pressed against his face. If the valves on the feet are adjusted to let air escape at a pressure equivalent to 50-60 inches water gauge, then the suit will tend to inflate until the pressure in it is equivalent to that of the water at the lowest point of the body, which would be the lips.

One of the principal claims made for the old-fashioned Standard Divers' Equipment is that the suits are tough and that they are the only ones suitable to stand up to the wear encountered in constructional work. In fact, this is no longer true as many thin synthetic proofed fabrics have a far higher abrasion and tear resistance than the rubber proofed canvas of the old suits without incurring the penalty of weight and stiffness necessary to achieve the strength of the latter suits.

For most work underwater where the diver is expected to remain submerged for some hours at a stretch, day after day, it is necessary to keep him dry even in tropical conditions, and it is usual to wear what is termed a dry suit over underclothing suitable for the conditions in which he is working.

The dry suit may be of two main groups and have a number of different methods of entry. The material may be rubber or neoprene-proofed cotton stockinette, which is heavy, and has no natural stretch, a synthetic stockinette proofed with the same materials and woven so that it will stretch either two ways or only one. Where the material can stretch in only one direction, clever tailoring can give it almost as effective a result as the more costly two-way stretch fabric.

Methods of entry into the suit may be through a small hole in a very elastic yoke over the shoulders with arrangements for sealing off the top of the suit with a hood or neck seal, through a large slit in the back at the shoulders of the suit with the opening closed by a water-tight zip, through the middle by a skirt surrounding a large hole and sealed in a variety of ways, or by getting into a trouser and jacket sectioned suit and then rolling them together to form a seal. These methods are known respectively as neck entry, back entry, front entry, and two-piece.

Each method of encasing the diver in a dry envelope has its protagonists and opponents, which is another way of saying that each method has its strong and weak points. A brief description and survey of the respective merits will be made before examining their use in practice.

The neck entry suit was developed for the Royal Navy swimmers during the last war, and was an attempt to provide a clean line that would offer as little resistance to the water as possible. The hole in the yoke through which the diver's body passes into the suit has to be as elastic as possible, combined with the minimum tolerable strength for the suit as a whole and the effort required to extend the material when getting into and out of it with a lot of underclothing on. The seal is effected by inserting a broad metal hoop inside the hole over which the yoke edge fits snugly. The hood or neck seal is made with a thick band that stretches over the edge of the yoke on the hoop, and the whole is clamped tight by a screw clamp (see *figure 11 (i) (ii) (iii) (iv) (v)*). The advantage of this suit is that when it is correctly tailored and constructed of stretchable material the streamline flow is greatly improved, and although the neck-sealing arrangements do protrude they are exceeded in the front presented to the water flow by the breathing equipment usually worn. However, with the advent of neat or streamlined breathing equipment, and the higher speeds obtainable by being towed on a sledge or small torpedo, added to the obstruction to free movement of the head, this method may not be considered as suitable as it used to be for the diver wishing to move fast through the water. One considerable advantage that it does maintain, however, is that the use of a neck seal or hood can remain a choice without changing the suit, depending upon the circumstances of the dive.

A type of suit that has been favoured for diving to depths below 100 feet in cold water is the constant volume suit previously mentioned. This suit completely encloses the diver except for his hands, and is connected to his air supply through the face seal of the mask which is a part of the suit. Exhaust valves are fitted to the heels and neck to allow the escape of excess gas from the highest points. This suit automatically allows sufficient air into the suit to maintain the volume of air in the clothing the same as it was at the surface throughout the depth of the dive. The diver thus keeps

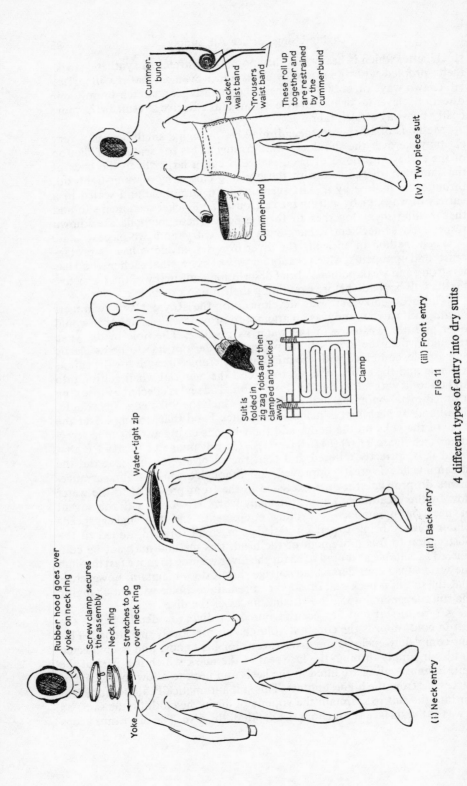

Rubber hood goes over yoke on neck ring

Screw clamp secures the assembly

Neck ring

Stretches to go over neck ring

Yoke

(i) Neck entry

Water-tight zip

(ii) Back entry

Suit is folded in zig zag folds and then clamped and tucked away

Clamp

(iii) Front entry

FIG 11

Cummerbund

Jacket waist band

Trouser's waist band

These roll up together and are restrained by the cummerbund

Cummerbund

(iv) Two piece suit

4 different types of entry into dry suits

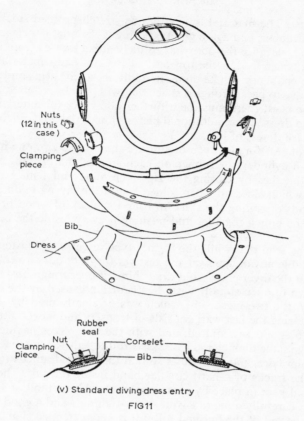

Nuts
(12 in this
case)

Clamping
piece

Bib

Dress

Rubber
seal

Nut

Clamping
piece

Corselet

Bib

(v) Standard diving dress entry

FIG 11

both warm and able to move freely. Although this type of suit is designed for use with the open-circuit system of breathing apparatus it is doubtful whether the complication and therefore expense of the outfit is superior either to the closed cell foam neoprene at shallow depths, or CO_2 suit inflation by means of a small bottle, hand-operated, for the greater depths, which can be fitted to any type of dress. It is certainly less efficient than the latter from the point of view of heat insulation, although care must be taken to allow the gas into the suit only through an expansion coil. Otherwise burns from liquid CO_2 may result.

The success or failure of a back entry suit depends entirely upon the efficiency of the water-tight zip used to seal the opening across the shoulders. If this is kept clean and easy running there is no doubt that it provides the diver with the cleanest line of all the dry suits, leaving the choice of suit to depend upon consideration of size, type of head covering, and material, to be examined later. It is also the only close-fitting suit that can be easily put on and taken off without help.

Front, chest, or middle entry suits are the most commonly encountered dry suits at present as they are the most easily made, and therefore the cheapest. The material is usually non-stretch proofed stockinette, or pure sheet rubber, and again good tailoring is essential if a clean line is to be achieved. Because the body has to be bent backwards from a forward posture in order to don the top part of the suit extra material must be allowed to enable this to be done. In addition, as the arms and shoulders together have to pass through a space that will only be required to accommodate the chest there must be a further allowance of material to allow the diver to dress. These additional pieces of material unavoidably detract from the cleanliness of line.

Types of seal for this type of suit are the double zip, one inside, one outside two cylinders of rubber on each side of the opening which are squeezed together by closing the zips; the male and female rubber V-moulding which close up when folded round the diver's middle, and the two methods of rolling the skirt up round a block of wood or on itself, clamping the bunch together and pushing it away inside the belly of the suit.

It can be seen that while the former type of entry and fastenings have a considerable advantage over the rest yet they are not so neat, and besides, when the diver crawls and drags himself over rough obstacles, have been known to open slightly with the distortion caused by the exertion.

Finally, the two-piece suit, which was originally used by the Italian frogmen during the last war, consists of trousers and jacket, fitted with a neck seal or hood as required, and with the two pieces having seamless skirts of the same diameter. These skirts roll together, sometimes round a hard circular core, and sometimes so that the finished, uncreased roll lies between the tracks of a hard circular band inside the suit. The whole is covered and kept in place by a cummerbund. This method of sealing has to be most carefully done to ensure water-tightness and a good result can only be expected of the finished roll if it is kept extended slightly beyond the relaxed diameter of the skirts. Hence the reason for the hard internal band. As the efficiency of the seal depends upon its being slightly extended the diver's girth will be a consideration that affects the water-tightness of the suit.

The principal advantage of this suit is that one suit can more easily accommodate a range of divers of different heights.

All the suits considered are equipped with 'boots', that is, a strengthened section enclosing the feet and an integral part of the suit; but the hands and head are often left uncovered or require separate items of clothing to give protection against cold or filth. Seals are usually provided at the wrists and often at the neck, and are made of thin rubber stretched firmly over the skin. However, lean people create hollows in both parts in certain postures, or when making certain movements, and the tension seal of the stretched rubber then no longer prevents water entering up the sleeve or down the neck. As the number of skilled or otherwise sedentary divers increases and the manual worker is diluted by these others, so this complaint is likely to increase for as long as the tension seal is retained. Where this is likely to occur so the neck seal is often replaced by a hood, while the wrists can be protected by the type of compression seal shown in *figure 7.*

The wet suit is one in which a layer of gas (usually CO_2) is retained in the material of the suit while water is allowed to enter between the suit and the diver's skin. Surprisingly these suits can be worn with a reasonable degree of comfort even in the winter seas around the South of England, as the author has tried, and they are also being used in the winter in Northern waters by the American and Canadian Navies.

The material of the suit is usually closed cell foam neoprene or rubber tailored to fit the diver as closely as possible without stretching. The most successful suits tried are those made in one piece with the entry through the front, closed by a long zip from the navel to the throat. It is only in these that the pumping effect, caused by changing position, bending down, and straightening up, is reduced to tolerable limits in cold water. Furthermore they are easier to put on and take off without any assistance. The pumping action is caused by some of the material being forced away from the skin by bending, at the stomach for instance, and water being sucked into the space formed. This water is then expelled as the diver straightens up and a constant circulation of cooling water is maintained. The majority of commercially produced suits are two-piece, consisting of trousers with additional material to cover the body up to the chest, and a jacket to reach down to the hips, this double thickness over the middle of the body helping to reduce the pumping effect. These suits usually require assistance to remove the jacket as they have to be a close fit.

The most comfortable surface for the inside of the material is one without a skin, or with a fabric lining. The small exposed cavities of the broken surface bubbles prevent the movement of air or water, and any considerable area of neoprene or rubber coming in contact with the skin, which is not done by the double-skinned material. However, it is then necessary to have a very flexible suit as the surface cannot be lubricated with french chalk as the double-skinned variety can. Obviously the thicker the material can be the better the insulating properties, but as the thickness increases so does the stiffness of the material, and it has been found that the best compromise is about $\frac{3}{16}$ inch thick, equivalent to $\frac{3}{8}$ inch–$\frac{1}{2}$ inch of woollens. A recent development of this suit has resulted in the inside lining being made of two-way stretch nylon fabric which not only strengthens this otherwise weak material but also provides a surface that slides over even hairy bodies without pain or prior lubrication with chalk or water.

As this material is of closed-cell construction it is not effective in very cold water below about 60 feet because of the compression of the gas in the bubbles and consequent diminution in the thickness of the insulating layer. However, down to that depth, it provides the most comfortable suit, or acts as the most excellent underwear below a dry suit, that has been evolved.

The material is easily patched, made up into suits, or altered to fit a particular diver, while tearing it does not remove or even noticeably impair the heat-retaining qualities while the torn material lies in place. Thus, tears in a wet suit, or flooding a dry suit when wearing foam underwear, is not uncomfortable.

A diver dressed in a properly tailored suit is so streamlined that there is practically no more drag than when he is swimming with only a bathing costume on.

Clothing for aircrews is often electrically heated, and it has been suggested that the diver's clothing should also be treated in this way, thus eliminating one of the major causes of discomfort and termination of a dive. This has not yet been done, at least in common practice, because, as the following tables show, the power required to maintain the temperature is far too high to ensure that the diver does not lose any heat at all. However, a combination of new techniques and materials should bring this benefit within the grasp of divers, thereby increasing their potentialities particularly at great depths. For instance, a suit that will maintain a layer of carbon dioxide around the body loses only about half the amount of heat in the same time as air, while neon would provide a three-fold improvement in insulation over CO_2.

TABLE V

Maintenance of bodily heat—power requirements and materials

Water temperature: 32°F.
Average Northern Man

Insulating layer: $\frac{1}{2}''$ thick
Heat production at rest 0·093/4 watts
Surface Area 2·0 sq. metres

Material	Conductivity Btu/hr/ft²/°F/ft	Power required to maintain body heat in addition to that supplied naturally at rest
Air	0·014	141 watts
Wool	0·0211	210 ,,
CO_2	0·0084	84·3 ,,
Rubber	0·08	802·5 ,,
Water	0·343	3400 ,,
Helium	0·0818	822 ,,
Neon	0·00256	25·7 ,,

Thus an open cell fabric with its volume maintained at a constant value, and the layer thickness preserved whatever the diver's posture, could provide a suitable foundation for a warmed suit without requiring an excessively large power supply.

In very cold or filthy water it is necessary for the diver to be completely enclosed in a water-tight envelope, and besides the suit this is done by wearing gloves of various types, which will be considered below, and a dry or wet hood.

As with the rest of the body it is necessary to maintain a layer of air close to the skin if the hands are to remain warm. This may be done by excluding the water from a layer of woollen fabric, or by trapping it in the cells of an elastic foam compound. An additional problem is presented when trying to keep the hands warm for they are the diver's principal sensory organs when he is submerged, and if they are muffled and obstructed by gloves will lose their effectiveness. Thus the aim must be to cover the hands under a thin, flexible, air-filled, layer resistant to abrasion yet transmitting small differences of texture through to the skin.

There are two main types of glove in use to-day, the dry and the wet. Dry gloves, like dry suits, are made of proofed fabric with the highest possible tear and abrasion resistance so that they remain thin and pliable. Room for additional layers of wool underneath is allowed and the dry seal is made at the wrist, often overlying the cuff seal of the suit. Where the diving is taking place in cold water for some length of time the gloves are sometimes sealed on to the sleeves of the suit and both cuff seals omitted. The disadvantage of this being that should the gloves be torn then the whole suit may get wet through a tear which is otherwise isolated to that one hand. If the depth of the dive exceeds about 50 feet it is advisable to ensure that air can enter the glove from the suit, otherwise with the increase in depth the air compresses and the heat-insulating effect diminishes with the decrease of thickness of the insulating layer. A roughened palm and underside of the fingers is usually a feature of these gloves and is necessary in order to grip smooth things like bottle valves, greasy spanners, or other tools, effectively.

The wet gloves, like the wet suits, derive their effectiveness from the layer of gas bubbles trapped in the foam material of which they are constructed. At present this is usually foam neoprene or rubber. The gloves should be close fitting so as to reduce the effect of pumping water in and out as the hand is opened and closed, and, because they are closed-cell and the volume of air cannot be maintained with increase in depth, are most useful in the first 60 feet. The advantage of this type of glove is that it keeps the hands warm, though wet, and can be removed while a job requiring delicacy of touch is executed. When the hand starts to get cold, or the job is done, the glove is put on again and the warmth quickly restored. A further advantage is that the result of puncturing or tearing the fabric is not nearly so drastic as it is when dry clothing becomes wet through a tear. Slight inconvenience may be caused and an increase in the pumping effect experienced, but the hand will not begin chilling immediately nor experience the painful effect of being plunged into icy water unprotected, which can be so demoralizing in difficult conditions.

Although different people will wish to wear gloves at different degrees of cold it may be taken that any temperature below 50°F. may be cold enough to need to protect the diver so that he retains the fullest use of the senses in his fingertips. This is particularly so if the work involves digging his hands into clay which soon numbs with cold even though the water temperature is not low.

Wet or dry hoods come in the same category as wet or dry gloves although it is usual to take more care to exclude water from the ears and hair if there is a likelihood of their becoming filled with sand or contaminated water, whereas the hands may be exposed under those conditions.

Dry hoods are made of a thin layer or rubber formed by dipping over a mould. They completely envelop the head leaving an opening for the face and for entry through the neck. The ears are allowed extra space and this is essential to prevent 'reverse ears' if no additional air can enter the suit from the face-mask or a suit-inflation system. The additional air trapped in these blisters will continue to diminish in volume unimpeded by any rigid structure and so keep the pressure between the inside and outside of the ear balanced. If these blisters or cups are not present the hood may seal off the outside of the ears as the air is compressed, thus giving rise to the same effect as a diver unable to clear his Eustachian tubes, but the other way round.

The hood may be sealed to the shoulders of the suit with which it is worn, or it may be a separate item sealing on to a neck ring and clamped in position. A vent valve is usually fitted into the neck of the hood.

Neck seals are often used in place of a hood but are seldom used when hard physical exertion is needed, or when the dive will extend over more than half an hour, as it is very difficult to make a neck seal that is really water-tight. If a neck seal is worn in cold water a 'wet hood' provides complete protection for the head and neck. Some types are made to seal round the neck with a thin rubber 'cuff', as some gloves do round the wrists.

Care should be taken to ensure that while the face opening is not so large that the edges of the material lie outside the sealing edge of the mask, yet it must also leave the eyes clear and uncrowded, and the mouth free. This latter point is particularly important if a soft-fronted mask is being worn in which the mouthpiece can be withdrawn while talking as great difficulty in replacing it will otherwise be experienced.

Wet hoods are various in shape and may be as slight as a bathing cap, or completely cover the head and neck. The edge of such a hood must lie outside the seal of the face-mask otherwise water will enter the mask from underneath the hood. These hoods must be firmly secured in place or they will float or get 'blown' off by the water streaming past.

If the diver has a good thick head of hair he will not require more than a thin rubber hood even in very cold water, provided it covers the back of his neck as well. A foam hood is recommended for those who are not accustomed to cold water, or for those with less hair.

The temperature at which a hood becomes necessary will be largely a matter of opinion and acclimatization, but it is more comfortable to use one in temperatures below 50°F. Acclimatization takes place very quickly, and it will be found that whereas a hood is necessary at the beginning of a session it may soon be discarded as an unnecessary obstruction.

The modern diver using a surface supply will wear either boots with heavy lead soles, or fins, depending upon the job to be done, and may sometimes wear fins for descending and ascending, and the boots while working on the bottom. This will then give him great mobility in getting to the work and leaving it, and increased weight and stability where it is most needed. Extra weights in the form of a belt can also be put on if required at the site.

The boots, as shown in *figures 12 (i) (ii)*, are usually made of rubber with room for lead soles to be inserted, and done up with stout lacing. There are a number of different ways of doing lacing up but they are all directed to ensuring that even the suction of deep and thick mud will not pull them off, while the diver can release them easily if necessary. This is sometimes ensured by fitting a slip-pin that can be pulled out and to which all the lacing on one side is made fast. All knots on lacings, and on anything else the diver may have to release quickly, must be bow reef knots.

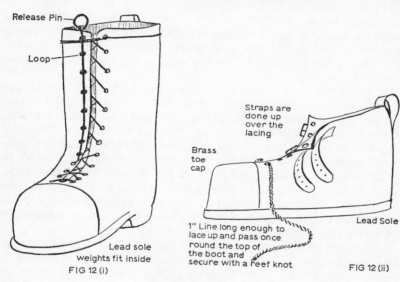

Diving Boots

Other knots, and particularly those without a bow, will jam. Some boots are fitted with a pocket for the knife to fit into, but it is an uncomfortable and unnatural position for it, besides proving a nuisance when crawling through narrow spaces, or over coils of ropes or wires.

The essential features of boots are that there shall be plenty of room for a heavily clothed diver to put his foot into it as well as the 20 lb. of lead weight in flat sheets that is often required. They should be very robust and flexible with no square or sharp angled cuts in any part that can lead to tearing, and the lacings should be stout, easily handled, and long enough to pass twice round the boot and be tied with a bow reef knot to secure the boot.

Fins have already been discussed on page 56, and it is only necessary to add that care should be taken to ensure that those used by the diver are sufficiently large to fit over the feet of a suit when he is wearing clothing beneath without cramping the foot. The majority of makes of fins are designed for a naked or lightly clad swimmer, and usually it is only possible to obtain sufficient room in the largest sizes sold. It appears that the manutacturers design the size of their dies on a figure of average foot widths throughout a population, whereas the majority of divers seem to me to have wider feet than the average, consequently discomfort is often experienced when a suit and clothing have to be worn.

The principles upon which the operation of a Standard Diver are based are valid for his more lightly equipped successor except that the required facilities can be lighter and simpler.

The diver still requires a shot-rope to guide himself down to a specified point on the bottom, and a distance-line for use as a horizontal guide when once there. However, the shot need not be so heavy, nor the shot-rope so stout, for if a tidal stream is running the diver can descend by swimming down, and ascend in the same way, so that little more resistance to the flow of water, and therefore lift on the shot, is exerted than that of the shot-rope by itself.

The platform can be reduced in size and for many jobs it is desirable that it should be as small and light as possible. Thus a booted diver can work from an inflatable dinghy of the type shown in *plate 9* provided that a short ladder is fitted for him to come in over the side. Otherwise rolling him in requires two men, or that he should remove his boots first. This size of dinghy is quite adequate if the diver is swimming and therefore able to manœuvre in depth and float on the surface. While such small dinghies have been used successfully in brisk weather in the Bristol Channel, and other areas, where a choppy sea raised by tide against wind is experienced, a slightly larger type such as that in *figure 8* is drier and more comfortable besides being faster.

Ladders can be fixed in these craft by making hoops that fit over the inflated tubes and stays into the centre of the craft, as shown in *figure 8*.

When diving from a platform that is part of a shoreside structure, or a larger boat, care should be taken to see that the diver does not have to enter the water from a great height, although the usual method of entry is by jumping, and that he can leave it easily and without a struggle. The ladder should be wide enough (2 feet) and go far enough underwater (about 3 feet).

As with Standard dress, if the diver has got his heavy boots on he should also be secured by a life-line and not allowed near the side of the platform until ready to dive. The attendant should secure the life-line to the diver by means of a bowline knot tied in the line which must pass next to the diver's body, and underneath the breathing apparatus. Usually in this rig the life-line is the air supply line. As the line leaves the diver it should be secured to the apparatus at one shoulder to ensure that if he is brought up in a helpless condition he will come up head first, and will not be liable to slip out of the bowline.

When the breathing equipment is put on the attendant must check the condition of the apparatus and that all connections are tight. The diver then puts on the mask and checks it for water-tightness by blocking off the breathing tubes and sucking from the mask. Provided the mask holds the vacuum it is water-tight. The diver should also check that he can clear his ears by blowing against the nose clip, and should have remembered to demist his mask by spitting into it and spreading the spittle over the window before flushing the mask out with water. If any communication or recording equipment is carried it should be finally tested at this juncture.

Having dressed, donned the breathing equipment, and begun breathing correctly from the equipment, the attendant should take the time and allow the diver to enter the water. This is most conveniently done by jumping in feet first provided there is sufficient room, and in very shallow dives, sufficient depth of water for him not to hit the bottom when he does so. When jumping in the diver must put one hand over his face-mask to prevent its being dislodged, and if he is wearing equipment with large cylinders on the back, must hold the cylinders down with the other hand to prevent their hitting him on the back of his head, particularly if the demand valve is situated immediately over them.

Another important point to remember when jumping into the water when wearing fins is that the diver should cross his feet over each other, as this will help to prevent their being dislodged on hitting the surface. This is particularly liable to happen when jumping in from heights over 10 feet. Above 20 feet there is more likelihood of breaking the straps or feet of the fins, while a misjudged leap, resulting in the diver landing on his face, can result in a broken face-mask. The diver should never dive in head first as he will probably lose his face-mask in doing so, while the outcome of hitting a submerged obstacle would be serious indeed.

When entering the water from small boats the habit of going in head first and backwards by means of a backward somersault from the gunwale should be discouraged. It results in the diver or swimmer being out of control until he has righted himself, and by that time, if he is diving in a tidal stream, the current will have carried him away so that an effort to regain the boat will have to be made. Entry from the gunwale of the boat should be from a sitting position facing outboard with one hand on the gunwale, or a line secured to the boat, and jumping off with a half turn in the direction of the hand holding on. This is quiet and the diver retains control for the minimum effort, while no undue strain is brought to bear on any part of the equipment. Furthermore, if any part of the equipment is faulty and has escaped the notice of the attendant during the dressing routine it will be apparent immediately on entering the water, and the diver can be rescued with the minimum of fuss.

The attendant allows the diver sufficient life-line for him to rest upright in the water with his face-mask just awash, and when this has been taken up by the diver's momentum he checks him and hauls him up so that he can grab hold of the ladder. Once on the ladder the diver allows excess air to escape from the suit, either through the blurp valve at the back of the hood, or through his cuffs, if he is not wearing dry gloves or grays (soft rubber bands around the cuffs to reinforce the seal). At the same time the attendant can examine the equipment to ensure that there are no air leaks from the various breathing tubes, supply lines, and connections.

Provided that all is well the diver is hauled to the shot-rope in the same manner as the Standard Diver, and when ready can drop to the bottom as quickly as his ears will allow. With practised divers this will take approximately one minute per 100 feet. It is at the point when the diver is ready to leave the surface that he is handed any tools or instruments that may be necessary for the job, and which cannot be sent down to him, or to await his arrival. When it can be done the tools should be secured to a shackle riding on the shot-rope, and to the lowering line. They will then arrive within the vicinity of the shot on the bottom and can be easily found.

Signals are passed using the single life-line code, but otherwise the diving technique is similar to that adopted in Standard practice, except that the danger of being squeezed by a fall does not exist.

If the dive is in water more than 50 feet deep it is usual to equip the diver with a suit inflation system so that he can keep the volume of air in his suit constant, and can therefore retain the thickness of the layer of insulating material.

When the diver is ready to ascend, having made up his distance-line, he will exchange the correct signals with the attendant and start to haul himself up the shot-rope. Assistance should be given by the attendant as the diver does not get much lighter through the expansion of the small amount of gas in his suit unless he inflates it with the suit inflation equipment. This will usually give him sufficient buoyancy to float to the surface for a short time before all the excess gas can leak away through the blurp valve or cuffs.

The routine during the ascent and on arriving at the surface will be very similar to that for a Standard Diver. Care should be taken at all times to help the diver, and once he has taken his mask off to ensure that he cannot fall into the water. Thus the life-line should be the last piece of equipment to be taken off.

Whenever the bottom conditions consist of thick soft mud the diver will probably be more effective wearing fins rather than boots. He can still be heavily weighted, but will have a great deal more mobility over the mud if he can swim or propel himself through the water without needing to get a purchase on anything solid. He will of course still require a life-line, and need to be attended as though he were wearing boots.

There will be many occasions when the diver needs to be swimming freely in dark water where a life-line is essential for safety. Under these circumstances the most satisfactory equipment to use will be a surface supply set, for the supply line is no more bulky than a life-line and the diver will be free of the greater part of any encumbering equipment.

The diving technique will still be based on what has gone before with the heavy divers. A shot-rope is desirable as a guide, and a distance-line from the shot-rope. In clear water these may be dispensed with as the line of the life-line is sufficient guide, while the diver being light and in control of his vertical movement does not require a shot-rope to maintain his depth at the decompression stops, although the decompression routine can be more effectively carried out if the constant movement otherwise necessary to do this is eliminated by passively hanging on to a rope.

When descending the ears should be cleared frequently as this will prevent a pressure difference building up in the Eustachian tubes, tending to hold the entrances shut despite muscular effort to open them.

If a diver gets into trouble using this equipment the attendant should be able to analyse the nature of it quickly. Failure of the breathing gas supply can be spotted immediately on the surface, and the diver signalled to come up quickly. As he can only carry a small reserve of gas for emergency purposes it is important that the attendant should be paying constant attention to the noise of the diver breathing, or the vibration of the breathing through the air-line in his hands, and if he can see them, the bubbles from the apparatus after each breath.

However, the tell-tale from bubbles should not be relied on as evidence either that the diver is well or not. When diving near a ship, floating objects like catamarans, or submerged structures, the air bubbles get deflected, trapped, or released at odd intervals to give a totally false impression of where the diver is, or what he is doing. Sunlight on broken water, or broken water itself, quickly mask or destroy the trail, and in these conditions the diver should never be alone without a line to the surface.

If the bubbles stop, or the breathing noises stop, and the diver does not answer a signal quickly, then he should be hauled up, if this is possible without his becoming snagged by obstructions on the way up. If it was a false alarm no great harm will be done and the job can be resumed or the diver descend to begin a proper decompression routine. There is no danger of the diver 'falling' when wearing this equipment, even if he surfaces a little way from the shot-rope, because of the buoyancy of the expanding air in his suit. The diver can become unconscious or have a flooded breathing equipment which causes him to drown quickly. Thus, speed under these circumstances will be vital.

Diving should never be undertaken in conditions that fall short of being ideal using a half-mask, or visor, and a separate mouthpiece. Full face-masks only should be worn. The reason for this is that if anything happens to make the diver faint or lose consciousness he will almost always let go of the mouthpiece as his jaw slackens. This immediately turns a mishap into a case of drowning in which all haste is necessary to save the diver's life. A really secure and stoutly constructed face-mask, or a full face-mask with a mouthpiece, are minimum requirements in all diving other than that in shallow, clear, water close to shore or a boat.

As a cautionary note, no equipment of this type should be used that does not have an emergency supply of gas carried by the diver, independently of all other reducers or demand valves, and sufficient for him to reach the surface by whatever means may be available.

If the diver is thought to be a case of drowning artificial respiration must be applied within a few seconds if he is to have any chance of recovery. This is best done by hauling him to the platform facing away from it.

With two men he is easily dragged inboard. With one he may be dragged or rolled. Take the face-mask off and the mouthpiece out, if one is being worn. With his face lower than his chest any water should run out, then the drill explained on page 125 is carried out with all despatch. As speed is vitally important never hesitate to use a knife to cut away equipment. If the heart has stopped beating or cannot be felt it will also be necessary to carry out heart massage as explained on page 126, but to do both this and artificial respiration requires two men.

This will be an exceedingly rare accident if the divers are competent, and a proper emergency supply checked before every dive is carried out. More frequently the diver is likely to feel unwell, or faint through diving when unfit. In these circumstances he must again be hauled to the surface, but if his face-mask is in place and empty of water, and his breathing equipment working (this may not be apparent until he is inboard), then he will probably recover after a few seconds in the open air. If he is at all cyanosed (blue lips) it will be best to let the fresh air revive him provided he is still breathing. If he is not breathing of course then artificial respiration must be applied. Oxygen should be administered if the patient is breathing as it may be the only way in which a water-logged lung can be adequately oxygenated until the water therein is absorbed.

If the diver is fouled up no attempts to pull him free on the air-line must be made. If he thinks that he could be pulled free then he must signal for a rope to be sent down to him (two pulls), make it fast round himself, and then signal for it to be hauled up. Under these circumstances it would be usual for the attendant to dress (if no other diver were available), put on a spare set, and investigate the trouble. This spare set should be self-contained unless a third man is available to watch the surface air supply, otherwise it is possible for the attendant to find himself in as much trouble as the diver if the main supply fails for some reason, whereas with an independent apparatus it is unlikely that that would become defective at the same time.

Although these accidents are very alarming when they occur, all effort should be devoted to preventing panic or random movement. Speed is essential, but conservation of air and low CO_2 evolution are equally important if effective action is to be taken.

It is possible to control panic only if it is stamped on immediately it appears. In the individual himself it can be detected sprouting out in flashes of extreme apprehension. At this stage it is possible to control if the individual is ruthless with himself and rests absolutely. But if he has lost control he must be quieted, if necessary violently, for not only does the malady quickly overtake the victim, it is contagious amongst others and very dangerous.

A more likely, but none the less potentially serious, occurrence is when the diver's air-line has become snagged around some obstruction and signals cannot be passed through from the surface. Probably the diver is quite unaware of the occurrence until he attempts to move about or to surface. This is obviously a serious predicament, for if the diver has any accident he will be unable to reach a place of safety, or to signal his distress. If, for example, he continued working until the tide became too strong on the bottom, on attempting to surface, and ascending into the stronger stream above him, he might be unable to reach the position where the line was fouled. Thus it is the job of both the attendant and the diver to do their utmost to prevent this occurring. When it does, an alternative method of signalling the diver, such as a spanner banged on a steel structure, or a detonator, must be used to tell him to come up. This will be sufficient to inform the diver that his line is fouled, for why otherwise signal with a spanner and not on the air-line? This signalling can be done according to the single life-line code.

To prevent these mishaps the diver should always proceed slowly and carefully, making sure that his life-line is clear from the shot-rope (the attendant should also play his part in this) after going a short distance along the distance-line, never doing more than one circle in one direction when engaged on a circular search, and always keeping the life-line in hand when on the move. An occasional signal to the surface, particularly in moments of doubt, are also useful to ensure the line being clear.

If these precautions are observed it will be found that snags occurring along the length of the life-line or snag-line are soon felt and quickly cleared. In order to maintain the distance away from the shot when doing a circular search in dark water it is often necessary to keep heading out away from the shot, rather than at right angles to the direction of the distance-line. This is because the distance-line takes up a curve backwards from the resistance of the water and the bottom as it is being dragged along.

If the life-line does become fouled it must be followed up and carefully disengaged from the obstruction. It must never be jerked free as this may serve to tighten the knot, or even *sever the line* on a sharp edge.

5

Deep Diving and Self-contained Equipment

Surface air supply is usually used down to 100 feet as it is the simplest method of diving provided no distant horizontal movement is required. However, few of the modern types of equipment have been made to operate satisfactorily much below that depth as there is practically no commercial requirement to do so. Thus extended commercial diving below 100 feet is nowadays done by divers wearing regenerative self-contained breathing apparatus, while naval or experimental diving is done using Standard Equipment with deep-diving attachments for depths below 240 feet. Below this depth observation chambers are used although other methods could give the diver greater freedom and make him more useful.

Deep diving in the Royal Navy has always been carried out with the specially adapted Standard Diving gear. This is in principle a regenerative apparatus for the atmosphere in the helmet is circulated through carbon dioxide absorbent, and then rebreathed by the diver. Other experiments in deep diving have been carried out using self-contained apparatus and in 1937 an American dived to 420 feet in Lake Michigan, using an oxy-helium mixture in a self-contained helmet suit.

From this arbitrary depth of 4 atmospheres, downwards air is rapidly becoming a less suitable mixture of gases to breathe. The density is rising, the poisonous effects of increasing partial pressures of nitrogen and oxygen are becoming apparent, and decompression is becoming rapidly more important for even short periods of exposure to the pressure.

Increasing the density of the inhaled atmosphere increases the frictional resistance to flow through the passages of the breathing system, and impedes the rate at which CO_2 can diffuse out into the alveoli from the blood. This results in the breathing effort being increased both by reason of the increased rate of breathing caused by the impaired rate of diffusion of the CO_2, and by the greater work required to overcome the friction and move the increased mass of gas in the system at each breath.

The effects of the higher partial pressures of oxygen and nitrogen are an increasing likelihood of oxygen poisoning and the gradual development of nitrogen narcosis with time. The threshold for both of these ailments being lowered by the presence of CO_2. Eventually at a depth of 297 feet oxygen is being breathed at a partial pressure of 2 atmospheres, while nitrogen narcosis is already overpoweringly evident to the diver, and becoming worse the longer he remains at that depth breathing air.

In order to overcome the related problems of nitrogen narcosis, breathing resistance, and decreased ventilation of the lungs, a gas which is much lighter is used to dilute the oxygen. Generally, despite the expense, it is helium that is chosen rather than hydrogen, simply because of the difficulty that oxy-hydrogen mixtures raise of explosion, while oxy-helium is completely safe in this respect. To be safe from the risk of explosion the oxygen proportion of any oxy-hydrogen mixture must be less than 0·04. This mixture can only be used as an atmosphere below 132 feet where the partial pressure of the oxygen would also raise problems because it would be necessary to substitute another respiratorily inert gas before ascending above this depth so that the mixture in a diver's chest is never explosive.

Although these lighter mixtures have been used in the open-circuit demand valve self-contained type of equipment, the waste is so extravafant at the greater depths that insufficient quantities of gas can be carried to enable the diver to make proper use of the advantages of this technique. As the waste is greater using Standard Equipment, even though it is fitted with a recirculating system for deep diving, and the cost of this gas is so high, this type of diving is seldom carried out except for experimental purposes, or submarine rescue, and operations now are conducted with an observation chamber in conjunction with a grab worked from the surface. The only equipment that can make use of the advantages of this technique, while keeping the cost of the diving within bounds, is the regenerative self-contained gear.

An understanding of the use of this equipment, both the deep diving Standard Equipment and the regenerative self-contained equipment, is dependent upon having the gas laws, which have been examined before (Chapter I, 'The Sea as an Environment'), firmly in mind.

Although air, as breathed at sea level, may not necessarily be the best gas mixture at the best pressure that each individual is most suited to breathe, yet on the average any considerable disturbance of the partial pressure, or the density, of the constituents is deleterious.

Thus, it must be the aim of the designer of equipment that is to be taken deep into the sea, or to support life for extended periods at shallower depths, where the very length of exposure to the unusual pressure conditions will develop symptoms of trouble normally too slight to be noticed, that the partial pressures of the active components of the breathed gas mixture, and the resistance to flow of the inert components, are maintained close to their sea-level value (see TABLE I).

Firstly it is necessary to maintain the partial pressure of the oxygen in the breathing apparatus between 0·16 and 2·0 atmospheres. Any less will lead to anoxia, while more raises the possibility of oxygen poisoning, particularly if the level of CO_2 is high, and the diver has been exposed to a high oxygen pressure for some time. In fact, it is advisable to keep the oxygen partial pressure as nearly as possible at 0·2 atmospheres.

The partial pressure of CO_2 must be kept below 0·03 atmospheres if the diver is to be spared discomfort and kept efficient, while the designer's aim should be to keep this pressure below 0·01 atmospheres.

If nitrogen is being used to dilute the oxygen its use for extended diving operations should be restricted to ambient pressures of less than 3 atmospheres, if the diver is to remain thoroughly efficient throughout the dive. At a partial pressure of approximately 4 atmospheres narcotic symptoms are apparent to the diver himself, and these symptoms will develop with time shortened by the presence of a large quantity of CO_2.

With any type of semi-closed-circuit regenerative breathing apparatus the rate of flow of the mixture to be admitted into the breathing system will depend upon the proportions of the gases in the mixture and related to the figures given above, while the proportions of the mixture to be used will depend upon the type of apparatus and the depth of the dive.

In closed-circuit apparatus it is only the diver's oxygen consumption and CO_2 elimination that are disturbing elements in the system to be corrected by the sufficient supply of oxygen and the absorption of the CO_2. So far, a really satisfactory system of regulating the oxygen supply in concert with the diver's consumption, so that the partial pressure of the oxygen remains constant, has not yet been evolved as it depends upon the development of a compact and reliable oxygen partial pressure metering device. When once this has been developed, however, no further advance in gas consumption efficiency will be possible. At present the only completely closed-circuit breathing apparatus in use relies upon the breathed mixture containing more than 99·5 per cent oxygen. Any less oxygen than this can give rise to anoxia if shallow breathing (if the diver is unconscious) follows after the system has been used during deep breathing and when the cylinders are almost exhausted.

Thus, all the regenerative apparatus used at present, whether by swimmers or deep divers in adapated Standard Diving dress, will need a flow calculated and set, either by the designer if the gear is automatic, or the diver if it is to be set for a particular dive, and its operation is only semi-closed-circuit.

In the deep diving equipment this is ensured by the design of the equipment and the nature of the mixture supplied. In self-contained apparatus the flow can be more easily adjusted to suit a wide variety of mixtures. However, the method is the same and depends upon the rate at which the gas under pressure will pass through a small orifice.

The volume formula given below enables the correct flow figures to be calculated.

$$\frac{O}{D} = \frac{MF - C}{F - C}$$

Where O is the proportion by volume of oxygen in the breathing system.

M is the proportion by volume of oxygen in the mixture supplied to the breathing system.

D = Absolute depth (reckoned in atmospheres)

F is the rate of flow of mixture into the breathing system by volume per unit time.

C is the rate of consumption of oxygen by the diver by volume per unit time.

Whenever the depth and duration of the dive are such that the diver can surface immediately in the event of emergency without severe danger the value for D is maintained at 1·0 in order to guard against anoxia overtaking the diver if he should surface under these circumstances.

The values for M will depend upon the maximum depth to which the diver could descend during the dive. During the periods that are possible with present apparatus the oxygen content is maintained as high as possible provided the partial pressure is kept below 2·0 atmospheres in order to reduce the flow of gas required, and thus increase the submerged endurance of the gas supplies carried on the apparatus. An additional effect of increasing the oxygen content of the system is to reduce the inert gas content and thus reduce the time required for decompression as this is dependent upon the partial pressure of the gas.

The value for C is taken at various figures for various purposes. When reckoning the maximum oxygen partial pressure that is likely to arise in the system for a given mixture the lowest figure of 0·25 litre/minute is used. It is unlikely that even an unconscious diver will use significantly less than this amount. The maximum sustained consumption may be taken as 3 litres/minute. However, the CO_2 absorptive capacity of modern equipment is not yet efficient enough to allow this high work rate to be maintained for more than a very short burst and it is therefore more practical to allow a highest continuous rate of 2 litres/minute. Less will be adequate if the diver cannot get into a situation where he must exert himself during the ascent to the surface. This maximum consumption is also used in the calculation for the flow of gas required for any work during the dive. Thus by calculating for a sufficient exertion at the surface, and on the shot-rope, that is less than the amount consumed during hard swimming, considerable saving in gas flow may be achieved over the greater part of the dive. During dives in depths where the diver must return to the surface, and in which any additional oxygen supply may be required for decompression stops, the flow should not be arranged to give the diver less than 2 litres of oxygen per minute at the surface.

When the diver cannot return straight to the surface because of the risk of severe decompression sickness, and surface decompression techniques are not being used, then the flows required can be considerably reduced, by giving D a value which economizes in gas at the diving depth but gives a minimum safe depth. At this point a different mixture must be substituted to bring the diver to the surface.

The process of calculating the flows, mixtures, time of the dive, and decompression routine, for a dive is given in the following example.

Depth of water in which the dive is to take place = 165 feet.

Total gas capacity of the breathing apparatus ..	800 litres mixture of gases.
Volumes at normal temperature and pressure—	
N.T.P.	200 litres oxygen (additional supply).

To find the mixture, flow, decompression routine, and length of time for the dive:

Absolute pressure at the greatest depth possible during the dive .. .. $\frac{165}{33} + 1 = 6\cdot0$ atmospheres absolute

∴ Maximum permissible value for O $= \frac{2}{6\cdot0} = 0.333$.

This occurs if the uptake of oxygen, i.e., the volume of C, is zero.
The minimum permissible value for O equals 0·2, and this will occur when C is maximum, i.e., equals 3·0 litres/minute.

Thus, using the formula, $O = \frac{MF + C:}{F - C}$

$$0\cdot333 = \frac{MF - 0\cdot25}{F - 0\cdot25} \quad .. \quad .. \quad .. \quad (1)$$

$$0\cdot2 = \frac{MF - 3\cdot0}{F - 3\cdot0} \quad .. \quad .. \quad .. \quad (2)$$

Combining the two equations:

$$\frac{2\cdot4}{M - 0\cdot2} = \frac{0\cdot167}{M - 0\cdot333}$$

$$M = 0\cdot344$$

Thus the mixture to be used is 0·344 oxygen, 0·656 nitrogen.

When M = 0·344, from (2), $F = \frac{2\cdot4}{0\cdot144} = 16\cdot67$ litres/minute.

It should be remembered that the flow formula is a volumetric expression and only describes the situation at the absolute pressure considered. In this case at one atmosphere, or the surface. If the situation at other depths is to be examined then the full expression

$$\frac{O}{D} = \frac{MF - C}{F - C}$$

must be used. ∴ Allowing ¼ of the capacity of the cylinders to be unavailable, used through the by-pass valve, or required to operate the reducing valve to give a correct flow, the total time that the diver can spend underwater breathing the mixture is:

$$\frac{800 - 200}{16\cdot67} \text{ minutes} = 36 \text{ minutes}$$

The mixture in the breathing system has been calculated so that the proportions of oxygen by volume will be equivalent to that of air if the diver has been exerting himself on the surface, and absorbing 3·0 litres of oxygen per minute. If he has been absorbing less, then he will have a larger margin of safety when ascending. It is with the depth and the total time that the diver can stay down that the decompression tables are entered, and the programme for the dive found. From Decompression TABLES I and II it can be seen that the diver can spend 15 minutes from the time of leaving the surface to the time of beginning the ascent, which must take him 15 minutes, and leave him with 6 minutes' spare gas. If necessary he can carry out the decompression stops using his oxygen supply alone, and, provided he empties all the gas in the system at every stop, and twice during the last stop, the decompression times can be reduced by half. This time could be reduced to two-fifths if oxygen can be breathed on open-circuit, which is not usually possible either in a decompression chamber or on a shot-rope, but as the nitrogen diffusing from the tissues is not eliminated from the breathing system and thus remains to diminish the difference of nitrogen tension between the lungs and the tissues so the more cautious figure of a half is given.

This procedure then gives him a further two minutes on the bottom which should be treated as a reserve period available in an emergency, and at the end of the dive he should have a remnant of mixture and approximately 80 litres of oxygen left.

In the event of there being no readily available source of mixtures made to the required proportions it is simple to make up mixtures from compressed air and oxygen.

The calculation for doing this is as follows:

If the required pressure in the supply cylinders = 200 atmospheres, and the mixture to be introduced is in the proportion by volume of 0·344 oxygen and 0.656 nitrogen, then the total pressure of nitrogen in the cylinders when they are charged will be 131·2 atmospheres (i.e. 0·656 × 200).

But compressed air and pure oxygen are the sole sources of supply. The proportion of nitrogen in the air is 0·79.

Therefore the total air pressure required to ensure the correct nitrogen pressure will be $\dfrac{131\cdot2}{0\cdot79} = 166$ atmospheres.

The compressed air is accordingly pumped in first as the cylinders will already contain 1 atmosphere of air, and oxygen will then follow after to bring the total pressure up to 200 atmospheres.

When changing over from one gas to another the pumping system should be vented and then blown through with the new gas so that the residual volume of the previous gas in the tubes and spaces of the pump does not get pushed ahead by the next gas into the cylinders to affect the mixture by an unknown amount.

The tolerable errors in making the mixtures will largely depend upon the figures for the particular dive, and a calculation should always be done assuming that all the errors have been weighted in one direction and then in the other, to ensure that the resultant gas mixture, flow, and decompression routine, will not put the diver in hazard. Where facilities for analysing the mixture are available these should be used. Portable analysing sets are available such as the Orsat, and the accurate laboratory apparatus required for the Haldane gas analysis method may be suitable where diving is being conducted in one place for an extensive period.

If the diving to be done is at depths below 150 feet, and it is necessary to keep the diver down for extensive periods, or a large emergency reserve is required, so that it becomes exceedingly perilous for him to ascend to the surface quickly, it may be desirable to reduce the oxygen partial pressure in the breathing system to a value close to that at sea level. As a result the diver will not be able to surface without becoming anoxed unless he augments or changes his supply of breathing gas. He would also be subject to decompression sickness if he surfaced quickly from these depths without decompression stops even if he could change over to oxygen or augment the flow by using the by-pass. The calculations for this dive would be approached in the following manner. Given the same apparatus as mentioned above in the previous example it might be necessary to dive for as long as possible to 165 feet given a total mixture supply of 800 litres, oxygen supply of 200 litres, and a CO_2 absorbent duration of 2 hours.

Obviously the richer the supply of oxygen in the mixture the smaller the flow need be and it has been shown that the mixture for the depth considered is $0.344 : 0.656$, $O_2 : N_2$.

If the minimum safe depth in order to use 2 litres/minute is considered as 33 feet on the descent and 66 feet on the ascent then the flows and procedure can be worked out to see which gives the diver the best advantage.

$$\text{Minimum safe depth} = 33 \text{ feet}$$

Then the oxygen in the counterlung at this depth when requiring 2 litres/minute must take up $\dfrac{0.2}{2} = 0.1$ of the volume.

The flow to achieve this is given by $0.1 = \dfrac{0.344 \, F - 2}{F - 2}$

$F = 7.4$ litres/minute, $\therefore$ Endurance of the equipment $= \dfrac{800 - 200}{7.4}$

$$= 81 \text{ minutes.}$$

The equivalent air depth (for entering the decompression tables) $=$
$$\dfrac{1.0 - 0.1}{0.79} \times 165 = 188 \text{ feet.}$$

This means that the diver could stay 40 minutes on the bottom and by using oxygen for all the stops could decompress in 69 minutes. Thus having 41 minutes flow of mixture in hand. But, allowing 3 minutes for the ascent to the first stop only 8 minutes for the maximum duration of the absorbent.

If the minimum safe depth is selected at 66 feet by similar arguments the flow required would be 6·75 litres/minute, the equivalent air depth 195 feet, and the endurance 89 minutes. In this case the diver could still only spend 40 minutes on the bottom and 79 minutes decompressing, leaving himself just over the maximum endurance of the CO_2 absorbent. If the previous example is compared in a similar manner and the decompression carried out using oxygen then the endurance on the sea-bed could be doubled to 30 minutes with 34 minutes decompression on oxygen and only 6 minutes' reserve of mixture left in hand.

Obviously the preferable technique is to use the flow of 7·4 litres/ minute, which realizes the maximum potential of the equipment without incurring any other penalty than the additional 35 minutes' decompression time. In cold water this would probably be a serious consideration swaying the decision in favour of the lighter flow and shorter time spent swinging shivering at the stops.

It should be noted that the decompression routine used in these calculations are all from TABLES II of the Decompression Tables and involve a risk of a small percentage of bends. Thus a decompression chamber should always be available on or near the site of diving using these methods.

Although designs have been produced of apparatus that will maintain the oxygen partial pressure at values near to that obtaining at sea level, at the time of writing these designs have not yet got beyond the experimental stage.

The alteration of the partial pressure of the oxygen in the mixture can be achieved by changing either the rate of flow of fresh mixture into the system, so that the diver's metabolism acts as the agency of change, or by admitting separate gases into the system to mix in various proportions as required. Some designs have been made that use both systems but without an accurate method of measuring the oxygen partial pressure to within an accuracy of 0·01 atmospheres the system must remain inefficient in order to ensure that the diver is neither starved of oxygen nor flooded with it to a dangerous degree. When once such a measuring device is developed then all breathing apparatus will eventually become entirely closed-circuit in design as this is the most simple, compact, and physiologically satisfactory method of supplying the right atmosphere to the diver.

However, all deep-diving apparatus using helium mixtures, and closed-circuit apparatus designed for depths below 200 feet, have employed gas mixtures that have a minimum safe depth for use.

For example, compressed air used in semi-closed-circuit apparatus will yield sufficient oxygen for depths down to the limit fixed by nitrogen narcosis, while a set with the capacity of that taken in the example could be used for 10 minutes at 300 feet if the mixture used is oxy-helium. The actual calculation of the dive is a series of compromises as shown above and it would be necessary to carry a slightly larger supply of oxygen for decompression from this deeper dive than is allowed for in the example.

Standard deep-diving equipment is similar to that used for shallow water work except that the helmet is larger, has extra connections, and is fitted with a recirculating system with mouthpiece breathing used to eliminate the CO_2 and thus reduce the quantity of gas required to ventilate the helmet.

The helmet is fitted with two air connections, one for the supply of air or mixture and the other to exhaust through the CO_2 absorbent canister. The breast-rope connection is the same as on a shallow water helmet, and a fourth connection is sometimes fitted, particularly to American suits, to enable the suit to be warmed electrically. This is important in deep, cold water, as the heat conductivity of helium is greater than that of air by a factor of 5·7.

The breathing circuit of this gear is shown in *figure 13*. The flows required for it are arranged without calculation by the diving team by ensuring that a definite pressure to the injector is always maintained. In some oxy-helium gear this is 32 lb./sq. in. above ambient when breathing air, or 50 p.s.i. above when breathing either 13/87 or 9/91 (oxygen/helium) mixtures. The injector orifice is changed from one with a diameter of 0·055 inch to one of 0·025 inch when changing from air to either of the oxy-helium mixtures. The approximate consumption of gas is 14 litres per minute.

No deep diving with Standard gear is normally undertaken without the use of a very large platform or deep-diving ship that can carry large

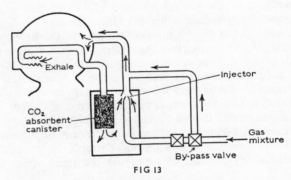

FIG 13

Deep-diving regenerative system

compressors, decompression chambers, submerged decompression chamber, and the necessary derricks and winches for handling the latter. In addition the diving team normally consists of at least 17 men plus the men required to work the derricks and winches. Thus, it can be seen that this is a large operation and closely limited by weather and tidal conditions. As a result little deep standard diving is now carried out commercially, most of the deep salvage work being accomplished by an observer in an observation chamber directing the ship and grab around the site. Most navies seem to be abandoning this method of conducting deep operations.

By contrast the use of self-contained equipment enables the diver to operate with few surface resources, particularly when using a 'free' pressure chamber with which to ascend to the surface (see *figure 13*), and no known limit has yet been reached although it is thought that the narcotic effects of hydrogen will eventually set this between 1,800 and 3,600 feet.

When diving operations below 100 feet are being carried out a decompression chamber should be easily accessible as it may not always be possible to recompress the diver by putting him back underwater. The likelihood of this being necessary will be greatly reduced if care is taken that the diver is fit, the breathing mixtures and absorbent correctly adjusted so that the significant breathing conditions do not vary from atmospheric conditions, and the equipment properly designed, built, and assembled. To date lack of quality and careful attention in design has been responsible for the poor reputation of deep diving or self-contained apparatus, and the indirect cause of accidents. It is not uncommon for incidents to occur whereby tubes have come adrift, leaks have developed in the gear, or the reducing or demand valves have suddenly ceased to work. Also, the deeper any equipment is taken the more obvious any defects in its design become, and the more dangerous these defects are.

When selecting or designing equipment that is intended for use in deep water certain principles should be rigidly observed.

Firstly, the partial pressures of the active gases must be kept as close as possible to those observed at sea level. Remembering that the so-called inert gases become obviously active as their partial pressures, and as the time they are breathed, increase.

Secondly, breathing resistance must be reduced as far as possible. Breathing underwater will always be more difficult than in air because of the difference of hydrostatic pressure between various parts of the breathing system, but a great deal can be done to keep resistance to the minimum

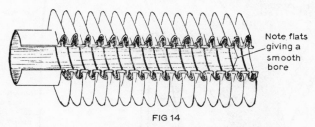

Note flats giving a smooth bore

FIG 14

Spiral wound breathing tube

by seeing that all the air passages are of large diameter and with a smooth lining, that as few bends as possible are used, and that all curves are gently radiused. In practically no commercial equipment produced to date are these criteria observed.

Thirdly, leaks must be prevented. This is principally a matter of good human and mechanical engineering and is not often observed. Face-masks should not leak, nor should it be possible to displace them with a knock, and breathing tubes, outlet valves, and counterlungs should not leak without a great deal of wear far beyond their designed life.

These points are always important, but they may become vital when deep diving as the diver's life is no longer dependent upon his own capacity for holding his breath and making a free ascent to escape from mechanism that has become dangerously defective, but upon the proper functioning of that equipment at all times.

The principle of the closed-circuit breathing apparatus is that the diver is supplied with oxygen at a sufficient partial pressure for him to breathe properly, and a method of removing the CO_2 that is formed as a waste product, without drawing on gas resources outside the system, or exhausting any gases to waste.

In practice this has only been achieved so far by making the breathing mixture contain pure oxygen, otherwise a flow of gas in excess of the diver's requirements is required to remove the inert gas supplied with the new supplies of gas. This fraction of inert gas would otherwise build up as the diver consumes only the oxygen but not the carrier used to dilute it. Except in the case of the deep Standard Diver, the gas supplies are carried by the diver so that his equipment is self-contained as well as being regenerative like the former.

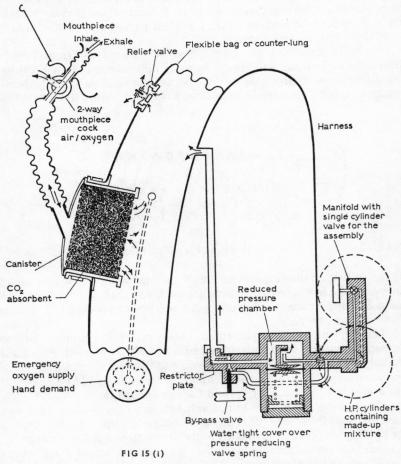

FIG 15 (i)

Semi-closed-circuit pendulum breathing apparatus

The description, regenerative, is given because the gas exhaled by the diver is regenerated by having the CO_2 removed and the depleted oxygen fraction restored before being inhaled again.

There are two main types of semi-closed-circuit self-contained equipment (see *figure 15 (i) (ii)*). One employs the pendulum breathing system whereby the inhaled and exhaled gas travels up and down the same tube, while the other directs the flow round and round the system one way only.

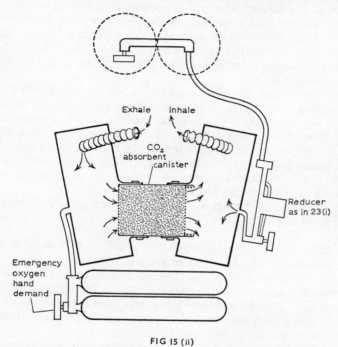

FIG 15 (ii)

Semi-closed-circuit 'one-way' breathing apparatus

The advantages of the pendulum breathing system are that it dispenses with valves in the circuit and reduces the number of breathing tubes by one, while it also ensures that the moisture content of the soda-lime used to absorb the CO_2 is maintained. Its principal disadvantage is the large and steadily increasing dead air space caused by the reciprocating movement of the gas, and the exhaustion of the soda-lime close to the breathing tube, first.

The one-way system reduces the dead space to practically the diver's natural dead space and ensures much fresher and more efficient breathing and CO_2 absorption. On the other hand valves have to be fitted to direct the flow and the apparatus is slightly more complicated, particularly to ensure that the soda-lime does not operate in a dried-out condition. Usually, to ensure this the exhaust has to be arranged to pass directly through the absorbent before collecting in the counterlung ready for the inhale part of the cycle. If it is arranged the other way round the water vapour condenses out in the counterlung and after a period of efficient absorption the performance of the soda-lime suddenly collapses, while this does not occur if it is kept slightly damp by condensation on the walls of the canister. From a physiological point of view this is a less satisfactory arrangement as it will generally require more effort to drive the exhaled gas through the canister and into the counterlung than it would to drive it into the counterlung alone, and as the diver's breathing is constructed so that he is better able to draw breath than expel it, it is less exhausting if this relation of effort is preserved in the apparatus. However, if the design is efficient the breathing effort will be very low, and this effort may then be discounted.

The canister must be so designed that when it is filled with soda-lime granules of approximately $\frac{6}{10}$ grain size there are no spaces left and the charge is not loose. This can only be ensured by being able to fill the canister through an opening that has the same diameter or measurements as the canister, and securing the charge in place with a spring-loaded mesh. By this means any change in shape of the filling can be taken up by the spring and gaps avoided through which the gases can channel, and the CO_2 pass by without being absorbed.

The soda-lime is exothermic in reaction with CO_2 and works most efficiently between 4–27°C.

Another method of absorbing CO_2 is with lithium hydroxide which is more efficient and safer but more expensive.

The counterlung must be constructed of a material that is gas-tight, very resistant to abrasion or tearing, and pliable. Proofed synthetic fabrics such as nylon or terylene are the most satisfactory, and newly developed materials give greatly increased safety and more satisfactory results than the rubber-coated stockinette used for so many years.

Positioning the counterlung is important as this will determine the amount of breathing resistance built into the apparatus. Ideally the bag should envelop the thorax from the sternal notch to the top of the diaphragm. This would then ensure that the breathing resistance did not change significantly with attitude. Other positions that have been chosen are, round the back of the neck, on the back by the shoulder blades, and on the front of the chest. A later type is carried on the front but has wings going round under the armpits. Besides the consideration of breathing resistance there is resistance to passage through the water, which will depend largely upon cross-sectional area. The more this is reduced the less the drag that the diver will have to overcome when swimming, walking, or holding on against a tide, for in all these activities he will be lying practically prone.

The breathing resistance for each particular apparatus must be judged in relation to the job it was designed for, and therefore the position that the diver is most likely to be in for the greater part of the time. For example, an apparatus designed for a man to use who will be standing up, or working vertically, may be quite satisfactory even though the breathing resistance is greatly increased if he lies down on his back. Resistance is measured as static pressure and the units usually employed are inches water gauge pressure. This is the height of a column of water than can be supported by the pressure under consideration. Normally the whole apparatus, not counting resistance due to pressure, should have a resistance no higher than 3 inches w.g. at peak flow rates at the maximum operating depth.

If it is taken that the maximum rate of flow at N.T.P. is at 300 litres/ minute in the centre of the inhalation or exhalation cycle then the resistance to this flow should be measured at a pressure equivalent to that experienced at the maximum depth for the apparatus. Commonly flow rates and resistances are quoted which appear satisfactory because they are evaluated at N.T.P. but which would not be so good if the truly operational conditions were simulated.

Resistance due to position should not be allowed to rise above a further 3 inches w.g., giving a total allowable resistance of 6 inches w.g., which is the greatest amount that can be tolerated for any length of time, particularly as the resistance in the lungs also increases significantly below 100 feet when breathing air.

Surplus mixture is allowed to escape through a relief valve that can be adjusted for the particular circumstances, either of steady breathing or ascent. It can be seen from examination of the example on page 101 that of the 16·67 litres of mixture flowing into the breathing system per minute a maximum of 3·0 litres per minute will be absorbed by the diver, leaving the remaining 10·94 litres of nitrogen and 2·73 litres of oxygen to be blown to waste if the volume of the system is to remain constant. Likewise, if the diver ascends from 165 feet to the surface in one minute and the total volume of the gas in his lungs and apparatus is 6 litres there will be an additional 30 litres of gas to be eliminated.

Other considerations are that the gas blowing off in the form of bubbles should do so as silently as possible both because noise interferes with communication, is an additional psychological impediment, and the bubbles may interfere with vision or the behaviour of organisms being observed. In military equipment it is also necessary to avoid the tell-tale trail of bubbles escaping to the surface and betraying the presence of the diver. Until recently safety and freedom from bubbles could only be ensured by using a pure oxygen mixture and a totally closed-circuit apparatus, which gave off no bubbles when properly managed. However, it has been found that provided the bubbles are broken up into a cloud of very small ones with a diameter of less than 0·03 inch they would dissolve a short way away from the diver.

Thus the relief valve must allow the escape of small amounts of gas steadily and at set escape pressures, it must accommodate large amounts on occasions, it must emit the bubbles as silently as possible, and it must not allow any leak back from the outside water into the breathing system.

Few valves are yet fitted to disperse the bubbles silently, and so are constructed of a simple spring-loaded valve seat that lifts under an excess pressure that is predetermined and set by screwing down on the spring. This type of valve is liable to allow water to leak back into the counterlung when working in mud, sand, or fine grit, and it has been known for the diaphragm to be forced over the mushroom piece when the by-pass valve has been accidentally knocked on so that a large amount of gas had to pass through it in a short time. If a subsidiary non-return valve is fitted underneath this trouble can be avoided and all relief valves on the breathing system should be fitted with this safety valve below.

However, some apparatuses have two valves fitted, one for relieving large volumes of gas and lifting at a higher differential pressure than the one that allows a steady escape of the excess gas from the flow of mixture coming into the set.

A type of valve that has been found to be effective consists of just a punctured rubber sheet, the holes being made by a sewing machine, which is rolled up depending upon the amount of gas that there is to be allowed to escape.

A composite relief valve incorporating a large blow-off valve and a fine adjustment for the steady flow is shown in *figure 16*. This valve is

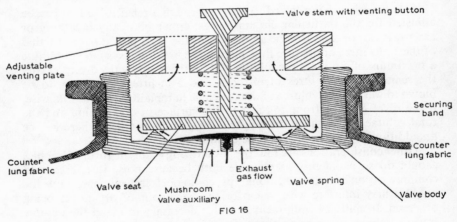

FIG 16

Counter-lung relief valve

fitted into the front of a face-mask rather than the usual position high up on the counterlung, as this is most likely to be the highest place and the 'smoke' of fine bubbles will drift away behind the diver if he is on the move, as he usually is.

The gas mixtures are usually made up before the dive and stored in large cylinders carried on the back from which the supply is taken to a reducing valve which also meters the supply to the breathing system. An emergency, or auxiliary, supply of pure oxygen is also carried, which is independent of the reducer or its supply route, and is under the manual

1. A diver wearing light-weight surface-supplied gear

(*Underseas Ltd*)

2. A diver wearing semi-closed circuit gear

3. Bottle, reducer, and weight pocket assembly of semi-closed circuit apparatus

4. A diver climbs into Zodiac-type diving boat, having first passed his gear in. This is shown in the foreground

5. Standard diver
on ladder
(*Underseas Ltd*)

6. Closed circuit
breathing equipment
and two-piece suit
(*Siebe Gorman Ltd*)

7 and 8.   Diver proceeding along the bottom, dressed in surface-supplied open circuit gear

9.   Small inflatable diving boat

10. Searching submarine

11. Zodiac-type diving boat fitted for off-shore survey, with Decca echo-sounder and diving gear and canopy for wet or cold conditions
(*Underseas Ltd*)

12. Light-weight diving bell
 (*Underseas Ltd.*)

13. Light-weight diving bell
 (*Underseas Ltd*)

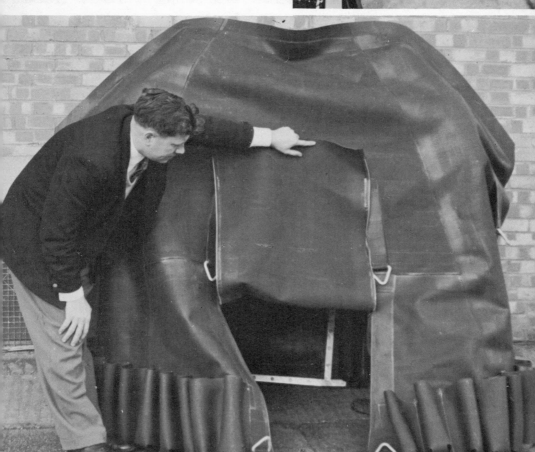

14. Decompression chamber with lock and submerged chamber attachment

(*Siebe Gorman Ltd*)

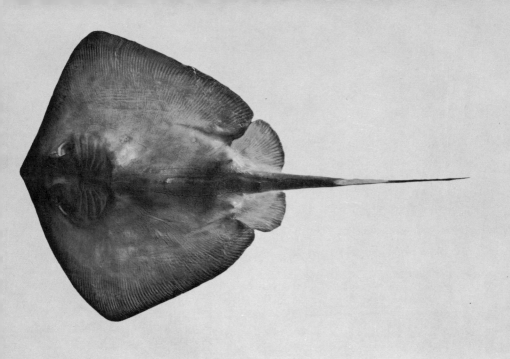

15. Sting ray

16. Killer whale

(*British Museum, Natural History*)

17. Sea urchins

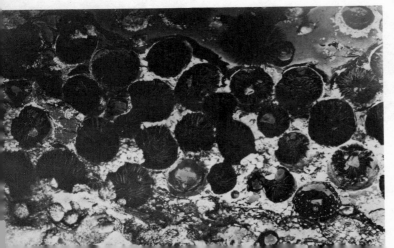

18.   Lion fish

19.   Cone shells
(*British Museum, Natural History*)

20. Stone fish
(*British Museum, Natural History*)

21. Portuguese man-o'-war
(*Dr. D. P. Wilson*)

22. Underwater
cine-camera case

23. Diver's sonar
(*Research Laboratory*)

25. Arc ruler showing
a range of wheels that
can be fitted to give a
radius of curvation
from 14 to 240 inches

24. Sextant

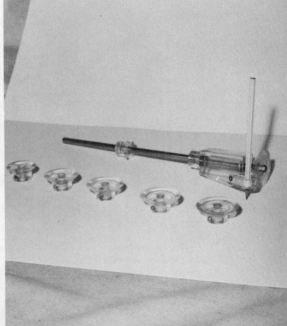

26. Diver connecting
up charges for area
blasting programme
(*W. Travis*, F.R.M.S.)

27. Divers setting up
Wagon-Drill on sea-bed
for strata drilling tests
(*W. Travis*, F.R.M.S.)

control of the diver. In addition there is a by-pass valve fitted that allows a supply of mixture to be taken directly from the main supply without going through the reducing valve. Thus, unlike open-circuit apparatus, the diver is not dependent for his life upon the integrity of one valve or one gas supply.

The rate of flow of gas through the reducer is effected by reducing the main bottle pressure to a predetermined figure that is higher than the greatest ambient pressure that will be experienced, and allowing the gas at this reduced pressure to escape into the system by way of a small orifice. If the reducer pressure is kept sufficiently high, and the orifice is small enough, the rate of flow through it will be independent of the ambient, or back pressure, provided that the ratio of the ambient to the reducer pressure is less than 0·527. The gas will then be travelling at the speed of sound through the orifice. It cannot travel faster and will not travel slower, so the mass of gas passing through will be constant. This is known as a Constant Mass Flow Reducer, and does not alter its characteristics within its depth range of operation for any given driving pressure.

Sometimes reducers are 'compensated' for depth by allowing the increasing ambient water pressure to bear directly on one side of the reducer diaphragm so that the flow is increased with depth. As the flow formula shows, this is an unnecessary waste of gas as the flow should decrease with an increase in depth.

An improved reducing valve whose flow decreases with depth could be made if the orifice was large enough so that the flow was not constant but the driving pressure was not so low that it fell below the ambient pressure.

A constant flow of gas into any system wherein the consumption is variable is bound to be wasteful as the flow must be arranged to cope with the maximum possible consumption, which very rarely occurs.

Thus, while the ideal totally closed-circuit apparatus would merely replace the oxygen taken out by the diver, as mentioned before, some advance towards the ideal can be made by varying the mixture as the diver descends and metering the mixture to him on demand. In essence this latter system would bear the same relationship to the present semi-closed-circuit apparatus as the open-circuit demand valve apparatus does to the Standard gear.

One method by which this can be attained is by using compressed air in one cylinder and oxygen in another. By supplying the right amounts to the diver at a definite point in the breathing cycle both the mixture and the amount can be varied without a meter to detect gas partial pressures to fine limits, with a result that considerable savings can be effected and the diver's range increased (see *figure 17*).

With all self-contained apparatus being used in any but the best diving conditions and under constant supervision the face-mask must cover the whole face. This must ensure that the diver will not lose his breathing system provided attention is paid to securing the mask by robust attachments to the head, and ensuring a good, water-tight, compression seal round the face. Breathing tubes are unavoidable with gear

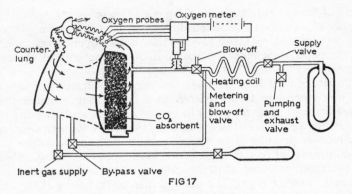

FIG 17

Closed-circuit metered breathing apparatus

that does not employ the suit as a counterlung, and as these lead to breathing resistance and form obstructions that can catch up on obstacles they should be kept as short, and of as large diameter, as possible, while the inside bore should be made smooth (*figure 17*). The face-mask is also a convenient place to put the relief valve for the system as it is usually at the highest point for the greater part of the dive. If the face-mask has no mouthpiece it is usual to ensure that a flow is maintained through it, pre-loading the valves, and reducing the effective dead air space, by means of an injector unit operating in the absorbent canister in the same way as the deep-diving attachment on the Standard gear. This method is not suitable if the mixture is supplied on demand, and in this case an oro-nasal mask inside the main one may be desirable.

When diving with self-contained apparatus the procedure and resources are far less cumbersome than with the heavy gear, and this freedom may give the impression that there is less need for caution, safety regulations, and discipline, than in Standard Diving. This is untrue and dangerous. Because the diver is so much more free he is also very much more dependent upon himself and his colleagues diving with him. If the Standard Diver faints or becomes ill and helpless he will generally be hauled out of the water on to a solid platform while a number of hands become available to assist him. If the self-contained diver suffers a similar disturbance and has failed to take the proper safety precautions, he may well be lost.

The diving boat, or platform, can be very small and light provided the diver can climb in easily. If he is wearing boots then it will be necessary to have a ladder fitted unless he can be attended by two men, who can easily launch him inboard while he faces outboard. If he is swimming then it is simple to slip the set and hand it to the attendant who lifts it inboard, and then to climb inboard afterwards, being considerate about the water that will tend to splash up and come in with him.

Inflatable craft are quite the most satisfactory as diving boats in all weathers for this type of diving as they are seaworthy, low to the water, and can be adequately powered.

If the diving is to be done in dark or tidal water a life-line should be worn, and the divers should operate independently. But in good visibility the divers can often work more efficiently in pairs, being linked with a 'buddy line' so that they maintain contact.

A shot-rope should always be used except in the most ideal conditions and shallow water, as the diver will rapidly become lost without some tangible or visible guide. The shot-rope can be suspended from a small float adequate to bear the weight of the tide that may run in the area. If the depth is such that decompression is likely then the shot-rope should also be distinctively marked off in tens of feet from the surface.

The procedure when diving with self-contained gear must be followed rigorously to avoid accidents. When the gear has been put on and the diver is just about ready to enter the water he will finally put his mask on. The whole system must be cleared of any gases that may be in it and of unknown composition by sucking from it and exhaling into the air. An air/mixture valve is usually fitted in the apparatus to enable this to be done. If he wishes to demist the mask then immediately before putting it on he should spit on the face-glass and spread the spittle over with his fingers. This is quite the most efficient demister that has been produced for diving apparatus.

When once the system is cleared of gas the main supply is turned on, the time noted, and the volume of gas in the system augmented by judicious use of the by-pass valve which need be only just opened to fill the counterlung very quickly.

The diver should be allowed two minutes to adjust the relief valve, the volume of gas in the system, and to become accustomed to the new mixture of gases being breathed. There is some evidence to show that the high oxygen partial pressure has some influence on the respiratory system and symptoms akin to shock are sometimes discernible. If the diver is likely to be significantly influenced by this these two minutes and a postural change from sitting down to standing up at the end of that time will have given the symptoms adequate opportunity to develop if they are going to. During this time the attendant should check that all connections are tight on the apparatus and the way clear for the diver to begin.

As in every other form of diving both the attendant and the diver should be very clearly aware of the purpose of the dive and the intended methods by which the aim will be achieved.

The diver must always enter the water feet first, whether he jumps or merely launches himself in. This procedure will protect him against the possible dangers of striking any unsuspected submerged object and will enable him to retain control the whole time. This is particularly important in tidal waters where a great deal of effort can be wasted getting back to the diving boat against the tide if the diver drifts down tide for a few seconds while he sorts himself out from the flurry of entry.

Once in the water the diver should hang on to the platform or boat with the breathing apparatus just below the water so that the attendant can detect any leaks from the apparatus that may have been overlooked, or caused by entry. When satisfied the attendant gives the signal to carry on and the diver proceeds to the shot-rope, if one is being used for the dive. For decompression routine purposes, whether the attendant or the diver is conducting it, the time of leaving the surface is the time from which the calculations are started.

It is usual to use a nose clip as most people find difficulty in clearing their ears rapidly without its assistance. As soon as the descent begins the diver should consciously clear his ears every three or four feet. This will ensure that they do not get jammed shut by the pressure as can happen during a rapid descent, thus preventing any further clearing and bringing the descent to an abrupt halt.

During the descent the relief valve is kept shut off so that gas is not wasted, for every bit will be required as the depth increases and the volume of gas in the breathing system decreases.

The descent should be as rapid as the diver can manage without hurrying. He should take care to keep his ears clear and the breathing system adequately full of gas, compensating for the decreasing volume as the pressure increases by use of the by-pass valve. Descending in a tideway may be quite an effort and care should be taken not to become breathless with the work but to proceed steadily down. This is particularly important where there is no visibility as the breathless man is not in a position to think clearly and is more likely to take alarm at an unexpected turn of events.

Having once reached the bottom, which is generally a great relief and very comforting in its tangibility, a brief rest should follow, if the descent and conditions were difficult, before proceeding with the job. Also the attendant should be informed that the diver is on the bottom by one tug on the life-line.

The procedure that should be followed once the bottom, or the site of operations, has been reached will of course depend upon the job, but at least the diver should move carefully and deliberately, both because any unnecessary effort is more wasteful of available physical resources than ever it would be on the surface, and because of his limited appreciation and adaptedness to his environment. Thoughtless movements may have unfortunate consequences. While this will be instinctively obvious to the man diving in dark water it may not be so apparent to the happy one in clear water until he plants his hand firmly on the spines of a tropical sea urchin that was just out of vision of his mask.

Before beginning the ascent and having informed the attendant, or his other colleague, of his intentions to ascend, the diver should exhaust all the gas that he can from the breathing system and refill it with completely fresh mixture by means of the by-pass valve. This will ensure that the CO_2 tension in the system is low during the first part of the ascent and will thus avoid a slight dizziness that is sometimes felt and which may become a serious contributory factor to disorientation in dark water when the diver has left the bottom and has no longer any aural, visual, or tactile horizons to keep him properly orientated.

Refilling the counterlung with relatively fresh gas with a low proportion of CO_2 also contributes to safety as a high CO_2 partial pressure is well known to lower the threshold of resistance to oxygen poisoning and decompression sickness. If these symptoms overtake the diver he may feel panicky, dizzy, sick, and start to take foolish and abrupt action. It can also lead to his fainting. This is not only a good reason for 'flushing through', as this ventilating process is called, but also for providing a shot-rope and guidance system when diving in dark and tidal waters.

When nearing the surface, if the ascent is fairly rapid there may occur another moment of dizzy breathlessness. This is largely due to the rate at which the gas in the breathing system is expanding, and the slightly increased pressure in the system over and above the ambient pressure required to vent it through the relief valve. This causes the diver to suffer slightly from hyperventilation, or forced breathing. A similar feeling is sometimes felt if the ears are slightly resistant to the escape of gas from the Eustachian tubes. The former is easily combated by slowing the rate of ascent and opening up the relief valve a bit more to allow the excess gas to escape. On very few valves is it safe to pull the valve open as this lets water into the counterlung as well as air out. However, the later types do allow this to be done.

Occasionally it may become necessary for a diver to abandon his equipment and ascend to the surface with only the breath he can hold in his lungs when he leaves the bottom. This method of escape, known as Free Ascent, is the standard method used in most submarines of to-day, and while it has been demonstrated to be possible from a depth of 300 feet, it is practised by many hundreds each year from 100 feet. However, there should be no misconception that the method is entirely without danger. It should only be used if the diver is forced to do so and it is unlikely to be successful unless he can ventilate adequately before starting and leave with his lungs full, except in very shallow water.

When a man takes in a lungful of air at a depth of 100 feet and then ascends to the surface this volume will have increased fourfold. Thus, to avoid any risk of rupturing his lungs he must allow this excess gas to escape during the ascent and for many people this requires conscious control of their throat and mouth muscles which will otherwise block the breathing passages.

Men trained in free ascent are taught to purse their lips as though whistling and to start breathing out very gently from the moment they leave the bottom. With instructors around, clear, warm water, and adequate previous ventilation this is easy in practice. In the event of an emergency, however, the circumstances are so different that the risk is very great and this method of escape is truly a last resort.

6

Submarine Medicine

In previous pages the physiological and psychological factors affecting a diver have been examined and the features that are largely novel to terrestrial medicine are those in which gas poisonings, differences of pressure, and drowning occur. While divers suffer injuries such as might occur to them on land it is not the treatment of these cases that will be considered here except in so far as there may be any complicating factor that is due to diving.

The gas poisonings which the diver may be subject to result from oxygen, CO_2, CO, and nitrogen. Purely pressure effects producing decompression sickness, embolism, and damage in the various air spaces of the body are typical diver's complaints. The less obvious troubles arising from heat, cold, explosions, animals, polluted water, stress, and dietary deficiency will also be mentioned. Although drowning is not specifically a diving hazard yet it is always present as a threat after any accident to the respiratory apparatus and is accordingly examined here.

Finally, an Appendix is devoted to the principal factors that should guide the medical examination of divers.

The rhythmic activity of breathing is the result of an interaction of three control systems. Firstly, the pH of the blood decreasing as CO_2 is excreted from the tissues as the result of metabolism leads to stimulation of the breathing centre in the brain, which initiates the contraction of the muscles of the chest wall and diaphragm as well as stimulating the circulatory system. When the muscles have completely contracted and the lung volume is at its maximum a reflex action, known as the Hering Breuer reflex, operates to reverse the process and those muscles which contracted now relax allowing the previous elasticity of the stretched tissues to restore the chest to its resting, exhaled, position.

The effect of any sudden exertion, reflected as an increase in the rate of metabolism, is met initially by an increase in the depth of breathing, that is, an increase in the degree of contraction of the muscles of the ribs and diaphragm; it is followed by quickening pulse rate. Both the increased quantity of blood flowing past the alveoli and the improved ventilation of the lungs increase the rate of diffusion of the CO_2 and O_2 through the lung wall, particularly as the increased lung expansion opens up new areas of alveoli exposed to the air. Finally, the breathing rate is also quickened.

The third system is the feeble one mentioned before in connection with the stimulation resulting from anoxia. This is, however, so slight that it does little to initiate a breath and generally only affects the degree of ventilation. It can be seen from this brief résumé that the balance of CO_2 is vital to stimulate breathing despite its otherwise being a waste product and poisonous. The partial pressure of CO_2 in the alveoli is kept extraordinarily constant at 0·055 atmospheres, and the variation of this figure by one-thousandth of an atmosphere has an effect on the breathing rhythm and rate of circulation making it deeper and faster as the figure increases, and slower and shallower with a decrease. The relative strength of each of these stimuli taken separately has been shown to be excess CO_2, decreased lung volume, and lack of oxygen, in that order. While the powerful effect of excess CO_2 is apparent in the appearance, struggles, and feelings of a choking person it has only recently been shown that decreased lung volume by itself is also a sufficiently strong stimulus to initiate the breathing rhythm. This was shown when the experimenters hyperventilated to wash out the CO_2 from their tissues then took a lungful of oxygen and held their breaths for 10–14 minutes. The 'break point' when they were forced to inhale again occurred when their lung volume had decreased to the residual volume while the CO_2 partial pressure was still well below 0·05 atmosphere. This experiment should not be undertaken except in a laboratory with doctors in attendance as the individual reactions to these conditions may not all be uneventful.

Anoxia is almost the most important of the physiological hazards affecting the diver because it is the final effect underlying many of the other accidents and if unrelieved will kill the victim.

The subjective symptoms of anoxia precede unconsciousness so briefly, if the supply of oxygen is drastically interrupted, that it has often been said that there are no subjective symptoms. However, in many of the diving accidents which happen, and are due to anoxia, the oxygen partial pressure is diminished in association with other events and the symptoms then become obvious. This is particularly true if the diver has been active when the accident occurred, although even then it has been found necessary for him to be sensitive to the effects to notice them in time. Otherwise unconsciousness intervenes before he can take effective action. There appears to be even less warning when the ambient pressure is reduced as in flying, and it is suggested that the presence or absence of self-recognizable symptoms may depend upon the rate of diffusion of CO_2, an amount of CO_2 retained in the tissues, undisplaced by oxygen, serving as a slight warning. The most recently developed central nervous centres are the most sensitive to oxygen lack, and it is found that the inability to concentrate occurs first followed in rapid succession by greying and darkening of vision with increasing tubular effects, 'distant hearing', loss of control of the facial and hand muscles, and finally amidst a general feeling of being apart from the environment, complete unconsciousness. The objective symptoms are, rapidly increasing vagueness, increased rate of shallow breathing, blueness of the lips, slackening of the facial and throat muscles, twitching movements, and unconsciousness. If the patient has been anoxed for some time the characteristic blueness of the lips in particular, and the general hue of blue through the skin, is a sufficient indication of the cause. No time should be lost in freeing the breathing passages of any obstructions, and, if necessary, beginning artificial respiration as laid down in the section on drowning (page 125). Oxygen should be administered as mentioned before (page 96).

The effect of giving the victim pure oxygen may be, paradoxically, to stop his breathing altogether. This can occur because oxygen at a high partial pressure initiates a reflex action which tends to restrict the supply of blood to the brain, and if the CO_2 in the blood is lowered sufficiently the breathing centre fails to stimulate the breathing response. Provided the victim is made to breathe air his blood will become saturated with oxygen within a few seconds and in the case of the normal healthy person we are considering as a patient here additional oxygen in the breathed atmosphere would not result in an increase in oxygen in the tissues unless his lungs are water-logged to any extent, when oxygen would be urgently required.

This is not the case where CO (carbon monoxide) poisoning has taken place although the effect of such poisoning is to produce a state of acute and prolonged anoxia. When poisoning from CO is suspected, for example if air is being breathed as the whole or part of the breathed supply when compressor exhaust fumes may have been included, then the correct treatment is to give the patient pure oxygen to breathe as he cannot suffer from the ill effects of the relatively high oxygen partial pressure while the CO remains combined in his blood. Such a patient will also appear flushed because while the de-oxygenated haemoglobin is blue, carboxyhaemoglobin, the result of the combination of carbon monoxide and haemoglobin, is bright red.

Although the response to being exposed to the fresh air in an ordinary case of anoxia is followed quickly by complete recovery, yet the longer he is suffering from anoxia the longer recovery will take and the more likely he is to suffer permanent damage to the central nervous system.

The criterion of how quickly one may have to act is whether the pulse has stopped or not. If it has there is no time to lose at all because although some individuals may survive a limited amount of anoxia others suffer irreversible damage and death, very quickly. Unlike other cells in the body the nerve cells of the brain and spinal cord are incapable of replacement, and having a high metabolic rate are soon affected by lack of oxygen. Once seriously damaged they may die and the patient with them. The brain tissue cannot be left without a reoxygenated blood supply for more than three minutes without incurring damage. Thus there should be no delay in giving artificial respiration and heart massage as quickly as possible if there is any failure in these functions.

Anoxia is the underlying cause of the symptoms resulting from hyperventilation, unconsciousness after CO_2 poisoning, the final stages of oxygen poisoning, and 'shallow water blackout', or oxygen syncope.

As mentioned before, there is a physiological reaction to low oxygen tension by receptors in the aorta and carotid arteries, but this is feeble, as it only needs to be in natural surroundings. The reduction of the oxygen supply is generally too quick when it does occur in breathing apparatus for this response to evoke a powerful enough reaction in time.

The effect of increasing the ambient partial pressure of CO_2 in the atmosphere being breathed is to decrease the rate at which this gas can diffuse from the lungs. While this external partial pressure remains below 0·01 atmospheres the increase in ventilation rate is tolerable, but at 0·03 atmospheres the effect is becoming noticeable to the diver himself, and as the value of the normal alveolar level is approached so the symptoms of poisoning become rapidly more apparent.

Finally, as the partial pressure of the CO_2 in the inspired air becomes equal to that in the alveolar air, so the CO_2 tension in the blood starts to rise in spite of maximum respiratory effort. Under these conditions un-controllable panic will be followed by unconsciousness, when the partial pressure rises to 0·1 atmospheres, muscular spasms at about 0·15 at-mospheres, and death if the conditions are not relieved.

The initial subjective symptoms are a desire to get a complete breath, and noticeable deep breathing. In situations where there is additional stress frequent flashes of baseless apprehension, and later panic, may be experienced. Where panic is allowed to gain control the subsequent symp-toms will be accelerated as the metabolic activity of the victim increases. As the deep breathing develops into a hard panting, and racing pulse, without relieving the situation, so the distress of the victim increases. Finally, the breathing and pulse rate drop and he becomes unconscious. A headache accompanies the other symptoms if the onset of the poisoning is sufficiently slow, while it always persists after the patient is otherwise recovered because of the vaso-dilatory effect of CO_2 particularly in the brain.

The objective symptoms are easily followed by the course of the sub-jective ones as the patient is obviously in distress and will make con-siderable efforts to relieve this distress. As noted before, the breathing rate and depth, and the pulse rate, increase to their maximum, and the patient becomes flushed and gasping. As the direct cause of becoming unconscious is anoxia of the central nervous system no time should be lost in restoring a supply of fresh air and adequate ventilation to the patient's lungs. Al-though in this case the supply of oxygen for breathing would not incur the same dangers as before, because there is quite sufficient CO_2 present to stimulate the breathing centre, yet the method of artificial respiration ex-plained later is advised as a normal first-aid practice if breathing has stopped. If the patient is retrieved before his breathing has stopped he will rapidly recover if he is able to breathe fresh air, and should suffer nothing worse than a headache of more or less severity and slight shock.

With some modern types of breathing apparatus it is possible for the diver to experience CO_2 poisoning through working as hard as his muscles will allow him, and therefore as hard as he might expect to be able to work on the surface. If this occurs he should reduce his effort as much as possible, even relaxing completely to rest for half a minute or so while breathing deeply and consciously during this time with his eyes shut. If by-pass or ventilation facilities are available on the apparatus that he is wearing these should be used as well to reduce the CO_2 partial pressure in the system. It is important to realize that while the basic cause of the poisoning is lack of alveolar ventilation there may be several conditions giving rise to this situation. These may be over-exertion, resistance to breathing in the apparatus, and impaired diffusion because of the increased density of the gases breathed with depth.

While the presence of a greatly excess pressure of CO_2 is obviously dangerous, yet even in moderate quantities insufficient to be noticeable in breathing apparatus it lowers the threshold to toxic reactions when high concentrations of oxygen, or gases giving rise to narcosis, or tensions of gases liable to come out of solution as bubbles to give rise to decompression sickness, are present, besides probably having a narcotic effect in itself. Thus it is most necessary that the design of all breathing apparatus should pay considerable attention to reducing the CO_2 tension.

It has been seen both how necessary the presence of CO_2 is to the correctly functioning breathing cycle, and how disastrous a small increase in the quantity can be, but now we must consider the equally important effects, although much less unpleasant, of a drop in the CO_2 tension.

If someone breathes very deeply and often for a time so that his lungs are thoroughly ventilated the CO_2 tension in the alveoli drops and this is followed by the diffusion of CO_2 from the tissues so that the pH of the blood rises. It will take a little time for the metabolism of the tissues to restore the original balance but in order to restore the balance oxygen is consumed. Since there is no store of oxygen in the body other than that contained in the lungs and the very small amount carried round by the blood, and this store is already saturated by the normal breathing cycle in the absence of increased metabolic acivity, the oxygen can only be exchanged between the red corpuscles and the cells by means of a com-plicated series of chemical reactions which depend upon the higher partial pressure of the oxygen in the blood to that in the tissues. To supply the oxygen required for metabolism and to maintain the CO_2 which will continue to stimulate the respiratory system requires that the circulation should be increased to supply the necessary oxygen. This does not take place in the absence of stimulation by CO_2 and an impasse can be easily reached whereby the patient becomes unconscious and ceases to breathe because of anoxia brought on by the arrest of the breathing cycle through lack of CO_2. A dangerous game played at parties illustrates this reaction which is enhanced by rapid postural change or pressure on the chest forcing blood from the head into the peritoneal cavity.

It can occur to swimmers who breathe deeply before diving and then hold their breath for a long time. If they swim down and stay down too long the CO_2 tension may not have built up sufficiently to force them to the surface before the partial pressure of the oxygen retained in their lungs has dropped to a dangerously low figure. This is the only significant store of oxygen in the body and within a few seconds of the partial pressure dropping to 0·1 atmospheres the swimmer will become unconscious. Usually in accidents of this nature, as the swimmer's lung volume has been reduced by pressure at the outset of the dive, so the partial pressure of the gases in the air contained therein will have increased. If he now remains submerged until the partial pressure is close to the danger point before surfacing then as he ascends the danger point will be passed through and unconsciousness ensue before, or on, reaching the surface. Furthermore, there may be no inclination to breathe, which although protecting him from drowning, may make rapid treatment on the surface difficult.

Another moment when the diver may suffer from symptoms of slight hyperventilation is on return to the surface after a dive which does not involve decompression and in which the diver may reach the surface quickly without harm. During the ascent the diver is probably exercising very little, allowing the buoyancy of the expanding gas in his suit and breathing apparatus to bear him upwards. As the pressure decreases so the partial pressure of all the gases in the breathing system, including the CO_2, is also decreasing, but if the apparatus was functioning correctly at the sea-bed the alveolar CO_2 tension was nicely adjusted to stimulate the correct breathing rate. The partial pressure is now suddenly collapsed before the tissues have time to produce a compensatory decrease in the pH of the blood and so restore the balance. As a result the diver experiences the initial effects of hyperventilation due to a depletion of the CO_2 supply.

While other causes of hyperventilation exist and may afflict the diver, such as anxiety, exhaling against a pressure, and the initial efforts of breathing through a mouthpiece, the effect is less than that which exists during an ascent.

The subjective symptoms are apprehension giving rise to an urgent feeling to surface even more rapidly, which must be resisted or the symptoms get worse, and an increase in breathing rate which enhances the hyperventilation. Treatment by the diver himself consists of resting, or at least reducing his effort, and remaining at one depth, or even descending a little deeper, until the symptoms have subsided.

If the diver is breathing pure oxygen at 33 feet, or air at 297 feet, the oxygen will be present at a partial pressure of 2·0 atmospheres. It has been found by experiment that this pressure can be tolerated by the majority of divers for the short periods that are usually experienced and that the apparatus used at present will continue operating. If any partial pressure in excess of 0·2 atmospheres is maintained for some time the symptoms associated with oxygen poisoning develop. The higher the partial pressure the shorter the time the neurological symptoms will take to appear. The symptoms which are apparent in the cells of the exposed tissue of the lung wall indicate a disruption of the complicated metabolic processes in the cells. When this happens to nervous tissue at similar oxygen partial pressures the resulting stimulation gives rise to a typical epileptic fit preceded by a short bout of minor convulsions and twitching. Some protection is given by the fact that a high partial pressure of O_2 gives rise to constriction of the blood vessels, particularly of the brain, so that the deleterious effects are delayed. The presence of CO_2, however, lowers the threshold to oxygen poisoning as it has the opposite effect of vaso-dilation, thus eliminating the protective delaying reflex of high oxygen partial pressure by itself.

The subjective symptoms are vague and once again similar to those felt at the onset of anoxia except that twitching face muscles may give a short warning before the onset of unconsciousness and a convulsion.

Although the majority of accidents, or experimentally induced convulsions, occurred when the victims were subjected to partial pressure of oxygen at, or in excess of, 2.3 atmospheres, it is generally accepted that for the limited times of exposure given by most apparatus, and at the shallow depths, a partial pressure of 2.0 atmospheres is tolerable. For deep diving it is arranged never to exceed 1.75 atmospheres. If long exposure to high pressures is expected then the partial pressure of the oxygen in the mixture should not exceed that in the atmosphere at sea level by more than 0.1 of an atmosphere.

The objective symptoms of oxygen poisoning are an increasing loss of control of the muscles and twitching starting at the face and spreading rapidly through the limbs until the whole body is involved and the epileptic fit mentioned before is observed. If the oxygen tension is not reduced the patient will die, and reduction of pressure is the immediate first-aid treatment. The patient should recover quickly without any residual effects other than fatigue or injuries sustained during the convulsion and is unaware of the fit shortly after the facial contortions begin. The time and pressure at which symptoms of oxygen poisoning appear are variable both between individuals and at different times in the same individual. No effort should be made to restrain the convulsion beyond trying to keep the patient from causing himself or others damage and getting a gag between his teeth to prevent him biting his tongue. This gag should be covered with cloth to prevent him damaging his teeth on it. Although the spasm might be strong enough to break a bone this is unlikely to happen with the normal diver.

As the density of the atmosphere being breathed increases so the rate at which CO_2 can diffuse out from the alveoli is reduced and it is thought that this restriction is a contributory factor to the symptoms of narcosis that are observed at different depths and which appear to depend upon the molecular weight of the gas forming the so-called 'inert' fraction of the atmosphere being breathed.

The subjective symptoms of narcosis are gradual and increase both with depth and time, eventually becoming fatal if the exposure is continued long enough. The first and immediate symptoms have been outlined before and will be briefly recapitulated. The air feels heavy (because of the increased density) and may taste slightly metallic, the lips may tingle slightly, and there will be a distinct feeling of detachment from the surroundings as if they were of less concern than normally. Concentration is affected, and besides being unable to concentrate the patient may find himself feeling disinclined to do so. Some people feel light-headed and hilarious, while others become deliberate in their movements and thought. Whistling is impossible below an equivalent depth of 90 feet, and very difficult before that, while the voice becomes strained and higher-pitched. Musical instruments, however, are unaffected provided the density/speed of sound ratio of the gas mixture is the same as in air. This shows that the effects are entirely physiological, perhaps affecting certain parts of the nervous system very early. Furthermore, it is an effect that varies directly with time and there appears to be some relationship between narcosis and decompression sickness. This is apparent because subjects who are more sensitive to narcosis also appear more susceptible to decompression sickness.

Manual dexterity and balance are unaffected in the early stages even when subjected to partial pressures up to 8 atmospheres of nitrogen.

The objective symptoms are similar to that observed during the successive stage of alcoholic poisoning in the particular individual.

The symptoms are almost immediately relieved with the decrease in partial pressure of the inert gas. The lighter gases do not cause the symptoms to appear until a depth porportional to their molecular weight and in helium and hydrogen it has not been observed in practice although it might be expected to appear at 964 feet breathing helium, with the oxygen partial pressure maintained at 0·2 atmospheres.

CO_2 can also give rise to narcosis but generally is only found in patients whose breathing centre has become habituated to high CO_2 tension and whose respiratory stimuli are obtained from the chemo-receptors in the carotid arteries and aorta which respond mainly to low oxygen tensions. This condition is only found associated with disease and such a patient would not be diving as he would swiftly lose consciousness through CO_2 poisoning on being exposed to the high partial pressure of oxygen in the breathing equipment which would remove any stimulus to breathe to eliminate the CO_2.

Drowning.

The mechanics of drowning have been thoroughly investigated and it has been found that patients fall into two types. When the CO_2 partial pressure in the blood rises to 0·06 atmospheres, and the O_2 tension drops to 0·07 atmospheres, the breathing reaction overwhelms all other controls and an expiration is swiftly followed by an inspiration. If the patient's swallowing reflex is working efficiently then the incoming water will be diverted into the stomach, the patient will lose consciousness through anoxia, and will eventually die of anoxia, becoming a characteristic blue colour. If the reflex does not work then the water will be taken into the lungs. The membrane lining the lungs is impermeable to water in one direction, as it must be to keep the water in the tissues from filling them up, and highly permeable in the other in order to pump out into the blood stream what little normally finds its way in. When fresh water enters it is assimilated by the vast area of lung tissue (about 900 square feet) very quickly. The enormous increase in fluid volume and pressure overwhelms the heart which fibrillates and stops. In fresh water this takes place in a matter of 15–30 seconds, while in salt water, where the osmotic pressure of the salt water causes dehydration of the blood, the time is slightly longer. The patient dies of anoxia caused through lack of oxygen in the lungs or heart failure. Only very swift action to get the lungs ventilated and the heart functioning again can be effective. The total time allowed before irreversible damage is caused to the brain is usually assumed to be three minutes although individual cases have been known of survival after the heart has been stopped for ten minutes. Until recently it required great courage and exact anatomical knowledge to carry out the operation which would expose the heart to view so that it could be massaged and restarted. Fortunately it has recently been shown that a simple external form of massage is generally effective, that is, if any massage is likely to be so.

This massage is carried out by stretching the patient on his back, putting the heel of one hand under the sternum with the fingers extending on to the sternum, and the other hand on top to give greater pressure Then, pressing down on the heel of the lower hand and also along

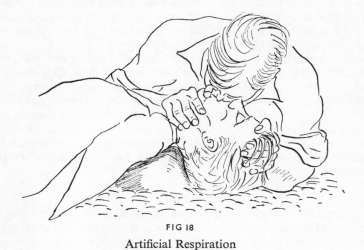

FIG 18

Artificial Respiration

towards the patient's chest. This action should be repeated 40 to 50 times a minute which is about the speed of counting 'one—and—two—and—three— and—four' slowly. Generally it will be necessary to respirate the victim artificially, as mentioned below, but two people are then necessary to apply these measures together. Massage should be continued until all hope has disappeared that the circulation can be restored, which may not be for an hour after the original failure.

Although it may not be obvious at first sight into which of these two categories the patient falls, great speed is vital if the patient is to survive. Generally the patient who is simply anoxed is blue and the one with flooded lungs, white. Mouth-to-mouth artificial respiration should be carried out according to the drill set out below (see *figure 18*).

Firstly remove obstructions to breathing, if necessary with your fingers wrapped with a piece of cloth. To prevent the tongue obstructing the air passages it is essential that the neck should be extended and the head pressed back while the lower jaw is pushed upwards. This will then draw the tongue forward. To assist this movement the patient should be laid on his back with a support under the shoulders allowing his head to drop back.

No time should be wasted in trying to drain water from the lungs or stomach other than the trachea and main bronchi as it has been found to be impossible to accomplish anything useful in this respect. It will remain until eventually absorbed.

It is also necessary to ascertain whether there is any pulse, or only a very slight one, without delaying the artificial respiration. In this event the external cardiac resuscitation method mentioned above must be used.

When the patient is in position the most comfortable position to administer the mouth-to-mouth respiration should be adopted with the administrator to one side.

Hold the patient's lower jaw and head as shown in *figure 18* and blow gently until you see his chest rise, then stop, remove your mouth, and it should subside again. Repeat the procedure half a dozen times as quickly as possible and then continue at about twenty times a minute.

If the patient is in convulsion or, for any other reason, his mouth is obstructed then he can be ventilated through the nostrils, but it may be necessary for him to be allowed to exhale through his mouth as it is possible for the soft palate to prevent this happening.

Of the other well-known methods, Eve's rocking method is the most efficient as it helps to restore the circulation as well as ventilating up to the normal tidal capacity of the patient. However, as the requisite apparatus is seldom at hand and is bulky it is of little practical use. The pumping action is derived from the viscera rolling up against the diaphragm and away from it as the body is rocked head up, heels down, then head down, heels up, at a rate of about 10 times per minute.

The Holger Nielson method achieves a ventilation of approximately $\frac{4}{5}$ of the tidal volume and requires no apparatus, but it cannot compare to the Biblical method explained before.

Other methods usually fail to do more than ventilate the dead air space, consisting of the throat and bronchii, which is of course quite useless.

Of the hazards arising from the differences of pressure caused by the relative incompressibility of fluids and solids as compared to gases the first to be considered is decompression sickness, which is physical in origin and mechanical in effect.

The cause has been shown before to be the result of reducing the pressure on the body so fast that the inert gas dissolved in the tissues has insufficient time to diffuse out via the circulation and the lungs, and after a super-saturated solution is formed gas bubbles suddenly appear. These micro-bubbles which form when the tissues reach a super-saturated condition grow at a definite rate as the ratio of the partial pressure of the inert gas to the ambient pressure increases, and resemble colloidal particles in suspension. They finally form bubbles of sufficient size to cause mechanical damage by coalescence. Formation of the bubbles, when once the conditions of super-saturation have been achieved, seems to be initiated by movement of the gas-holding tissues relative to another surface. As the blood and tissues appear to lack any gas nuclei it would normally require very much greater differences of pressure to cause bubble formation than is found in diving conditions, and this is the only mechanism to account for the fact of their formation. The sudden eruption of this bubble may cause mechanical damage at the site and in the case of nerve tissue this can lead to serious symptoms.

The symptoms depend upon the degree of seriousness of the cause. When the pressure is being reduced in a decompression chamber, warning that the decompression may be too rapid is given by the patient's experiencing an itchy skin.

The next symptom is pain in the most used muscles and joints giving rise to contortions in order to relieve the pain which can be very severe, hence the divers' name of 'bends' to describe the disease. This symptom is the most usual and is not serious provided it is treated and provided that no pair of limbs are involved which may indicate a bubble in the spinal cord. If this occurs then the case is serious.

Pains in the chest and pins and needles indicate a severe stage of decompression sickness and must be treated without delay and properly if permanent damage to nervous tissue is to be avoided. Obviously if the pins and needles have passed into weakness and paralysis there is even more reason for speed and concern.

If the diver is in a state of complete collapse, which is caused by a mass of bubbles throughout his circulatory system, only immediate treatment can save his life.

Treatment for decompression sickness consists of recompression and very gradual decompression according to a definite routine. The patient must be got under pressure again as soon as possible to mitigate the damage and prevent damage becoming more extensive with time. This occurs because centres of super-saturation can still form bubbles while the average value of the dissolved inert gas partial pressure is well below that required to form bubbles.

The therapeutic decompression procedure is as follows:

If immediate recompression is not possible either because no chamber is available or because the diver cannot be resubmerged by reason of his physical condition, considerable benefit may be given by getting him to breathe pure oxygen, particularly in cases where the decompression sickness is severe and there is reason to believe that bubbles have formed in the 'fast' tissues and blood stream. There is no benefit to be obtained from breathing pure oxygen for longer than 30 minutes as these tissues will then be desaturated and the speed at which the remaining tissues desaturate will not be greatly affected as regards eliminating symptoms of 'bends'. If the patient is breathing slowly or shallow it may be found to be an advantage to use 5 per cent CO_2 in the mixture to increase the ventilation rate. Pure oxygen is most simply breathed from a closed-circuit apparatus, such as the 'Novos' set produced specially for this eventuality, or any closed-circuit diving apparatus.

For most diving accidents likely to occur at present the pressure required in the recompression chamber is that to which the patient was diving, or 165 feet, whichever is the less. The reason for limiting the depth being that the size of bubbles in the tissues is so reduced at 165 feet that until the pressure (or equivalent depth) is very greatly increased beyond this there is no further appreciable reduction in volume. This of course only applies in cases where the 'bend' is discovered at the surface. Where it is discovered during a decompression stop at depth then the patient must be taken to a depth where the pain stops, or to the depth from which he came. Sometimes soreness persists even when the original diving depth has been attained because of the damage already caused to the tissues by the expanding bubbles, and this soreness may well continue for some time after all useful treatment by slow decompression has been completed.

During treatment for decompression sickness the patient must be tended for shock, being kept warm and given plenty to drink. He should also be kept quiet but not in one position for any length of time as it is necessary to maintain the circulation rate through all the tissues, but particularly those showing the symptoms, as high as possible. To this end certain drugs may be used with advantage, particularly those which increase the total respiratory and circulatory rate. With this treatment in mind it is important that the decompression chamber should be properly fitted out. The patient should be accompanied by a doctor or trained nurse conversant with diving medicine with good communication available to the operators outside. Light should be available either from outside through a window in the chamber, or installed in a shatter-proof mounting. An air-lock for food and medical supplies should be fitted as well as an air-lock for the passage of personnel. The doctor should also ensure that no easily inflammable material is taken into the chamber and that buckets of water are full and to hand. This is because any inflammable material becomes even more sensitive to fire in the presence of the high partial pressures of oxygen in compressed air. Other requirements for the pressure chamber are mentioned later (see page 134).

The first successful decompression tables evolved by Haldane were based upon the observation that however long a man was under pressure of under 2·3 atmospheres, the pressure could be reduced quickly without his getting a bend, and on the supposition, based on experimental evidence, that there are five main tissues that contribute to decompression sickness having 5-, 10-, 25-, 40-, and 75-minute half-saturation times. Each tissue was viewed mathematically as being a well-stirred fluid contained within a permeable membrane surrounded by blood. From the fact that a man could decompress from approximately 2 atmospheres to 1 atmosphere pressure while breathing air, Haldane deduced that decompression stages could be arranged so that the first stop was arranged at a position where the ratio of the absolute ambient pressure to the nitrogen partial pressure in the tissues would be equal to 0·625. This partial pressure would obviously depend upon how long and how deep the diver had been and thus how much nitrogen had been able to dissolve in the various tissues.

A new approach started by Hempleman, developed by Rashbass, and translated into tables for Royal Naval use and on the 600-foot dive in 1956, by Crocker, considered one slab of tissue only which was visualized as being bathed by blood on one side only so that the gases diffused into or out of the slab in a manner described by Hall. Furthermore, it was decided that Haldane's ration of nitrogen tension to ambient pressure should be altered to a finite pressure head of nitrogen tension over ambient pressure.

Calculation for helium decompression tables are based on nitrogen tables by applying factors for helium absorption at rest and working as the two states give markedly different results.

Although the calculations made by these methods provide the basis for the Royal Naval tables yet the published figures have in fact been adjusted by small amounts as a result of practical use and extensive trials.

Quite recently remarkable advances in decompression technique have been effected by the efforts of a Swiss mathematician, Hannes Keller. His criticism of Haldane's model of the decompression problem is that the experiments were carried out to determine the critical saturation factor where bubbles began to form, when the subjects were fully saturated, and therefore the gases were diffused homogeneously through the tissues. This homogeneity is a special case and is only realized in practice either under conditions of saturation or when two gases, separated by a semi-permeable membrane, diffuse into each other. However, the decompression tables were then calculated from this special data with no allowance being made for the fact that under practical conditions of partial saturation there would be variations in concentration of the inert gas throughout the solution although the average value would be as predicted by Haldane's formulae. Thus, while Haldane's tables are suitable for the average rate of decompression for the averaged tissue diffusion values they will not, and in fact do not, give enough security for prolonged or deep dives. This is acknowledged in practice by the adjustment of the critical saturation figure by all the compilers of tables, a practice which dodges the issue and disguises it under the label of individual peculiarities.

Keller's calculations, backed up by deep dives and laboratory experiments on himself to pressures equivalent to depths down to 1,000 feet, take account of these local variations in partial pressure. He introduces into the Haldane calculations the conception of the specific excess of saturation (E) which is the product of a factor (S) expressing the comparison between the maximum saturation obtained at a precise point in the tissues and the mean saturation, and a second factor (H) defined as the proportion between the mean saturation of a tissue and the value given by Haldane's formulae. This latter factor is a function of time which depends on the form and prehistory of the tissue. Thus $E = S.H.$

The factor E is then used to multiply Haldane's formulae to determine the true maximum saturation in the body and thus the minimum safe depth, or depth of each stop. At the time of writing Keiler's detailed workings are not available but will be of the greatest interest when they are eventually published.

The Royal Navy's tables differ from the American tables which also provide the basis for the French Navy's tables, and it can only be assumed that these differences arise as an expression of material differences in physique, average diving conditions, or as an unwitting acknowledgment of the criticisms levelled by Keller.

These tables can be constructed by use of a formula which traces out the history of saturation in a variety of different types of tissue arbitrarily chosen and is empirically adjusted to provide as short a decompression period as possible.

Every unit volume of tissue may be visualized as containing some spaces which are unfilled by tissue materials and which are available to each type of gas. Also it appears that each gas behaves separately so that it is the partial pressure of each gas, the volume available to that particular gas, and the ambient pressure which determine the amount that can be dissolved. However, the chemical effects of reactive gases such as CO_2 do affect this purely mechanical behaviour.

If the block of tissue is visualized as a porous mass it will be appreciated that it takes time for a gas to flow through all the restricted passageways to fill the space available to it and that the time taken will depend only upon the number and size of the pores within the limits that the gas can be treated as an incompressible fluid. In practice this means within the moderate depths and times prevailing in diving operations to-day. This restriction upon the rate of diffusion of a gas can be represented by a constant factor for each different type of tissue. Then the time taken for any volume to fill up, or saturate, will depend upon this diffusion factor and the proportion of the available volume that remains to be filled. This relationship may be expressed as:

$$S = \frac{NP}{P_D} + K\left(1 - \frac{NP}{P_D}\right) \log t \quad \text{for Saturation}$$

$$S = \frac{SP_{An}}{P_{An+1}} - K\left(1 - \frac{SP_{An}}{P_{An+1}}\right) \log t \quad \text{for Desaturation}$$

where, S = proportional saturation of the available volume expressed as a fraction of unity.

N = proportion of inert gas in the breathed mixture.

P = absolute starting pressure from which the diver was saturated (i.e. usually the surface and therefore = 1).

K = diffusion constant.

t = time in minutes.

P_{An} = Absolute pressure at selected stop.

P_{An+1} = Absolute pressure above selected stop.

P_D = Absolute pressure at diving depth.

As saturation is regarded as a mechanical process it is assumed that it is also a reversible one and that desaturation will occur in a similar manner to saturation with one important difference. Whilst saturation occurs without the formation of bubbles even in tissues that may be regarded as desaturating inwards because the ambient pressure is always greater than the partial pressure of the dissolving gas yet bubbles do appear when desaturating because this relationship is reversed unless the absolute ambient pressure and the partial pressure of the dissolved gases are maintained within close, variable, and empirically determined limits. It is these bubbles which give rise to decompression sickness.

It was observed by Haldane that however long men had spent breathing air at a pressure of 2·3 atmospheres they could be decompressed quickly to 1·0 atmosphere with no apparent ill effects. This figure provided him with the basis for his stage decompression system as it determined the maximum difference between the absolute pressure and the calculated partial pressure of nitrogen in the tissues, or tissue pressure, that could be allowed to exist on arrival at each new stage on the ascent. Naturally the larger the difference that could be tolerated the shorter the decompression. However, possibly for reasons pointed out by Keller, it has been found in practice that Haldane's original figure incorporated in his tables (1·9) were too high, and in TABLES I and II as evaluated by the Royal Navy and reproduced in this book the value chosen appears to be 1·4 for the lower stages, or stops, and about 1·6 for the last stop, where the length of time required to observe the lower value leads to excessively long stops.

To arrive at the values to be taken for K for different tissues is a matter for empirical determination at present. Generally an attempt is made to cover the possibility of any tissue exceeding the pressure difference limit however fast it may saturate, and therefore desaturate, and to provide this cover to tissues that are taken to be fully saturated after 24 to 96 hours. It is usual to consider tissues which have become half saturated, and are therefore labelled the 'half-saturation time', in 2, 5, 10, 25, and 40 minutes.

As stated above, each tissue's history is pursued throughout the course of the dive to determine at what point on the ascent the excess tension of gas in any tissue above the ambient pressure will determine the length of the decompression stop. As the calculation proceeds the determining tissue gradually shifts from the fast to the slow which shows why decompression routines must never be extrapolated as each one is a separate and organic unit.

Decompression tables beyond those shown are published but have not been included here because they have not recieved the same detailed experimental and operational testing. Also if diving is required beyond these limits the necessary tables can be calculated but must always be extensively tested with proper experimental facilities available both in a decompression chamber ashore and under controlled conditions afloat before being used operationally. If helium is used as the inert gas instead of nitrogen then an adjustment for both the rate of diffusion and the tolerable difference of

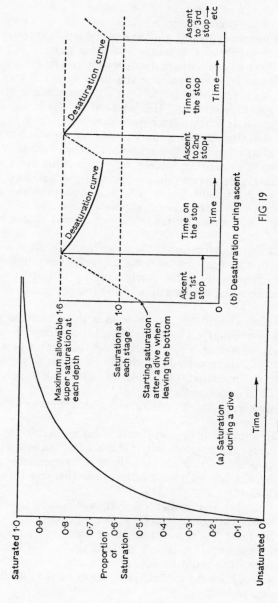

Saturated 1·0
0·9
0·8
0·7
Proportion
of 0·6
Saturation
0·5
0·4
0·3
0·2
0·1
Unsaturated 0

Maximum allowable 1·6
super saturation at
each depth

Saturation at 1·0
each stage

Starting saturation
after a dive when
leaving the bottom

(a) Saturation
during a dive

Time

Desaturation curve

Desaturation curve

Ascent
to 1st
stop

Time on
the stop

Time

Ascent
to 2nd
stop

Time on
the stop

Time

Ascent
to 3rd
stop → etc

(b) Desaturation during ascent

FIG 19

Illustration of gas saturation and desaturation process

ambient and tissue pressures as compared with nitrogen must be made. These are taken as being a rate of diffusion 1·7 times faster than nitrogen, and a tolerable difference of pressures of 1·7 instead of 1·6.

An illustration of the decompression procedure is shown in *figure 19*.

Sometimes it is necessary to put a diver down deep to investigate an object on the bottom briefly and then take him up as quickly as possible and move on to another position where the operation can be repeated with another diver. This can be done provided the diver does not stay down long and on surfacing is immediately put into a decompression chamber and repressurized within 5 minutes. The tables show the limits for the practice which is known as Surface Recompression (see p. 217).

If no recompression chamber is available during an operation requiring stage decompression arrangements should be made to ensure that equipment is available so that even an injured or unconscious diver can be lowered to the necessary depths and decompressed by stages. This can be done by means of a light-weight diving bell, as shown in *plates 12, 13*, while breathing apparatus that can be supplied from the surface, or changed underwater, is adequate for the unharmed diver if he can be kept warm.

In the open sea and rough weather the diver must use light gear and work from a shot-rope secured to a buoy on the surface or a light dinghy if he is to be re-submerged. Then he merely rides up and down with the sea, there is little differential movement, and the routine can be observed accurately.

If a decompression chamber is available in a ship then every effort should be made to ensure that it is immediately ready for use with qualified personnel in attendance whenever dives in excess of 100 feet are being made or shallower depths for long periods. It should be borne in mind by all concerned with the chamber that it is a medical instrument which may be required to save life at a moment's notice.

The points to watch if a decompression chamber is being provided are as follows:

(a) That the air supply (or helium if this is being used in the future) is adequate to increase the pressure in the chamber at the rate of 25 feet (12·5 p.s.i.) per minute and that this supply is not dependent upon an engine being started, but only on a valve being opened between the chamber and a bank of cylinders.

(b) That the chamber is pressure-tested to work at 80 p.s.i. or the depth to which the diver is going, whichever is the greater.

(c) That the operator has a pressure gauge that registers accurately to ± 1 p.s.i., and can reach the supply and exhaust valves easily when looking at the gauge. He should be able to ventilate the chamber every 30 minutes by opening both the exhaust and supply valves together while keeping the pressure steady.

(d) That any electric lights in the chamber are covered by pressure-tight glass covers protected by a metal grid on the outside, and that there are no other powered electrical fittings or other sources of heat that could initiate a flame or spark in the conditions of high oxygen partial pressure that prevail when the chamber is working.

(e) That the entrance to the chamber is wide enough to take a man easily, and that it is clear to get a man in on a stretcher.

(f) The doors should lock with one movement.

(g) The chamber is solidly mounted and cannot shift when men get in, or when the ship rolls.

Other fittings such as medical or air-locks and telephones may be installed but are not vital to the operation of the chamber, although they add considerably to the comfort of the occupants and the range of the operations that can be carried out. For example, a chamber with two air-locks can hold three divers in various stages of decompression which may enable a programme of Surface Recompression to be carried through continuously, as happened during the search for H.M. Submarine *Affray* (see *figures 19 (a) (b)*).

A second complaint, due to pressure differences arising through the greater compressibility of gases as compared with solids and liquids, is the formation of bubbles in the tissues as a result of gas being forced in from a nearby air space. This is known as gas embolism if the gas enters the circulatory system, or emphysema if it enters other tissues abnormally, unless a particular part is affected which has been given a specific label such as pneumothorax.

The effect of even a small bubble of gas in the circulatory system is extremely serious as it is the immediately vital organs that receive and need the greatest flow of blood through them. Thus any blockage occurring in the brain, spinal cord, or heart muscle will have an instantly dangerous effect which may be quickly fatal.

Bubbles just under the skin, subcutaneous emphysema, or, in the tissues around the heart and associated blood vessels, mediastinal emphysema are not serious unless the condition is extreme.

Pneumothorax is the condition in which air has been forced between the lung and chest walls which has the effect of collapsing the lung affected, and depending upon the amount of gas present, moving the heart and lung blood vessels. The gravity of this condition lies in the interference with breathing and circulation that may follow.

The basic cause, that is, difference of pressure across the walls of an air space, is usually brought about by holding the breath in the lungs against the expansion of the gas when the ambient pressure is falling. To a minor degree it could occur during an ascent if a blockage of the passages of the sinus or the Eustachian tube (given a very strong ear-drum or equally blocked ear) occurred at depth.

While breath-holding may occur during a free ascent or as a result of fright, gas may also be trapped in localized areas of the lungs as the result of previous disease.

The conditions described are most frequently found to occur relatively near to the surface where the rate of change of gas volume is greatest during an ascent.

The symptoms develop almost immediately during or after the ascent and as the arteries of the brain are usually involved they are dramatic and typically neurological. Thus the diver may feel weak, dizzy, paralysed, experience tubular effects of the senses, spots before the eyes, or other odd sensations, or he may be staggering, incoherent, or unconscious. If the lung tissue has been torn the patient may or may not have felt it and may show bloody froth at the mouth although the latter can also result from a bitten tongue during an oxygen poisoning convulsion, or after a squeeze. There may be blood also from the nose or ears.

The symptoms of emphysema are generally pain or ache in the affected part. There may also be blueness of the skin, difficulty in breathing, and shock, with mediastinal emphysema. In cases of subcutaneous emphysema there may be swelling of the neck, a crackling sensation as the skin is moved, a change in the voice and difficulty in breathing or swallowing.

Pneumothorax is accompanied by pain in the chest on the side affected, rapid shallow breathing, and blueness as in anoxia. If both lungs are affected the patient will be unable to breathe and will be suffering from both CO_2 poisoning and anoxia. As a result he will probably be unconscious.

Treatment of gas embolism must be by immediate recompression in which seconds are of vital importance. This point was illustrated by an accident which occurred in one submarine escape training tank in which the patient died from embolism after surfacing despite quick drill in carrying him down and recompressing him in the recompression chamber at the bottom of the tower. All escape training tanks now have a chamber at the top of the tower to deal with such eventualities and the few cases that have occurred have been successfully treated as a result.

Emphysema does not require recompression unless it is severe or complicated by other complaints.

A patient suffering from pneumothorax should not be treated by recompression unless complicated by other complaints that require this treatment immediately. If the patient has stopped breathing, artificial respiration must be started immediately coupled with heart massage if the pulse is absent. Oxygen should be used both for gas embolism and pneumothorax at the highest partial pressure permitted for prolonged use provided the lung is not irritated thereby, giving rise to coughing or pain. If the patient is breathing then treatment by a doctor is required as soon as possible to remove the air from the space with a long hypodermic needle and syringe of the type used in chest clinics for admitting air into the chest.

It should be borne in mind that although pneumothorax is a serious affliction, provided it does not affect both lungs it is a condition in which many people live who are working every day. For example, it is used to prevent the use of a lung affected by tuberculosis.

In Chapter I it was mentioned that all the air spaces of the body are connected with the outside although, apart from the lungs, these passages are small and therefore liable to cause trouble when the ambient pressure is being varied as in diving.

The passages to the ears are the ones that generally cause the most trouble as blockage of the opening of the Eustachian tubes in the throat may be obscured by the mucus which is constantly present to some degree. During a cold this form of obstruction is more pronounced and may form a block that cannot be freed by the methods mentioned in Chapter 1. Although the pain of continuing a descent is usually sufficient to deter a diver with blocked Eustachian tubes, if through enthusiasm or necessity, such as treating a patient suffering from embolism, the descent is pursued haemorrhage into the tubes may occur before the ear-drum bursts. If so then the ascent may be equally painful if the blood has clotted and reinforced the original block leaving a small body of air at a slightly increased pressure inside. Similarly the sinuses may become blocked and should not be forced except in emergency. The diver may be temporarily crippled with pain until the pressure is equalized by something giving way unless a weak capillary or ear-drum punctures early.

Sometimes one ear may retain the pressure of the expanding gases for a short time and together the two symptoms give rise to a feeling of dizziness. However, this only lasts a few seconds and is only important if the diver is under some other considerable stress.

In dark water where the diver is deprived of all his normal horizons when he leaves the bottom these symptoms may well give rise to disorientation, which can have serious results and can lead to panic and loss of control. At first the diver may doubt whether he is going up or down, he may get dizzy, and feel sick and apprehensive, but as continued progress upwards is usually halted further trouble is unlikely to develop.

It is obvious that should any diver suffer from any of these mishaps he must not dive until a subsequent medical examination has been made and he has been pronounced fit.

Gas may occur in other parts of the body from time to time to give pain when the pressure is varied. A decaying tooth may give an indication of its presence if a small pocket of gas exists in the root. Again this will give rise to pain during the descent until it fills with fluid to equalize the pressure if the dive is continued, and again on the ascent until the fluid is expelled or the gas absorbed. Gas may evolve in the intestines in the course of a dive to give considerable pain and possibly damage during the ascent. Should this occur the decompression time should be adjusted to bring the diver up as slowly as practicable. However, the diver should be aware of the possible risk and should either refrain from diving when windy or from eating habits which may cause it.

A diving hazard which is in reality a complaint resulting from differences of pressure in the air spaces of the body is that caused by explosions. In air the energy in the shock wave of an explosion is quickly dissipated as heat as the air is compressed and expanded in each position that the wave passes through in spreading outwards from the origin. Furthermore, when the shock wave hits a man's body a large fraction of the energy is reflected from the surface of the skin and does not penetrate.

However, in water which compresses very slightly under high loads little energy is lost in heat as the wave expands and is besides funnelled along between the surface and the sea-bed. This can be seen in films of depth-charge explosions when the surface of the sea leaps with the bang and is then followed by an eruption as the gas bubble surfaces. This shows that very little of the energy from the shock wave has passed into the air from the sea.

The naked body having a density similar to water transmits the shock wave and absorbs very little energy on the way. It therefore suffers very little damage except at those sites where a boundary between two media of different densities exists. Such are the air spaces. Over the small areas which are presented at an oblique angle to the direction the wave is travelling the energy will be more or less reflected but over those greater areas more at right angles to this direction the damage will be severe at greater distances than injury would be experienced from blast alone in air. The effect of the explosion wave on reaching the wall of the alveoli for instance is to produce much the same shredded effect as was seen momentarily on the film over the surface of the sea.

Although in peacetime there will be few occasions other than accidental when a diver is in the water at the time explosives are detonated yet there are jobs which produce minor explosions constantly and could give rise to a semblance of the damage described above. Such for instance is the effect of thermic boring in rock. In this work the use of a very hot lance of iron to melt away a hole in rock gives rise to steam explosions of steadily increasing force as the depth of the hole grows. At a distance of three or four feet from the hole entrance the diver can be shaken considerably and experience irritation of the lungs and breathing tracts.

The formula given to express the pressure of the compression wave formed by a charge of the standard explosive, TNT, is given by:

$$P = \frac{13,000 \sqrt[3]{W}}{D}$$

where P = pressure in p.s.i.
W = weight of the charge in lb.
D = distance from the origin of the explosion in feet.

This formula assumes that both the diver and the explosion centre can be contained within a sphere but it is sufficiently accurate for all but shallow water, and no accurate data can be given for this effect as there are so many variable factors. However, two observations give some indication of the effect of explosives in water.

A pressure wave of 500 p.s.i. is stated by the Americans to cause injury to the lungs and any air-filled part of the gut. British experience has shown that a 20 oz. charge will cause distress at a distance of 40 feet (i.e. a pressure wave of 175 p.s.i.) and will render the victim unconscious at 10 feet (700 p.s.i.).

Damage will not be confined to the lungs if the whole body is submerged as all the air spaces are affected and some central nervous injury also occurs.

There is virtually no practicable form of protection against underwater blast except distance, leaving the water, or at least raising the air spaces above the surface if there is warning.

Treatment must rest with the qualified medical professions beyond the first-aid attention to shock. Perforation or delayed perforation of the bowel, as well as damage to the lungs, sinuses, and central nervous system, may all be present. Thus, even if the patient appears to be fit and feels well a medical examination should be made as soon as possible.

The capacity of water for chilling the diver has been mentioned previously and little more need be said here of the effects beyond mentioning that acclimatization to cold is as important a factor as physical build in resisting the effects. This acclimatization is a complex adjustment of the heat-regulating mechanisms of the circulation and skin, and the metabolic processes of the muscles. For example in one experiment mentioned two experimenters only began to lose sensation after 50 minutes at 42°F. submerged in water while other men have died after an hour at 40°F. Quick restoration of deep heat to the body is the only treatment and, despite the pain which should occur on the outside and at the extremities as the circulation is restored, a bath kept at the normal hot-bath temperature of 105°F. is the most effective means of doing this. As air has far less capacity for carrying heat it is not so effective by a factor of approximately 24.5.

What is less commonly experienced or realized is that the more serious complaint of heat stroke may afflict the diver working in tropical water near the surface. An air temperature the same as his own would not cause a man any more than a little discomfort, but because of the large heat capacity of water and the inability of the diver to lose heat by evaporation so his temperature may increase rapidly. If he is unable to lose heat an hour's submersion will be sufficient to kill him.

Mild overheating with symptoms of dizziness, headache, restlessness, difficult breathing and rapid pulse would probably bring the diver to the surface where he can be treated by being given a mild solution of salt to drink and being cooled by whatever means may be available including complete rest and being allowed to sweat. If he collapses with heat prostration medical assistance should be obtained.

There is some evidence to show that in tropical conditions lack of salt may give rise to symptoms that seem to be related to pressure. The only cases known were complicated by other disturbances of a physical and psychological nature, but as the causes were vague and the symptoms were not the latter will be described. The first thing that is noticed by the diver is deep-seated apprehension that cannot be banished by reasoning, coupled with weakness of the limbs in most use as the pressure increases past a certain point. After a repeatable interval spasms involving both limbs commence which are uncontrollable. Ascent by only a few feet relieves the symptoms, resumption of the original depth restores them.

As the days pass the depth at which the patient becomes sensitive decreases but can be temporarily restored again by rest away from the conditions for a few weeks. When the condition affects the upper limbs it is noticeable how clumsy the hands are. Spasms may be precipitated by any small sudden movement on the part of the diver or surprise, such as a small fish darting away in his field of view. In the case where psychological stress was present the symptoms could not be reproduced in a chamber.

This emphasizes that when a diver is stressed, even unconsciously, when underwater, physiological events that may pass unnoticed at low pressures may become overwhelmingly apparent at a higher pressure.

Injuries that are peculiar to the nature of diving equipment result from what are colloquially known as 'squeeze' and 'proto cocktail'.

Injuries from the squeeze are confined to Standard Divers and more particularly those whose air supply is governed from the surface. The mechanics of this injury have already been dealt with (page 74) and it will be remembered that the injuries are the result of the diver's body being packed into the rigid helmet and corselet by the water at higher pressure outside acting on the flexible suit. A very slight form of squeeze may occur locally on the body where a suit is folded and not inflated with gas as the diver descends. The gas in the fold is then compressed and a portion of skin may be nipped by the water pressing on the clothing. Lines, welts, and sometimes bleeding may be caused which will serve to underline the desirability of using suit inflation in the future.

The symptoms of the very serious Standard Diver's squeeze may vary from bleeding from the nose, lungs, or eyes, to the diver having to be buried in the helmet. Treatment may have to take account of the air spaces of the body being filled to more or less extent by fluids forced into them from the surrounding tissue and the patient may therefore require to be given artificial respiration as for a case of drowning. However, the original precautions lie with the diver himself and his attendant in seeing that the gear is correctly maintained and that the diving drill is observed to prevent a fall through bad attending or as a result of blowing up.

The 'proto cocktail' is the name given to the caustic solution that may result from a leak into the counterlung of some types of regenerative breathing apparatus and which may be inadvertently swallowed. The result is that the mouth, gullet, trachea, and lungs can suffer severe alkaline burns. It is unlikely but not impossible that areas of the face such as the eyes may be involved. First-aid treatment is to wash the affected parts where possible with quantities of water. A solution of one part of vinegar to one of water or 2 per cent acetic acid may be used to drink, or wash the skin, and will help to neutralize the alkaline solution but should not be allowed near the eyes.

If the lungs have been affected a large quantity of fluid will be poured out into the lung and coughing will result. The patient should be assisted to drain this fluid out and should not remain sitting or standing up. Medical assistance should be obtained as soon as possible.

Divers are especially liable to the hazards of polluted water as so much diving is carried out in it. The dangers can be acute in some places and care should be taken to know what danger if any is known to exist before the dive is planned. Care should be taken by the diver not to swallow any water which finds its way into a mask and suitably antiseptic mouth-washes should be available when he surfaces. Eyes should not be forgotten as they may have been splashed or sprayed. Particular attention should be paid to protecting the hands against cuts and washing those that do occur, scrupulously. After the dive the diver should wash thoroughly, not for-getting to clean under his nails and around them. No equipment should be used which exposes the diver's ears or mouth and arrangements should be immediately at hand to wash the diver and his equipment with clean water. The risk of tetanus after injury in such water is of course higher than elsewhere and it is a wise precaution to insure that inoculations are given against this disease.

Various skin infections may afflict divers particularly in tropical waters where the heat, high humidity, and wetness, generally favour the com-plaints. They should never be disregarded as they can develop and become disabling. The most important single factor in prevention is the diver's personal cleanliness and care in washing and drying himself completely after the day's work.

The only major hazards that remain to be examined are those that stem from the presence of the animal population of the seas. On the land the majority of dangerous animals have been eliminated, segregated, or cowed, and as a result few people are conscious, as our forefathers must have been, of the stress that can be engendered by being exposed once again to this ancient risk.

The type of injury that may be expected from animals is either violent or poisonous and is summed up in TABLE VI (d). This is not a complete list but it does give the main categories plus a few particular species of dangerous animals.

TABLES VI (a) (b) and (c) sum up the main complaints that may be experienced and require immediate action. Where there is time to acquire medical treatment at any stage this is merely mentioned as the type of case with which the doctor will be confronted. Where the first-aid consists of medical action then it has been detailed even though the man in the field may be unable to carry it out.

A patient treated for any of the mishaps mentioned in this part should be submerged again as soon as he is fit enough and is free from shock or injury which might predispose him to faint and thus undo any of the good that a quickly repeated dive might do.

TABLE VI (a)

Gas Poisoning and Drowning. Symptoms and Treatment

Complaint	Causes	Symptoms/Signs	Treatment
Anoxia.	Reduction of O_2 partial pressure below 0·14 ats.	Subjective: Greying and tubular vision. 'Greying' aural faculties. Dizziness. A feeling of detachment. Objective: Cyanosed lips and fingernails. Pallor, loss of muscular control of facial and vocal muscles. Stertorous and increased rate of breathing and rapid pulse rate. Unconsciousness.	Restore a supply of O_2 to the patient in excess of 0·16 ats., i.e. fresh air. In extreme cases artificial respiration and heart massage may be necessary. If a high concentration of O_2 is required CO_2 up to 5% should be included in the breathing mixture.
CO_2 poisoning.	Partial pressure of 0·05 ats., CO_2 in the breathing mixture.	Subjective: At first flashes of apprehension giving way to general anxiety. Breathlessness and a feeling of insufficiency leading to panting, panic and desperate attempts to 'escape' and remove obstructions to breathing such as the mouthpiece. Nausea sometimes. After effect— invariably a headache. Objective: Increased depth and rate of breathing and pulse, leading to shallow rapid breathing and unconsciousness. Flushed face consequent on general vaso-dilation. Desperate efforts to remedy the situation.	By the diver: Cease all activity possible and concentrate on regular, deep breathing and relaxing. Closing the eyes helps. If the apparatus allows, flush out with fresh gas. At the base: Restore the supply of fresh air free of CO_2. Artificial respiration and heart massage may be required in extreme cases.
Oxygen poisoning.	Partial pressure of O_2 in excess of 2·0 ats. but higher in diving operations of short duration.	Subjective: Apprehension followed by interference to vision and aural faculties, and twitching facial muscles. Objective: General pallor caused by vaso-constriction. Twitching, and loss of muscular control of the extremities. Unconsciousness and epileptic type fit.	Reduce the partial pressure of oxygen to 0·2 ats., i.e. breathe fresh air. Artificial respiration may be necessary after a fit.

Complaint	Causes	Symptoms/Signs	Treatment
Inert gas narcosis.	Increased partial pressure of inert gas in excess of that, or the equivalent of N_2 at 4·0 ats. pressure.	Subjective: A form of intoxication similar but not identical to alcoholic poisoning. Metallic taste at lips, inability to whistle, voice change. An increasing feeling of unreality. Impairment of higher mental powers. Objective: Similar to but not identical with alcoholic poisoning, loss of mental accuracy and concentration leading to complete intoxication, unconsciousness.	Reduce the partial pressure of the inert gas either by reducing the depth or substituting an inert gas with a higher isonarcotic pressure.
Undue physical or unconscious psychological stress.	Excessive loss of salt in hot climates due to sweating. Apprehension concerning conditions or other stresses.	Subjective: Sudden increase of unreasoning apprehension and extreme nervousness below 4·0 ats. Very weak. After 15–20 minutes uncontrollable twitching of used muscles leading to spasms. Objective: Very weak, occasional muscular jerks leading to spasms after 15–20 minutes. Complete relief of symptoms at less than 4·0 ats. and renewed on return to depth.	Increase the salt intake by at least 15 gms. per day while ensuring copious fluid intake and excretion rate of 1½ litres day if lack of salt is thought to be the cause. Check in decompression chamber. If no symptoms there, lay off the diver for some weeks.
Drowning.	Inhaling when submerged in fresh or salt water.	Either blue skin and lips or white if unconscious. Pulse may or may not be absent. Breathing will have stopped if white but might restart spontaneously if blue.	Drain water from bronchi and begin artificial respiration by Biblical method as soon as possible, after clearing obstruction from passages, combined with heart massage if pulse is absent. If treatment is successful treat as for shock. Maintain treatment for 2 hours before abandoning the effort.

TABLE VI (b)

Complaint	Cause	Symptoms	Treatment
PRESSURE INJURIES: Gas embolism.	Ascending with breathing passages blocked, e.g. holding the breath when surfacing after equipment failure. Or breathing pressurized supply when leakage is ineffective.	Subjective: Interference with senses. Hallucinations, loss of sensation, pins and needles. Objective: Collapse, epileptic fit, paralysis, statement of above symptoms after events that could provide the cause.	Immediate recompressions. Decompress according to therapeutic tables.
Emphysema.	As above.	Subjective: Pain in the affected part which will be near or contiguous with an air space. Difficulty in breathing or swallowing, change in the voice. Objective: Blueness of the skin, swollen neck or other part of the skin. The skin crackling slightly when touched.	If gas embolism is not present then the case can be dealt with by a doctor removing the air as necessary. The air will be slowly absorbed anyway. Treat for shock.
Pneumothorax.	As above.	Subjective: Pain in affected side. Difficulty in breathing. Rapid shallow breathing. Objective: Blue skin and as above.	If the patient is breathing he will need complete rest and the air must then be removed by a doctor. If not breathing administer artificial respiration and possibly heart massage. Recompression is not desirable if there are no other complicating factors.
Explosive injuries.	Explosion close by or period with suffering a series of minor explosions.	Subjective: Tingling sensation in lungs in particular. Possibly other spaces as well. Coughing, difficulty in drawing breath. Inability to move although conscious for $\frac{3}{4}$ minute. Pain in stomach some time after. Objective: Patient unconscious or conscious but unmoving for $\frac{3}{4}$ minute then only feebly. Coughing with blood present, or just coughing. Bleeding from nose or ears. Bleeding anus.	Complete rest. If there is difficulty in breathing keep lungs drained and administer oxygen if necessary. Get patient to qualified medical care as soon as possible. Even if symptoms are slight obtain medical examination as soon as possible because of danger of unfelt internal injury.

Complaint	Cause	Symptoms	Treatment
Decompression sickness.	Too rapid decrease in pressure.	Subjective: In order of emergency: Itching skin. Pain in joints or muscles. Pain in the chest. Pins and needles in lower limbs and body. Tubular vision. Objective: Complaint of pain as above for up to 24 hours after diving. Complete collapse of the diver during the ascent or on the surface shortly after.	Immediate recompression or, where this is impossible, breathing pure O_2 in a closed-circuit system. Therapeutic decompression as laid down in the tables.

TABLE VI (c)

Complaint	Cause	Symptoms	Treatment
TEMPERATURE INJURIES: Chilling.	Exposure to cold in various degrees depending upon clothing.	Subjective: If water is 47°F. or lower, loss of sensation in the hands accompanied by pain. Considerable pain on restoration of circulation. Shivering with gradual loss of concentration, and clumsy sometimes random movements. Objective: Violent shivering. Blue, white or green skin. In some cases irregular pulse and breathing.	If the whole body is badly chilled a bath started at 98°F. and increased and kept as hot as bearable. Treat with stimulants after the bath has been started.
Overheating.	Undue loss of body fluid or salt by evaporation and sweating, or inability to reduce body temperature by sweating.	Subjective: Dizziness, headache, restlessness, and difficulty in breathing when uncomfortably hot. Objective: Incoherent, unconscious, body temperature in excess of 98°F. Feverish and delirious.	Rest and reduce the patient's temperature as quickly as possible. Treat for heat prostration if the patient displays the objective symptoms.

TABLE VI (d)

Animal	Where found	Type of Wound	Treatment	Remarks
PREDATORY ANIMALS: Sharks.	All temperate and tropical seas. A few tropical freshwater species.	Massive abrasive wounds or clean deep slashes caused by collision. Large lumps of tissue or limbs removed by biting.	Remove patient from water as quickly as possible. Apply tourniquet to stop bleeding if necessary. Treat for shock. Dress wounds.	Avoid diving in circumstances that may attract attack, or do so with protective devices. No attacks recorded in water temperature below 68°F.
Barracuda.	Tropical and sub-tropical waters.	Lumps of tissue removed by biting.	As for shark attack.	Attacks depend upon size of individual fish and numbers. Also situation and behaviour of the diver. Arrange protection as for shark attack.
Conger eels. Moray eels. Groupers.	Former in all temperate waters, latter two in tropical and sub-tropical waters. Found amongst rocks, wrecks, or structures.	Lumps of tissue torn out by the eels, or minor limbs removed. Grouper's attacks are by swallowing. Cavernous mouth.	First-aid as for shark attack. There is little danger of the victim being pursued if he escapes.	All inhabit rocks and will only attack if very large specimens become. Otherwise danger exists only if provoked.
Killer Whale.	All oceans and seas.	Unlikely to survive.	—	Leave the water immediately on sighting. They hunt in packs and are as intelligent as primitive man in pursuing quarry.
Seals.	All seas.	Generally nips as the result of curiosity, except Leopard Seal (Antarctic), almost as dangerous as Killer Whale.	First-aid if necessary.	Depending upon the type of seal and the circumstances so the attack will be more or less serious.
Clams. Crabs.	Former in tropical shallow seas, latter all seas. Found amongst rocks.	Crushed limbs, fingers, or toes. Danger of drowning if animals are very large.	First-aid as necessary. Free victim from clutches by cutting adductor muscle or killing crab.	Only of real danger to the unwary swimmer with no apparatus. Diver with a good knife should be able to cut free and should never have got caught.

Animal	Where found	Type of wound	Treatment	Remarks
POISONOUS FISH: Chicken, Lion, or Scorpion Fish.	Tropical and temperate waters. Inhabit rocky territories or structure.	Exceedingly poisonous back, anal, and pelvic spines.	Get the victim out of the water quickly, make an incision at the site of the wound(s) to encourage bleeding. Or apply tourniquet between site and rest of body as quickly as possible. Immerse in iced fresh water for five minutes then remove tourniquet and keep in iced water for at least two hours.	The fish are generally easily visible in clear water but the diver may blunder into them. The stings can be very serious and affect the central nervous system. There are no serums available.
Weaver fish.	Temperate waters. Commonly occurring in small trawls on east coast of England. Found on sand.	Poisonous spines along the back.	As above though painful and not so serious.	This fish is protectively camouflaged and quite difficult to see against the sandy bottom in which it lives.
Sting-ray.	Temperate and tropical waters.	Spine driven hard into nearest part.	As fainting is likely get the diver out of the water quickly. Wash the wound in sterile saline solution, or clean cold water. Remove any part of the spine that may remain. Soak in as hot water as can be tolerated for at least half an hour. If pain fails to abate local injection of 0·5 to 2% procaine, otherwise intra-muscular or intravenous. Cover the wound and elevate the limb.	The chief danger lies in the fish being trodden on in shallow water.

TABLE VI (d)—*Contd.*

Animal	Where found	Type of wound	Treatment	Remarks
OTHER POISONOUS ANIMALS: Sea Snakes.	Tropical seas.	Fang marks (two pairs of dots ¼ inch apart).	1. Keep the affected part quiet. 2. Apply tourniquet above the bite if possible. 3. Release it every 30 minutes for 5 minutes. 4. Medical assistance is essential. 5. If possible identify the snake. 6. Give antivenom treatment as soon as possible. (a) Give cortisone to prevent serum reaction. (b) Have epinephrine ready in case of reaction. (c) Use a polyvalent antiserum containing a Krait fraction as there is no serum for these snakes. (d) Give 20 ml. of antiserum by slow intravenous injection and be ready to give more. 7. Treat as a case of bulbar poliomyelitis or tetanus. 8. Provide sedation and anti-convulsant therapy, avoiding morphine.	The animals seldom deliver an unprovoked attack. There is no serum yet available for them and 25% of attacks are generally fatal. The symptoms do not develop until about 20 minutes—2 hours after the attack. The poison is one affecting the whole nervous system. The victim may sometimes be unaware of an attack beyond a prick.

TABLE VI (d)—Contd.

Animal	Where found	Type of wound	Treatment	Remarks
COELENTERATA Portuguese Man-o-War. Sea Wasp. Corals.	(JELLY-FISH): Tropical and occasionally temperate waters. Indian and Mid-Pacific Oceans. All seas.	Stings from contact with the long tentacles. Degree of severity depending upon number of stings. Cuts or abrasions and stings. The cuts tend to become ulcerous.	Remove tentacles promptly using gloves or protection to do so. Apply alkaline solution (weak ammonia or soda bicarbonate). Poison is a nervous one. For corals—wash with an alkaline solution as above.	Both these types are dangerous and the sea wasp definitely lethal at quite a small dose. Only the large corals are likely to cause trouble and only a few tropical ones are poisonous—then not lethal for the usual dose.
Sea-urchins.	World wide, on rocks and structures.	Piercing by spines, some long, hollow, brittle, and poisonous. Stinging by small pincers located near the spines in some species.	Remove the spines where possible. For some types and positions, surgical removal will be necessary. Remove pincers immediately as action continues whilst attached. Treat as for venomous stings (see above).	There are many species of sea-urchin and generally it is only those found in sub-tropical or tropical waters that create a hazard. The wound is made more painful by reason that the spines are aimed before contact is made.
Cone shells.	World wide. Generally found on or in sand in shallow water.	Stings followed swiftly by paralysis, coma, and death in severe cases.	No specific treatment other than that for venomous stings (see above).	There are more than 400 species and it is only a few tropical ones that are dangerous to man.
Octopus.	World wide. In rocky situations and struc-tures. The deeper the bigger.	Generally only lesions caused by the sucker discs on the tentacles, but they also have a venomous bite which can cause death.	No specific treatment other than that for venomous stings (see above).	Animals have been found up to 25-foot span which are big enough to regard man as prey. Chief danger is in causing drowning by their grip. They can be killed by stabbing between the eyes or turning inside-out despite the poison apparatus of the beak.

7

Underwater Fishing

When the beginner first takes up diving it is generally the sheer thrill of finding that he can fly in a new medium full of exciting promise that captivates him. Probably the first visits underwater will have been made in clear, if not warm, water, and the vividness of the colours, so brilliant by contrast in the relatively dimly lighted surroundings of predominantly green or blue, coupled with the silence and the strange feeling of moving about with the fish in their own enrivonment, will provide sufficient sensation for some time. Eventually, however, as the swimmer gains confidence he will feel the urge to accomplish something. This usually becomes an urge to hunt the nearest prey to hand, the fish.

Provided the hunting for the smaller fish is carried on without breathing apparatus, the stocks of fish neither suffer damage nor tend to disappear, and the swimmer will learn more about his new environment and how to survive in it so that he can move on to more rewarding activities later. To plunge straight into the intricacies of mastering strange equipment in an unfamiliar setting is to attempt running before even crawling.

In order to fish successfully it is desirable to know the elements of the fishes' sensory system to judge their likely behaviour. Fish swimming free from the bottom, apart from those that live on the bottom, survive attacks from enemies who also swim free from the bottom, not by hiding, but by sensing his presence and dodging.

An important sense organ of the fish is the lateral line. This is a line of sensory cells sensitive to acceleration and change of pressure, running on both sides of the body from the head to the tail. These organs serve to give the fish a sense of movement and hearing which are functions having an accelerative element. The function of 'hearing' is very acute and can detect sounds, or pressure waves in the water, of very low frequency and small amplitude with great accuracy in direction and range within one wavelength. It is sufficient to inform some fish of the presence of a small worm wriggling slowly several feet from them in dark water.

The sight of many fish is at least as acute as our own, but their discriminatory faculties are far less developed and tend to respond effectively only to movement, although colour enhances the vigour of the response.

Fish evade their enemies primarily by becoming aware of their presence in time to dodge by moving extremely rapidly over a short distance. Generally, their metabolism does not allow them a very prolonged period of heavy exertion and, like all animals in the wild, they use the minimum necessary effort to achieve a result, thus husbanding their reserves. The dodging behaviour patterns are stereotyped and each species has its own repertoire of tricks depending upon the degree of stimulation and the physical condition of the individual.

For example, the fish known as the brill (a flatfish) may evade by swimming away slowly if a swimmer approaches, or merely lie buried in the sand. The initial dash when disturbed may be for a distance of only 20 feet, depending on the visibility. If pursued, an alternative evasive tactic may be a great stirring of sand to give the impression of flight, and settling under the descending cloud in the same place.

It is because of these economical and stereotyped patterns that fish are run down and caught by the very much slower trawl.

With these facts in mind the fisherman can arm himself and set out to hunt. Underwater fishing is done with variously propelled spears or harpoons. The harpoon should be a steel shaft with a detachable barbed head so that it can be withdrawn from the fish without tearing it to pieces, having removed the barbed head beforehand, and is propelled by rubber, air, spring, or a cordite charge, from a gun to which it is secured by a line on a reel. It should be possible to reload the harpoon in the gun whilst in the water and swimming, for many bad shots will be made and to have to return to shore to reload is frustrating.

The swimmer should patrol the area that he has settled on slowly and gently, only diving either when he spots potential prey or to investigate the possible hiding places under rocks or in caves. At all times complete silence and slow movements should be studied to avoid surmounting the threshold of stimulation required to initiate the flight reaction. The swimmer cannot be unobserved, except by approach from behind a rock, but he can study his approach so carefully that flight is not precipitated until too late.

The blind spot of all round fish, that is, other than the flatfish, is the top of the head in a line immediately between and above the eyes. Only the most powerful guns should be used against the shark family, big or small, or the conger eels. The latter are immensely strong, have dangerous teeth, and are sufficiently vigorous to bend the average harpoon like a hairpin. The former have such hard skins that a heavy impact is required to penetrate, while members of this species are tough and bad tempered, having no hesitation in turning on their attacker. Even the small sharks, the dog fish, and nurse hound of British waters will react in this manner. As in any other type of hunting care should be taken not to shoot indiscriminately and only do so when the quarry is almost certain to be killed outright. The general principles which should guide the hunter are: shoot only what you are prepared to eat or use; do not attack quarry that is too large for your weapon; shoot to kill; and finally, if the quarry is wounded by mistake make every effort possible to despatch it quickly. The fish is as sensitive an animal as any other including ourselves and to wound it and let it escape is to inflict pain, considerable subsequent suffering from the attentions of sealice and small scavenging fish, and to attract the attentions of its larger foes. In waters where poisonous fish abound it is inadvisable to handle unidentified specimens alive or dead (see TABLE VI (c)).

Care should be taken to learn and recognize the various poisonous, bad-tempered, or dangerous animals that may be found in the area. British waters are remarkably free of creatures dangerous to the diver or swimmer but the few that do exist can hurt, for example the weaver, the occasional Portuguese Man o' War, the large conger eel (usually a female that has failed to breed), and in North Western waters the killer whale.

In tropical waters the spiny sea urchin, lion fish, coral eels, sea snakes, large groupers, sharks, and barracuda are only a few of the common hazards. Fortunately few of them afflict the swimmer unless he has committed an act of aggression. This is not true of the sharks, which remain one of the few wild animals that are a menace to man in wide areas of the world.

A few investigations into the danger of shark attack have been tentatively made but the nature of the problem makes it difficult to examine by controlled experiment. However, certain hypotheses may be drawn from observation made from records of attacks throughout the world. Firstly it seems that sharks do not attack if the water temperature is 68°F. or less, probably because the rate of their metabolism is low and they are neither so active, curious, bold, or ravenous as in the warmer waters. Secondly, the greater number of attacks have been recorded in the early afternoon, perhaps because that is when the greatest number of targets are also available. The conditions that they seem to find most favourable are sultry, overcast days, and muddy water.

Few swimmers have been attacked underwater but when they have the conditions have generally conformed with those set out above. An explanation of these results in the light of the known behaviour of other fish and their sensory system appears feasible.

Most carnivorous animals are extremely cautious by nature unless roused by injury or excitement. They have to be to survive, for theirs is a dangerous way of life calling for constant physical fitness, and they cannot afford to be injured in the course of routine hunting. As a result of this they will seldom attack anything over a certain optimum proportional size unless other stimuli lower the threshold, or alter their appreciation of the helplessness of the proposed victim. An attack may well be launched against large prey if the shark can do so from behind and there is a good chance of a quick crippling bite without risk. Like many other animals their eyesight is good and they are well aware of being observed or not. To attract the attention of the marauder the victim must look and behave like the food to which he is accustomed, and in the case of most sharks from the open sea this will mean displaying the colouring, type of movement, and position in the water of a sick, sluggish, or injured fish. Others educated by living in harbours, around slaughterhouses, or whale factories, will become more catholic in taste, hopeful, and inquisitive.

Thus, in general it can be assumed that if the swimmer is diving in dark, warm water with his skin exposed to the water, even if wearing overalls, and moving jerkily or sluggishly, he is laying himself open to attack. Likewise a naked white body splashing about on the surface in clear or murky, but particularly murky, warm water, is inviting attention. Shining or white patches will also catch the eye and stimulate the curiosity of the shark possibly because the colour of a flesh wound in a fish is white.

This is neither to state that anyone else is invulnerable, nor that anyone behaving in this manner in these conditions will invariably be attacked, but that a man swimming with assured movements, dressed in a black rubber dry suit well below the surface, and with no shining parts on the apparatus, seems to be less likely to be attacked, and almost certainly will not be attacked if the temperature is 68°F. or less.

Finally, it should be mentioned that no really effective shark repellent has yet been found and any unusual sensory stimulation will tend to attract these very inquisitive creatures. The use of explosives is exactly the reverse of what is often expected. The shark has no air bladder to act as a buoyancy control system and as a result is far more immune to explosive shock than the bony fish who may be stunned and paralysed by the charge. The result is that a crowd of hungry and excited sharks rush into the area to enjoy the banquet and soon become so wild that they appear to go mad. A swimmer might not last long amongst them.

As the swimmer becomes accustomed to the environment underwater so he will feel the urge to explore. This will mean that he will probably acquire more equipment such as a boat and breathing apparatus and will move further away from the shore.

8

Seamanship and Surface Navigation

It is imperative for safety and efficiency that the principles of seamanship and navigation should be thoroughly learnt before leaving the shoreline and accordingly a digression will be made to introduce these subjects which every diver must know and use.

The problems of seamanship are those raised by movement of the ship other than by means of its engines. The sea moves it, the wind moves it, and the tide or currents move it, and all must be understood in order to move about safely and with profit.

Firstly, the waves of the sea. The visible waves are caused by wind almost entirely; other long waves give rise to the tides but cannot be seen as waves while others initiated by earthquakes and similar disturbances may travel across deep water imperceptibly, only mounting up into 'tidal waves' as they reach shallow water.

Because any fluid, such as air, moving across a surface incurs a frictional drag at the surface so it forms the small eddies which comprise the boundary layer. These eddies vary the pressures they exert on the surface they are passing over and if this surface is a liquid such as water it will hump up under the low pressure areas and dip down under the higher pressure areas (see *figure 20*). But the wind is also moving and so these humps and depressions are given a movement in the same direction. However, the water itself does not move along unless the wave is breaking, it merely transmits the energy by means of these waves. Each particle of water in a wave may be visualized as describing a figure approximately like a circle in the vertical plane normal to the front. Friction in the water itself has the effect of reducing this movement until at a depth equal to $\frac{2}{3}$ the wavelength the diameter of this described circle is reduced to 3 per cent of its original diameter. From the diver's point of view wave movement may be said to have virtually ceased at a depth of one wavelength below the surface.

A wave travelling towards the land from deep water like a curtain of energy sweeping through the depth of the sea comes up to the slope of the sea-bed and the energy contained in the water is partly reflected back up into the wave, if the slope is gradual, and is partly lost in friction between the sea-bed and the oscillating water. The effect of the reflected energy on the wave at the surface is to increase its height and to alter the shape of the path travelled by each particle to a more circular ellipse.

A limiting height for the wave is set when the velocity of each particle as it moves round its point of origin and at the crest of the wave equals the forward speed of the wave front. The wave then begins to break. In practice this occurs when the slope of the sea is about 18°.

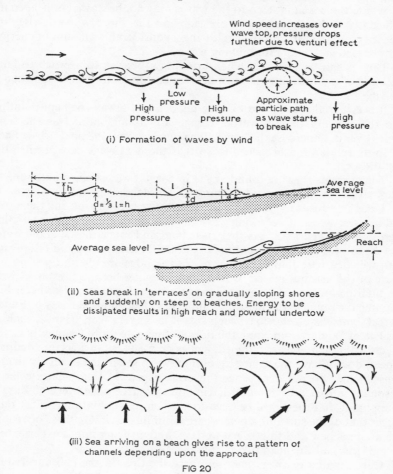

Wind speed increases over wave top, pressure drops further due to venturi effect

Low pressure

High pressure   High pressure

Approximate particle path as wave starts to break

High pressure

(i) Formation of waves by wind

L

h

$d = \frac{1}{3}l = h$

l   l

d   d

Average sea level

Average sea level

Reach

(ii) Seas break in 'terraces' on gradually sloping shores and suddenly on steep to beaches. Energy to be dissipated results in high reach and powerful undertow

(iii) Sea arriving on a beach gives rise to a pattern of channels depending upon the approach

FIG 20

Formation and behaviour of waves

When the wave breaks a lot of the energy contained is dissipated in turbulence and ultimately in the form of heat until the velocity of the circulating particles at the crest is reduced below the velocity of the wave front when the wave will continue inshore until the reflected energy has again accelerated the crest until it exceeds the forward velocity and a second break occurs.

On many beaches this constantly breaking series gives rise to a large body of water travelling inshore which periodically builds up against the beach and drains away. Usually it drains away down definite channels depending how the wind and tide make the sea strike the beach but which are plain to view on many beaches.

Where the beach is steep-to the waves may not be slowed or heaped up sufficiently to break until they are right on the shore where it rises up suddenly and the top falls over releasing a considerable amount of energy, transformed suddenly into moving water.

Thus is can be seen that when bringing a boat in to a beach to land the limit of practicability is set much sooner on a steep-to beach than a shelving one.

It is essential that the bow of the boat should always be kept pointing into the sea and that forward steerage way is maintained as the boat passes over it. Otherwise the bow will be swept round, the boat driven back on to its rudder and broached-to so that the next wave capsizes it if the first didn't.

The currents that are found at sea in coastal waters are mainly due to tides, rivers, or the spent sea running off a beach as mentioned above.

Tides are caused by the gravitational attraction of the sun and the moon and are sea waves of very long wavelength and small amplitude encircling the earth (see *figure 21*). As they near land and move into shallow water they heap up and slow down to give the characteristic rise and fall of tide with which we are familiar. In estuaries the tides are also heaped up because of the 'natural period' of the body of water becomes resonant with the tidal period so that a greater range occurs there than elsewhere. For example the range in the Bristol Channel is 42 feet and in the Bay of Fundy 66 feet, whereas on the coast each side it is only 14 feet. Islands, such as the Isle of Wight, often cause the tides to fluctuate more frequently as the effects from each side are mingled, while enclosed seas such as the Mediterranean do not have the same size of tidal wave generated as an ocean and consequently do not experience the same degree of tidal effects even in 'resonant' areas. As the moon is circling the earth once every 28 days it is apparent that there will be occasions when its gravitational effect reinforces that of the sun and others where it diminishes it. On these occasions the moon is new and full (every 14 days) and a spring tide is experienced, or half full and the neap tide occurs.

Currents due to rivers may reinforce the tide on the ebb and reduce it on the flood as well as being reduced itself for some distance back up the river as the tide rises. On occasions in estuaries the run of the denser salt water may begin in the direction of the flood tide at the same time as the surface flow of fresh water is still ebbing. This will occur where the salt and fresh water are comparatively unmixed.

Coastal winds play their part in the general structure of the environment in which the diver's seamanship will be exercised. Not only does it affect the surface flow of water, often holding up tides considerably, but it also affects the state of the sea in conjunction with the tide and has quite well-known periodic effects. Firstly it is commonplace that there is often a gentle onshore wind on a summer's morning which increases in strength through the day and dies away, or turns off-shore in the evening, due to the difference of temperature and rate of cooling between the land and sea. In the winter this difference is generally less marked and the breezes consequently reduced and may even be reversed. The effect of the wind acting against the tide is very marked and always results in a choppier sea than when they are both in the same direction. This can be understood when it is realized that the resistance offered by the sea to the wind varies

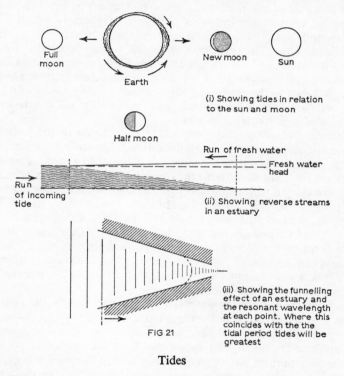

(i) Showing tides in relation to the sun and moon

Full moon
Earth
New moon
Sun
Half moon

Run of fresh water
Fresh water head
Run of incoming tide

(ii) Showing reverse streams in an estuary

(iii) Showing the funnelling effect of an estuary and the resonant wavelength at each point. Where this coincides with the the tidal period tides will be greatest

FIG 21

Tides

as the square of their speeds. If the tide flowing at 2 knots and a wind of 10 knots (force 3) is considered then it can be seen that when the wind is against the tide the resistance offered by the water, and hence affecting the size of the waves, is twice that when the two run together. If the wind speed is increased to 20 knots (force 5) the factor of the tide being with or against the wind is only $1\frac{1}{2}$, but of course the total effect is over three times the effect when the wind speed was only 10 knots.

When manœuvring at sea it is often necessary to have calmer water in which to work, for example if people are to be transferred from one ship to another. In this case it is usual for the deeper-draught ship to lie broadside on to the wind to form a lea in which the shallower-draught ship can operate. As the windward ship is being blown bodily through the water it will drift on to the smaller ship which should therefore be kept with steerage way to avoid damage as both ships roll.

As the sea acts on the rigid hull of a ship causing it to roll or pitch some parts of the hull will be moving through the water rather than with it. This causes the water to move and give rise to the pumping action mentioned in connection with decompression on a shot-rope.

Ships at sea or in harbours obey a rule of the road exactly as cars do on land. The International Regulations for Preventing Collisions at Sea express this rule of the road and should be studied by everyone engaged in using the sea whether inside or outside a harbour. In addition many harbours and ports have their own regulations which supplement the International ones. The principles on which vessels proceed is that each keeps to the starboard side of the channel. Each is visualized as being in a channel and obviously if there is risk of collision the channels must meet, so as each keeps to the starboard side without passing ahead of the other risk of collision should be avoided. Also every ship has a duty to avoid collision whatever its rights of way.

Channels and obstructions are marked according to the general rule based on the direction of the main flood tide. Thus starboard-hand buoys, those marking the starboard side of the channel in the direction of the main flood tide, are usually black, conical in shape, with triangular top marks, and carry a white light. Port-hand buoys are red, can-shaped, with rectangular top marks, and carry a red light. Obstructions in the channel are usually marked with buoys that are spherical if they can be passed either side and striped or checked in two colours. Wreck buoys are green and conform to the convention of the three shapes, conical, leave it to starboard, can, leave it to port, and spherical, pass either side. They carry green lights. By no means all these buoys carry lights but where they do they are usually of these colours.

Storm warnings are flown round European coasts on coastguard stations and by harbour authorities. Usually a rectangular shape means that strong winds are expected, a conical shape apex up denotes the direction from the north, and apex down from the south.

Whenever putting out to sea, or even moving around a port, a boat should always carry the proper equipment to enable the crew to take action in the case of emergency.

There should be a second method of propulsion on board by means of a second engine, oars, or sails. An anchor and cable should always be carried adequate to anchor in the deepest water in which this might be necessary. That is, three times the depth of water should be the length of cable carried. Some quick method of keeping the crew afloat without swimming should be on board. This will mean that rafts or lifeboats are available and ready for use. A compass and charts of the area complete the minimum outfit that should always be present every time a ship or boat slips from a quayside. In addition it is wise to carry fire-fighting equipment, torches, cordage, and methods of signalling.

Handling ships and boats requires a constant use of cordage, ropes, and wires, and the diver is quite useless who cannot use them properly. Ropes are made of nylon, hemp, manila, sisal, or coconut fibre (grass), and are measured in inches round the circumference. Wires are similarly measured and are made in many different ways for different purposes (*figures 22 (a) (b) (c)*).

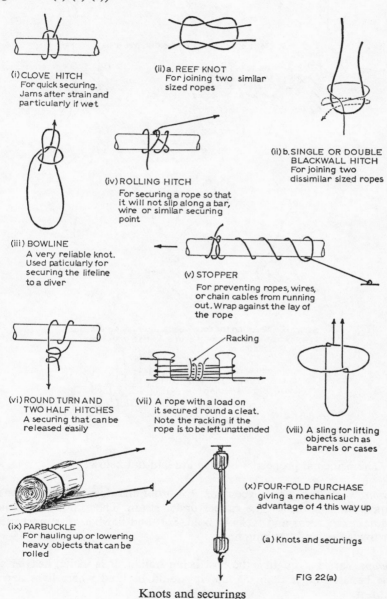

(i) CLOVE HITCH
For quick securing. Jams after strain and particularly if wet

(ii) a. REEF KNOT
For joining two similar sized ropes

(ii) b. SINGLE OR DOUBLE BLACKWALL HITCH
For joining two dissimilar sized ropes

(iv) ROLLING HITCH
For securing a rope so that it will not slip along a bar, wire or similar securing point

(iii) BOWLINE
A very reliable knot. Used paticularly for securing the lifeline to a diver

(v) STOPPER
For preventing ropes, wires, or chain cables from running out. Wrap against the lay of the rope

Racking

(vi) ROUND TURN AND TWO HALF HITCHES
A securing that can be released easily

(vii) A rope with a load on it secured round a cleat. Note the racking if the rope is to be left unattended

(viii) A sling for lifting objects such as barrels or cases

(ix) PARBUCKLE
For hauling up or lowering heavy objects that can be rolled

(x) FOUR-FOLD PURCHASE
giving a mechanical advantage of 4 this way up

(a) Knots and securings

FIG 22 (a)

Knots and securings

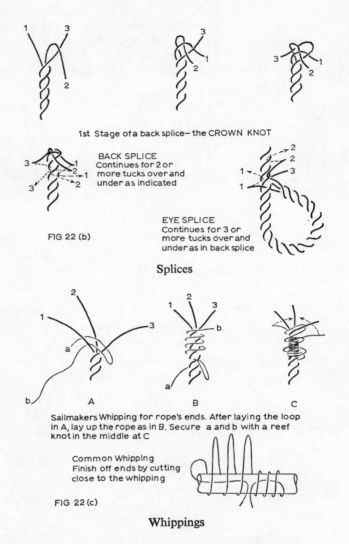

1st Stage of a back splice – the CROWN KNOT

BACK SPLICE
Continues for 2 or
more tucks over and
under as indicated

FIG 22 (b)

EYE SPLICE
Continues for 3 or
more tucks over and
under as in back splice

Splices

Sailmakers Whipping for rope's ends. After laying the loop
in A, lay up the rope as in B. Secure a and b with a reef
knot in the middle at C

Common Whipping
Finish off ends by cutting
close to the whipping

FIG 22 (c)

Whippings

The principal properties of each are laid out below:

Nylon: Very strong and expensive. Rot-proof and does not absorb water.
Slippery and stretches like rubber under strain. Thus knots and splices
require extra turns and tucks to hold. Soft and flexible. It is most useful
for tow ropes and berthing lines.

Hemp: Varies in quality, the best being Italian. It is white, heavier and
(the best) stronger than manila. It should be used where lives depend
upon it.

Manila: A good quality general purpose rope. Deep golden brown in colour.

Sisal: When new it is as strong as second-grade manila but is not so flexible nor so resistant to wear or weather. It is usually cheaper than the oregoing.

'Grass': This is made from coconut fibre and has the advantage that it floats. It is neither so strong, durable, nor reliable as the foregoing.

Fibre and Wire Rope: These are compound ropes which are strengthened by the addition of wire strands. They are used for berthing lines and springs where a strong rope is required.

Preformed: Wire that has each strand made into the shape it will adopt in the finished wire. This eliminates the danger of the wire flying back if it parts.

Flexible Steel Wire Rope: Generally used in small ships where strength is required but loads are unlikely to be applied suddenly. Care has to be taken when used in wooden ships as they tend to be stronger than the ship.

The basic minimum of knots and splices required by a diver are shown in *figures 22 (a) (b) (c)* and while these will suffice initially the more comprehensive information contained in Seamanship reference books should be mastered.

While this brief introduction to seamanship cannot replace the essential reading and experience required to qualify a man to handle a boat competently it may emphasize both how necessary it is for the diver to be a seaman and the range of knowledge that is required to achieve this.

An integral part of seamanship is navigation and it is necessary to examine this aspect as well, emphasizing meanwhile that in a work of this scope the book learning can only be briefly indicated while the experience must be collected at sea.

Navigation underwater starts from the surface and is related to the surface, for that is where the diver must finish up however far he has managed to travel underneath. Besides, the marks by which the unaided diver can guide himself even in the best conditions can be quickly confusing, while in dark water he need only lose touch with his handhold momentarily to become totally lost.

In air we direct our travels efficiently over long distances because we can see distant objects, often the sun is present to orient us, or shadows serve the same purpose. Our aural sense of direction is acute and helps us to hold our balance and place moving objects in the world about us. The weight on our feet gives us a plumb line which gives us accurate information on slopes.

The diver may enjoy none of these aids to direction-finding and as a result is never able to go in a straight line for very far even in the best conditions without an aid such as a compass, a stretch of ripple marks on the sand, a line of rock, or a jackstay.

However, the natural aids to direction-finding underwater should be used wherever possible and these will be considered first.

The direction of ripple marks has already been mentioned and they will frequently be found useful on a sandy bottom that is exposed to sea action or tide. If the ripples are large they may even be used as a measure of the distance that the diver has travelled, although this aid should be used with caution as the lines do not run exactly parallel to each order and the difficulty of counting accurately at even shallow depths is remarkable although to be expected when breathing high partial pressures of nitrogen.

If a slight swell is running so that there is movement on the bottom it will tend to line up the light debris across the direction that the swell is coming from while one surge usually appears a little faster than the other depending upon any current, thus giving a single direction. Seaweed will also move over rocks in a way that can be exceedingly disconcerting and may even cause sea-sickness, but is a good indication of direction. The nausea is caused by the diver being unconsciously moved by the wave in phase with the top of the weed. He feels that the weed is stationary like himself and that the whole sea-bed which he can see in the gaps between the strands of weed is oscillating back and forth.

Where rock outcrops are found there is system in the way the rocks are lying which can be of assistance in telling direction. Many rocks have been laid down in layers which later have become folded by pressure and then eroded. Thus the way in which these exposed layers lie, that is, the dip (direction of greatest slope down the layer) and strike (right angles to the dip), will give a good indication both of the features that may be expected in neighbouring outcrops and where they may be in relation to the starting position. Even when the rock is covered by thick weed these features will be readily visible underneath.

In shallow tidal water the zones which are inhabited by various plants and animals can give an accurate idea of distance from the shoreline and depth.

Around British coasts barnacles are usually the dominant animals from high water down to low water neaps where the weeds take over if the coast is not too exposed and the water is clear enough to allow a small amount of light to reach them at some state of the tide. On an exposed coast the barnacles will continue deeper and will finally give way to the large brown weeds with a strong stem and stout root-like holdfast called Laminaria. However, like all plants the weeds are dependent upon light for their life and in dark water they will not be found where light does not penetrate for a few hours during every low water. In clear water around the British Isles weed can be found down to 60 feet or even deeper on the south and west coasts.

Because of the refracting and scattering effect of water and the particles therein all the light coming from the sun and sky is channelled down a funnel of 45° and diffused so that only indistinct shadows are formed. As the depth increases this angle becomes less because the light is gradually absorbed by the water. Thus, there is no assistance in direction from the sun in the absence of sensitivity to polarized light.

These then are the sole aids that are likely to be experienced by the unaided diver. The effect of tides has not been mentioned as it is assumed that there will be other aids such as life-lines or jackstays available under those conditions.

Whenever an area is to be explored or is the subject of a search or survey operation it must be mapped so that quantitative results can be recorded and used to inform and order the mass of qualitative impressions that would otherwise be chaotically assembled.

A brief review of simple surveying methods and instruments will follow.

Whenever a search or surveying operation is to take place a reference point on the land should be selected which is both accessible and well marked. This must be plotted accurately with relation to the reference positions, or bench marks, shown on the best available maps of the area. In Great Britain there are Ordnance Survey Sheets to a scale of 25 inches to 1 mile for most places and 6 inches to 1 mile for the rest. These should always be used to tie in the selected reference position.

Having selected a suitable reference position the method of surveying chosen will depend upon the nature of the job, the size of area to be covered, and the climatic and topographical character of the neighbourhood.

If it is a matter of carrying out the operation along a single line which passes through the reference point then the best accuracy can be obtained by establishing a couple of marks to form a transit and a third point well to one side of the line which will give positions on the transit line by measurement of the angle between it and the third point. If no great accuracy is required a compass may be sufficient guide although taking bearings from a small boat in anything but a flat calm is exceedingly difficult to obtain within ± 5°. Also there are a number of places even around the British Isles where a magnetic compass is badly deflected by local magnetic anomalies. The most accurate method of measuring the angle is by means of a sextant, which can be used with great precision under the most difficult conditions (see *plate 24*).

An extension of the sextant angling method of plotting position is to select two points on either side of the original reference position, or three points in all, and plot their relative positions as accurately as possible with the best local map. If the angles between any two pairs of the points are then measured the position from which they have been measured will be fixed with great accuracy relative to the system of three points, provided the three points and the observer are not all on the same circle. Alternative points must be chosen if such a circle passes through or near the area.

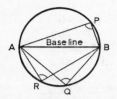

(i) If the distance between two points A & B are known and the angle subtended at any other point such as P, Q, or R, is measured, the circle on which they lie can be determined

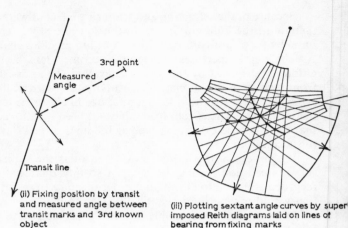

3rd point

Measured angle

Transit line

(ii) Fixing position by transit and measured angle between transit marks and 3rd known object

(iii) Plotting sextant angle curves by super imposed Reith diagrams laid on lines of bearing from fixing marks

FIG 23

Sextant angle fixing

Sextant angle charts are easily constructed for any area and once made can give an accurate position within 1 part in 900 of the distance between the marks for angles of 20° to 90°.

If it is necessary to plot the position of the boat whilst it is under way then two sextants operated at the same time are necessary to obtain accuracy. If the boat is stationary, however, it is sufficient to have only one man doing the plotting. When constructing a sextant angle chart care should be taken that while the angles measured are likely to lie within the range 30°–90° (otherwise measuring inaccuracies are liable to be introduced), the angle that each circle of equal angles makes with the other is as near to 90° as possible, and the marks are bold and fine and unlikely to be obstructed from view either by local conditions of haze, buildings, or passing shipping.

When lines are drawn from two fixed points on a circle to intersect at a point on the arc of the circle the angle they make at that point will be the same for any other point on the same arc and supplementary to the angles made by intersecting lines at a point on the other part of the arc (see *figure 23*). Thus each circle drawn through two points will be the locus of the positions from which the angle between those points is the same. If an angle is taken between a second set of points then this second circle will cut the first and an accurate position obtained.

Frequently it is necessary to construct a sextant angle chart of a small area well clear of the reference positions so that while the curvature of the sextant angle circles is considerable and not accurately represented by straight lines, the radius of them is so large that they cannot be drawn in practice without reducing the scale to an unacceptably small amount where accuracy is again lost by reason of the small scale. However, this difficulty can be overcome by simple calculation and drawing with the aid of railway curves or the instrument shown in *plate 25*, or the use of Reith diagrams.

The following example shows the working of the first part of a sextant angle chart.

See *figure 24*. The three points A, B, and C have been selected because as the coast is low lying and otherwise featureless the church, windmill, and lighthouse will be easily visible over at least five miles, are suitably situated so that circles passing through A and B and B and C cut at suitable angles in the small area D, E, F, G. Had either the other windmill or the coastguard station been selected then while the angles would have been a little wider than that between the windmill and the lighthouse the angle at which the circles cut would not have given such clearly defined positions.

To draw the arcs of the sextant angle circles correctly it is necessary

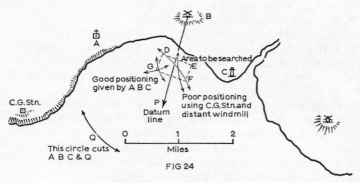

FIG 24

Making up a sextant angle chart

to select and plot bounding lines from one of the sighting objects, A, B, or C, to the right-hand and left-hand limits of the area if railway curves are going to be used. If on the other hand the arc ruler as mentioned before is used only a line from one of these positions and passing through or near the area is required. Such a line might be as shown in the figure by BP and will be referred to below as the datum line. This line is then used for calculating and drawing the arcs of the circles corresponding to the sextant angles.

To carry out these calculations it is necessary to find the radius of curvature of each arc, the angle that the radius of each arc will make with the datum line at the point where the arc cuts this line, and the distance along the line where any particular arc cuts.

Selection of the angles and distances to calculate will naturally be determined by the nature of the survey but it is usually found to be most convenient to plot the area to correspond to equally divided sextant angles at $\frac{1}{2}°$ or 10′ intervals, depending upon the scale of the chart to be used.

The radius of each arc is given by:

$$r = \tfrac{1}{2}b \cosec \alpha \qquad .. \qquad .. \qquad .. \qquad .. \qquad (1)$$
where r = radius, b = baseline, α = sextant angle.

The angle between the radius and the datum line is given by:

$$\beta = \theta - \cos^{-1} \frac{b}{2r} \qquad .. \qquad .. \qquad .. \qquad .. \qquad (2)$$

where β = angle between the radius and the datum line
      θ = angle between the datum and the baselines.

The distance along the datum line is given by:

$$d = 2r \cos \beta \quad .. \qquad .. \qquad .. \qquad .. \qquad .. \qquad .. \qquad .. \qquad (3)$$

If the radius of curvature given by (1) is the same for each set of points then the position from which the angles were taken cannot be fixed by using those points because they all lie on the same circle. For example in the illustration (*figure 24*) above, position Q cannot be fixed by angles taken between A, B, and C, because all four points lie on the same circle. This can be seen by inspection and proved by equal values derived for r in formula (1).

Where the three sighting objects and the survey area can be conveniently contained on the same sheet of paper without significant loss of accuracy then a good beam compass and the calculations for values with formula (1) alone are necessary. Generally, however, the objects are either too far away or the area is too large to be contained without an unacceptable loss of accuracy by diminishing the scale.

As the calculations involve values containing four figures it is necessary to use methods of computation, such as logarithms or a desk calculator, that give more accurate answers than the ordinary slide rule.

To set the arc ruler, determine the radius (r) as above converting it into inches for the plot, and select any wheel, radius x. Then the distance (s) that this wheel must be set along the shaft from the pen wheel is given by:

$$s = r(1-x) \text{ where pen wheel radius} = 1 \text{ inch.}$$

Having positioned the wheel and ensured that they are correctly lined up so that all the arrowed engraved lines on the shaft and wheels coincide, lay the ruler along the radius. Then roll the ruler across the paper and the pen will draw out an arc of the required radius and through the correct points.

If railway curves are being used then two datum lines must be used for the set of curves from each pair of sighting objects, making four lines for two pairs, and the calculations by formula (1) to determine the curves to be used, and by formula (3) to determine the distance along each datum line that each arc will cut, must be made.

The simplest method of making up a sextant angle chart is, however, by use of the Reith diagrams. These diagrams are rays of lines drawn from a point on transparent material such as Permatrace. Each diagram shows these lines spreading out at 10' or $\frac{1}{4}°$ intervals for the greatest distance likely to be used which has been taken to be 10 metres. This corresponds to a scale of 1:1000 over a distance of $6\frac{1}{4}$ miles and is almost the practical limit for this method of surveying. Two sets of diagrams are required and the plotting sheet must be transparent. The sheets are aligned as shown in *figure 23 (iii)*, and the equal angle positions connected up. The arc ruler will assist in doing this more accurately and quickly as it only requires to be lined up with three points. The advantage of the method using the diagram is that it enables all the arcs for two points to be drawn without further calculation. It is of course most suited for those who are constantly working with angle charts for whom it is worthwhile both having the equipment and who require copies of the charts to be reproduced. For those who seldom require to carry out this type of plotting or surveying it may be easiest and most accurate to make up diagrams for themselves just to cover the area they are particularly interested in on one working sheet by means of the railway curves or the arc ruler alone.

Other methods of accurate positioning on the surface are available and each is most suitable for particular applications having regard to the available financial resources, the accuracy required, and the area.

For distances up to 1,000 yards from well-established marks, the 1-metre base rangefinder is a useful instrument although it can be difficult to use in a small boat at sea. At ranges over 1,000 yards the errors to be expected are increasing rapidly and may be too large for survey purposes. It is, however, convenient when diving in an area marked out by marker buoys where the accuracy is not very great anyway.

The Decca system which is well established throughout European waters is accurate to a hundred feet in good areas and daylight hours and suitable for use in the open sea when landmarks are absent, or poor, or the visibility is bad. However, few diving surveys are sufficiently important to warrant setting up a special survey station in areas that may otherwise be poorly covered if at all. If the full equipment is to be kept running continuously the power required at the time of writing must be arranged so that the generator is at least 6 feet from the aerial, and this can only be achieved successfully in a boat about the size of a launch if any other equipment or diving space is required. In smaller craft large batteries that can be frequently recharged must be used. Should the power requirement be reduced by transistorizing the equipment so that a small battery can provide a prolonged constant voltage supply then the Decca system will become suitable for all accurate surveys around European waters and quite sufficiently accurate for all underwater surveys.

A line-of-sight electrical system of very great accuracy is the Tellurometer, which depends upon transmission of a continuous and accurately defined carrier beam of constant frequency with signals imposed on it, retransmitted by the slave station, the difference of phase between the transmitted and received signals being a measure of the distance apart of the two stations. A marine version of this instrument is the Hydrodist. The accuracy is to one part in 100,000 and is consequently a very great improvement on all other field methods over distances of a few miles and in addition is very much quicker in operation.

9

Underwater Navigation, Searching and Surveying

Having once established the position in which the diving is to take place on the surface then the scheme for the underwater navigation can be laid down and the type, again, will depend upon the purpose of the operation and the local conditions.

As the diver underwater is extremely limited in range of observation it is usually preferable to use instruments for detection or collection of specific data so that the man need only be used in the few places where the observations to be made are complex, require decisions to be made, or would entail instruments that are more expensive or difficult to operate than the job will stand. However, occasions do arise when the use of divers to correlate data collected by instruments or to operate in difficult conditions is necessary.

There are many possible patterns of searching areas with swimmers but the principal ones that have been found to be practicable have been drawn up in TABLE VII, with the general circumstances under which they might be expected to be of value.

No part of the diving operation should begin until the area in which the work is to take place has been thoroughly mapped, the surface features explored, tides and local peculiarities of weather ascertained. In smaller operations where the object may be to search for a lost object this preliminary investigation need not cover the same area or in so great detail, but it should be just as thorough for the purpose.

Many people have hazy ideas about the strength of tides and currents and the effect that these will have on objects lost in the water. Where possible, while all the evidence from any witness to the event should be listened to with care, the facts only should be given any weight in assessing the area to be examined. Even local fishermen and boatmen may be found to be profoundly ignorant of the actual conditions of the sea-bed in their area and the other factors affecting the operation, but will sound as completely confident in their inferences as upon the other subjects in which they are truly expert.

Facts that are likely to be of assistance and will be largely used by fishermen are transits of local features as these are the navigation marks primarily used in the fishing areas.

Again, the amount of dependence to be placed on any transits other than those based on accurate marks should be carefully assessed in terms of figures. It is not uncommon to be told—'The big tree in the middle of High Woods just clear of the church.' Such a transit may appear accurate yet lead to the diver being put down hundreds of feet away from the target. Thus transits should be judged for accuracy according to how finely the markers are defined. For example two poles can be seen to be in line with great precision, whereas a square tower and a farmhouse will probably be exceedingly doubtful. Attention should also be paid to the distance between the transit marks themselves as compared with that between the observer and the seaward mark. The transit line will be most accurately defined when this former distance is greater than, or at least a large proportion of, the latter.

If fixes are given by magnetic compass from a small boat, or even a small ship, they should merely be regarded as approximate positions. In a small boat a good bearing has an accuracy of $\pm 5°$, which at 2,000 yards from the object will give a position accurate to ± 525 feet. If 50-foot circular searches are being conducted it would need approximately 150 searches to cover the inaccuracies in this position whereas a sextant angle position would be accurate to ± 5 feet, even from a small boat.

In a small area where the water is not more than two hundred feet deep and the tides are not very strong, or more than two knots, marker buoys can be exceedingly useful. If the buoys themselves are to be used for fixing the surface positions then they should be tightly moored with only sufficient line to allow for tidal movement; even this can be disregarded if the buoy is fitted with a long pole above the buoyant part which will protrude above the water as the tide rises. In this instance the mooring to the buoy should only be as long as the depth of water at low water while the mooring itself should be very heavy to withstand the pull of the tide on the taut wire.

Buoys are unsatisfactory surface navigational marks if accuracy is required because of the difficulty of keeping them within less than a few tens of feet of the sinker position in any degree of tide or moderate depth of water, their real use being to define an area approximately and act as guides from the surface to an accurate position on the sea-bed.

Navigation underwater is still most accurately carried out by means of marked lines and compass from known and established positions. Efforts have been made to construct influence devices such as acoustic torches and leader cables but their success lies only in providing the diver with a homing device so preventing his getting lost.

Although the diver is in a very similar state to the aeroplane and might therefore be expected to carry a small dead-reckoning plot with him, yet in one important respect his circumstances are totally different. The pilot can rely on his radio methods of navigation to give a moderately accurate answer, whereas the diver's analogous influence, sound, is so refracted, reflected, and absorbed in the narrow film of medium in which he is immersed and by the comparatively large variation of bottom contour where he is usually operating that the system is wholly unreliable except as a homing method.

If the operations are taking place in an area of magnetic anomalies, but on a featureless sea-bed, then the area will have to be mapped to show the compass deviation throughout the area. Where features are apparent as suitable reference marks then these should be related to the surface and mapped.

Marked lines may then be laid over the area, care being taken to avoid curvature in the line by laying it taut from above any obstructions on the sea-bed and the degree of stretch measured by means of a pole laid along the line from one marking to the next. The beginnings and ends of lines should be related to the surface and checked against each other both above and below the surface. Every operation introduces an unavoidable error of some sort so that results are unlikely to tally exactly and provided the errors are within the tolerable allowance for the purpose of the survey there is no point in pursuing perfection beyond this.

The simplest method of laying a long line is of course from a boat, and this is generally more accurate and faster than a swimmer. However, if the swimmer must do it then the line may be made up on a reel so that it unwinds as he swims away on a compass course. The reel should be non-magnetic and both ends of the axis secured to the diver's front so that the reel rotates freely (tension on the line being applied by braking the reel slightly), and the diver can swim on an even keel, steadily, and accurately. If the line is to be wound in again then the reel must have two handles through the bearings that can be turned at the same time as the diver swims back to the point of attachment. Trying to reel in a few hundred feet of light line with one hand while holding the reel in the other and swimming with survey instruments flapping about meanwhile is most frustrating and tiring.

After swimming out laying the line the diver should hold it high off the bottom and pull hard to straighten it. He should then check the run of it by sighting his compass along the line. If the line is not lying strictly along the intended course then it should not be moved unless it is taken in and the lay started again, as the curve which is introduced into it, and very difficult to avoid however tightly it is pulled, by altering the position when at the end can give rise to large errors.

If the purpose of the survey is served sufficiently accurately by knowing the speed of the diver swimming at a certain number of strokes to the minute, and knowing the speed of the tide or any other currents in the area, then it may be sufficient to direct the operations by means of watch and compass swimming. If great distances or complicated courses are being swum then the most accurate method is to carry the watch and the compass side by side on a small board that can be carried comfortably in front of the diver. The board can also be fitted with a small map. To ensure accuracy one man's attention will be wholly absorbed by this navigation and if any visual searching is to be done one or two other swimmers should accompany the navigator so that while he acts as their guide they can make and record the necessary observations on the way. With practice, accuracy to $\pm 1°$ of steering and ± 5 per cent of distance can be achieved, given no currents in the area. If the sea-bed is reasonably smooth of course an accurate measuring apparatus giving a true position plot might be constructed on the lines of the meter drawn behind a sledge.

For short traverses it will often be most accurate and quickest for the swimmer to adopt the taut-line technique in which he swims down a given course unreeling a line, but keeping tension on it, as he goes. If the line is marked, or a counter is connected to it, and the sea-bed is not so irregular that he cannot swim clear of the obstructions, the swimmer will achieve considerable accuracy in one direction. He must then recover, or abandon, that length of line and start again if he wishes to alter course or break off the previous run.

Underwater navigation by the diver using a powered vehicle will still conform in principle to the methods outlined above but modifications will be imposed by the fact that unless the vehicle is fitted with expensive instruments the diver's hands and attention will be taken up with driving and the accuracy of the navigation will suffer as a consequence.

Instruments that can be fitted to vehicles will generally be acoustic, leader cable, or taut wire.

The acoustic instruments are unlikely to give great accuracy in the majority of places where diving takes place, as the surface is relatively close to the bottom compared with horizontal distances, and obstructions found on the bottom are usually large compared with this depth. As a result the sound waves are subject to considerable distortion. This will not affect the use of acoustic safety devices such as the Directional Listening Aid, which depends for its success upon the ability of a diver to track in to the source of the signal, rather than being able to determine his position relative to the source by the content of the signal.

Acoustic instruments will be of one or two types. The first, in which the source of the signal is carried by the diver and which can be trained upon an established and easily identifiable target to give an echo. The 'time of flight' of the sound wave and its direction then give the diver his position. Subtle variations on this technique have given excellent results as searching aids but are unsuitable for most surveying work.

The second type depends upon the diver carrying a receiver and interpreting signals emitted from at least two sources of sound. Again, any distortion of the sound wave will give rise to large errors in the calculated position. Furthermore, as this method has no other application than positioning, it has not found much favour.

The Leader Cable is essentially a magnetic method of navigation, which depends upon the magnetic field around a previously laid cable when a current is passed through it. This magnetic field is detected by coils carried in the vehicle and arranged at right-angles to the direction of travel. When the two coils are in balance electrically then the vehicle is over the top of the cable and this is usually shown on a voltmeter which can read both positively and negatively. Then the pilot has only to keep the needle central to remain over the cable.

The limitations of this method are that the vehicle is bound within close limits to the line of the cable, that the cable has to be laid beforehand, and that there is no registration of distance travelled.

The taut-wire technique has already been mentioned in connection with swimming navigation, and the principle remains the same when it is mounted in a vehicle.

The highly complex and exceedingly expensive methods of inertial navigation used in submarines will not be considered here, as they involve instruments that are unsuitable for the use of the diver/navigator.

When the area of operations has been thoroughly explored and surveyed, as necessary for the job in hand, then the major part of the operation can begin. However, it is worth repeating that generally one cannot survey an area too much. The better it is known and measured the better the planning can be for the operation.

Of the innumerable tasks that may be required to be carried out underwater, the type frequently encountered are searches. Ranging from searching for a lost cigarette case to a lost shipwreck. Each particular situation will require to be planned according to certain principles and the prevailing circumstances. The following table of searches briefly summarizes the considerations that will determine which will be used, but it may be useful to mention the principles that have led to the evolution of these methods (see *figures 25 (i) (ii) (iii)*).

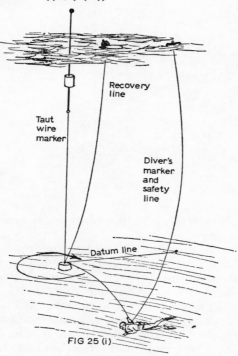

Recovery line

Taut wire marker

Diver's marker and safety line

Datum line

FIG 25 (i)

Circular search

Firstly, however good the visibility underwater, the diver can still only see a very short distance by comparison with the distances that are considered short on the surface. As a result, visual methods of searching, other than over a small area of good visibility, are slow and unreliable. Where the bottom is covered with rocks and other obstructions of a similar size to the target then this may be the only practicable method when the visibility permits. Otherwise, the search will be by feel alone (unless some

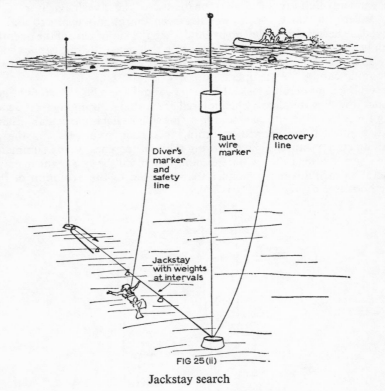

Diver's marker and safety line

Taut wire marker

Recovery line

Jackstay with weights at intervals

FIG 25 (ii)

Jackstay search

influence method, such as magnetic or acoustic, is applicable), which is very reliable but very slow.

The various towed searches are those depending upon the diver's visual observation of the sea-bed. The speeds at which they can be conducted are dependent on the clarity of the water, the clearer water allowing wider spacing of the search lines, and depends upon the object that is being looked for, and the type of surroundings that it will be lying amongst. For instance, a large dark object on a light sandy bottom is easily spotted and only requires the diver to be briefly aware of it for its successful detection. Therefore, a high angular velocity of the bottom passing his eyes is acceptable, and a high towing speed can be adopted. When the object

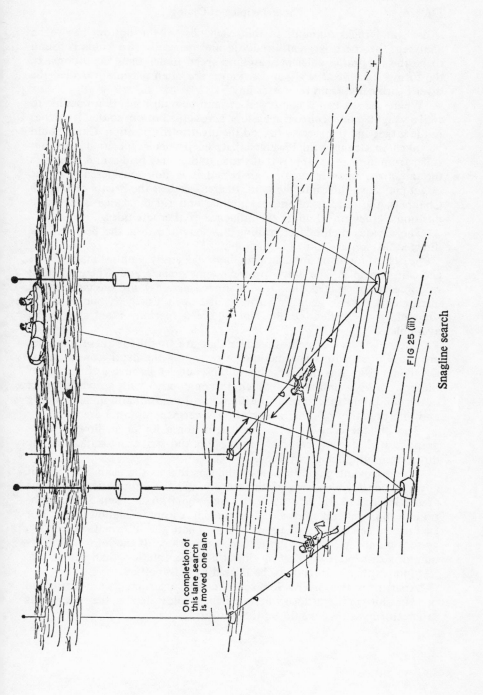

On completion of
this lane search
is moved one lane

Snagline search

FIG 25 (iii)

is dark and rocks abound, so that each part of the bottom has to be analysed, the speed is greatly reduced and generally two knots is found to be the maximum efficient searching speed under these conditions. In the former instance speeds of ten knots are often feasible provided the diver is protected from the water flow.

Where the sea-bed is composed of sand or mud it is often possible to trail a weighted line, called a snag-line, across the bottom so that it catches in the target and then serves to lead the diver to the position. Care should be taken in strongly tidal waters that the particular position does not suffer from large sand ripples that the snag-line may bridge and thus miss the target or, again in such an area, that it is not considered that the target may have sunk into the sand. In areas such as the Bristol or English Channels, the sand is often very mobile and ridges change shape and position as they travel under the influence of alternate tides.

The various methods of trailing the snag-line over the bottom in a directed fashion are shown in the table.

Searches involving influence methods generally employ magnetic or acoustic principles. The simple proton magnetometer, and, where financial resources are restricted, the Diver's Sonar (*plate 23*), are the most useful instruments. Other acoustic instruments, such as the Oblique Echo-sounder, give excellent results but require a specially fitted ship to be available.

The only types of echo-sounders that are useful for these purposes are those fitted with some method of recording the depth continuously. On the recorder it is then possible to pick out details such as the form of the bottom, fish, and wrecks which, in conjunction with a diver's report of the conditions in that same position, lead to meaningful understanding and interpretation of other observations over neighbouring areas.

The oblique echo-sounders are useful for a lot of shallow oceano-graphic work as they can pick up the dip and strike of strata, and the direction of alignment of furrows.

The disadvantage of an echo-sounder is that as the beam is a cone it covers a considerable area on the bottom and the information from this area is integrated and returned as a single signal. As a result the information given is 'general' and seldom particular, except in shallow water. For example, a set with a 20° beam will summate the information inside a 35 foot diameter circle in 100 feet of depth water. If the information required is of a poorly reflecting object considerably less than 920 square feet in area then it is likely to be missed by this method.

Apart from the Diver's Sonar all the other instruments are carried on board a ship on the surface where, for the shallow depths, they operate as satisfactorily as they would on the bottom.

TABLE VII

Search Patterns

Type of Search	Target	Visibility	Currents	Sea-bed	Personnel	Equipment	
Circular search. (see *figure 25 (i)*)	Any.	Nil to less than 50 feet.	Up to 1 kt.	Not very rocky.	1 diver, 1 attendant.	Shot and shot-line, distance-line, dinghy.	Usually a small search used for objects in shallow water. The search is conducted by circling half one way round and returning the other way, gradually going out along the distance-line from the shot. Radius of the search not more than 100 feet.
Circular snag-line. (see *figure 25 (i)*)	Anything that a line will catch in.	Nil to less than 100 feet.	Up to ½ kt.	Flat sand or mud.	1 diver, 1 attendant.	Shot and shot-line, distance-line, dinghy.	This is a quicker search that the first as only one complete circle need be made. The maximum radius that can be achieved is 100 feet because of the drag on the line; and at this distance or on a resistant bottom the diver should walk rather than swim.
Jackstay. (see *figure 25 (ii)*)	Any.	Nil.	Up to 2 kts.	Any.	Minimum— 1 diver and 1 attendant.	2 shots and shot-lines with marker buoys, 1 dinghy.	This is a straight-line search and can be conducted even over very rocky ground with no visibility. If a tide or current is running then the limitation is set by the diver's ability to reach the bottom from the surface. The search is moved sideways using one jackstay after another.
Jackstay. Snag-line.	Anything that a line will catch in.	Nil to less than 100 feet.	Up to 2 kts.	Flat sand or mud.	2 divers, 1 attendant.	4 shots and shot-line with marker buoys, 1 snag-line, 1 dinghy.	This again is a straight-line search and can be conducted in any tide or current that the divers can swim to the bottom in. 100 feet of snag-line is the approximate limit because of the drag.

TABLE VII—Contd.

Type of Search.	Target	Visibility	Currents	Sea-bed	Personnel	Equipment	
Snag-line.

(see *figure 25 (iii)*) | Any that a a line will catch in. | Sufficient to read a compass. | ½ kt. or more. | Flat sand or mud. | 2 divers, 1 attendant. | 1 dinghy, 1 snag-line, 2 diver's compasses, and watches. | This is only suitable when a current is running and where a 'one pass' search is adequate. The width of the searched front can be increased by adding more divers at not more than 100 feet apart.

Good swimming discipline is essential to maintain the line and navigation. |
| Towed search (visual). | Any that is visible on the bottom. | Over 4 feet. | Any. | Any, provided that the height of rock outcrops or obstructions do not exceed the visibility distance. | 1 attendant, 1 diver, 1 crew. | 1 powered dinghy, 1 towline and either sinker, aquaplane, or glider. | The speed of the search depends upon the type of bottom and the target, and also upon the device by which the diver is towed. At speeds over 2 kts. the diver must have something other than a weight to keep him down, and at 4 kts. requires protection against the water flow. Navigation is from the surface. |
| Search by vehicle. | Any that is visible on the bottom. | Over 6 feet. | Any within the capacity of the vehicle. | Any, provided that the height of rock outcrops across the line of search is less than the visibility distance. | 1 attendant, 1 diver. | 1 powered dinghy, 1 powered vehicle. | This is an inaccurate method of searching particularly where the visibility is poor. Navigation is difficult unless a very sophisticated machine is being used in which influence methods are substituted for the visual ones for navigation and search. Under these conditions visibility can then be reduced and the target may even be buried. |

Type of Search	Target	Visibility	Currents	Sea-bed	Personnel	Equipment	
Acoustic torch search (circular).	Any that will reflect sufficient energy to be detected at the range.	Nil.	½ kt. without protection.	Free of large boulders or other good reflecting surfaces or places in which the object can be 'shadowed' from the beam.	1 diver, 1 attendant.	1 powered dinghy, 1 accoustic torch.	There are several techniques for searching and registering the returning echo from the target, but all depend upon some part of the energy transmitted being returned and the time interval between the two being measured to give a range. The instruments are very portable and can be handled in rough weather by one diver and his attendant. The torch can also be used for navigation purposes.

When large areas have to be searched it is generally more satisfactory to conduct the operation from the surface if the sea-bed structure permits, as this is faster. For instance, a pair of otter boards can be towed over the bottom 150 feet apart with a wire between them at speeds up to 4 knots. This rate of coverage can only be exceeded by the diver equipped with a Diver's Sonar Unit (*plate 23*). Later it is suggested that this rate of surveying or searching could be greatly increased by the use of simple instrument-carriers launched in salvoes along predetermined courses, and their records recovered and analysed at leisure afterwards.

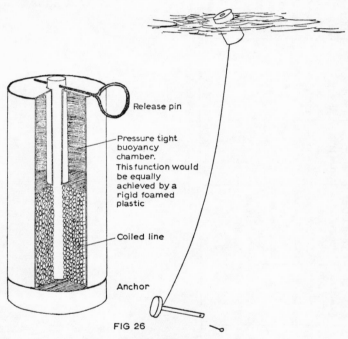

Release pin

Pressure tight buoyancy chamber. This function would be equally achieved by a rigid foamed plastic

Coiled line

Anchor

FIG 26

Neutrally buoyant marker

Whenever the object, or target, at which the search has been directed is found its position must be marked. This is particularly important when towed searches are being used in which it will be very difficult to return to any spot exactly, and a few tens of feet error may lead to many hours of arduous searching later to rediscover the object. While Decca or other accurate fixes may be obtained on the surface and marker buoys laid it is inevitable that considerable errors will be introduced into the final position where the sinker comes to rest as a result of small delays, inherent in the signalling system, reading the fixing instruments, and launching the marker. Many of these delays can be eliminated if the diver is carrying a neutrally buoyant blob and sinker (see *figure 26*) which he releases the moment anything of interest is sighted. It is then possible to return to the right position and lay a more permanent marker, or take more accurate fixes at leisure.

The methods at present available to the diver for directing his journeys underwater and relating these journeys with the established survey systems have been examined in some detail, as unless he can go where he wants and record where he went his efforts will be wasted.

Before any underwater work begins a survey will precede it, even if it is only the cursory glance, or exploratory feel, given by the working diver with his hammer already in hand. As with surveying and exploring an area, a survey of the work in hand will always be well worth the extra time and effort spent in doing it carefully and accurately. The degree of accuracy will obviously depend upon the nature of the work being considered and the tolerances allowed will vary from thousandths of an inch when fitting has to be carried out, to feet when a sandbank has to be moved.

For the diver to return with an accurate and comprehensive picture of a situation in his mind is extremely difficult and where possible recording instruments, even if only a slate and pencil, should be used to their full extent. In waters where the visibility allows, photography is a useful, simple, and accurate method, which anyone can use who takes the trouble to understand the principles that underly the technique and apply them. These will be briefly examined now.

Firstly an understanding of the way in which light behaves in water and across the boundaries of air-water, glass-water, and glass-air surfaces is necessary. When light passes from one medium to another of a different density some of the light is reflected and absorbed and the remainder is bent, or refracted, if the beam is crossing the boundary obliquely. When it crosses at right-angles then only the losses due to reflection are observed. As the obliquity of the beam to the surface between the two media is increased there comes a point where all the light is reflected and will not penetrate into the second medium. Furthermore, as the beam travels from one medium into another it will be bent in a definite direction depending upon the relative densities of the materials. For example, glass is denser than air so light striking the glass surface at an angle less than 90° will be bent so that this angle is increased, but is bent more than if the light had been travelling through water on to the glass.

This explains why the diver, and the camera underwater, will see objects 4/3 their measured size, alternatively the camera's field of view has been narrowed. Other observed effects resulting from these facts are that the diver can never see below a horizon of 45° to the horizontal when looking from underwater to the surface, and all the light from the sun is funnelled down this 45° cone. Thus, after the sun has passed below 45° from the horizon the only light available underwater is that reflected from the sky and any objects that may lie above this horizon at the point above the diver.

Another peculiarity of water is that it absorbs light of long and very short wavelengths more than that of the blue-green part of the spectrum and as a result the general coloration of the surroundings will become blue-green in very clear water. In silt-laden coastal waters the colour is predominantly yellow and green. Thus, for example, the Mediterranean is more generally blue, while British waters, although sometimes as clear as the Mediterranean, are usually green.

Finally, a third factor to be considered in photography is that the water is itself the nutrient medium for the ocean's plant life which exists as a finely divided mass diffused throughout the layers that the diver will be moving about in and particularly near the surface. Also many of the animals of the sea-bed are hatched and pass their early lives feeding on this. In tidal waters near rivers, or shallow waters exposed to an open sea of ocean, the constant stirring will keep the finer particles of silt in suspension.

All those small bodies contribute to reflect a small part of the light so that it becomes scattered giving a universally foggy appearance. Even in the clearest waters of the Sargasso Sea the visibility does not exceed 70 yards, which would be considered to be a fairly dense fog on land.

The underwater photographer is therefore faced with the situation whereby the lighting is poor at the best of times, the contrast is always bad except at the closest range in the clearest of water, and the field of view of his camera will be restricted by refraction so that even a conventional wide-angle lens will be of little use beyond a certain width because of fading at the corners of the picture.

To overcome these disadvantages the range of the subject must be reduced as much as possible so that the contrast is improved and to this end colour should always be used so that both the colour and tone contrast are made available. Wide-angle lenses are necessary, although if the camera is mounted in a case and protected from the water so that the picture is taken through a plane glass window, then the limiting useful solid angle will be 67°. With special lenses designed to be in contact with the water a 130° field of view is possible and will then give the same field of view as a pair of eyes give a man on the surface. Underwater he is of course restricted in the same way as the camera except that certain wide-angle masks increase his field of awareness to the extent he enjoys on the surface.

The choice of film will be determined by the particular job and the circumstances, but on the whole as fast black and white films tend to give poorer contrast as compared with the slower ones, the slowest one that can be used with the available lighting is best. As a general rule, the colour film will give the most useful results, particularly now that fast film is available. If quick results are required and good lighting is available, then the Land process of obtaining positive pictures directly from the camera should not be forgotten. The films available in this process are very fast and do not suffer from the same degree of graininess as similar conventional fast black and white films, while the results are entirely adequate for engineering or record purposes, provided single shots are adequate.

Artificial lighting is necessary for the highest quality work except at shallow depths in brilliant weather and clear water. It does, however, involve its own particular problems.

Flashlight photography for the still pictures taken by a single diver gives excellent results over a very limited range, but even in reasonably clear water this range is so restricted that loss of contrast through scattering is of very little importance. Here it is the power of the flash which sets a limit to the range at which an object can be photographed. An advantage is that the speed of film used is of less importance with flashlight than with natural illumination, and the reds and yellows come through as well as the blue-greens, particularly if the flash is stronger in the long wavelength part of the spectrum.

This lighting is of course quite useless to the cine photographer or for shooting larger subjects, and to date this has only been possible with sources of strong steady light, provided from continuously burning flares, powerful lamps driven from a generator on the surface, or expensive silver-cell batteries contained in a vehicle such as Rebikoff's Torpedo. So far as is known a synchronized flash has not yet been produced for cinematograph work.

The powerful lights giving the greater photographic range once more encounter the problem of scattering, and just as a headlamp from a car in a fog can diminish the driver's visibility, so the badly sighted lamp can reduce the effective illumination on the subject so that it disappears altogether from the finished photograph. The light source should be as close to the object as possible without appearing in the picture and should be arranged to shine at right angles, or on to it, from one side, and not from immediately next to the camera as the usual flash attachment.

If the water is too dirty for directly illuminated pictures it is often feasible to put the light behind the subject and get a clear silhouette shot.

Most underwater camera cases built for each particular camera are usually costly as few of them are built at one time and to safeguard the valuable contents of the case must be made robust and accurate. Controls through the side of the case must be free to move and quite water-tight down to more than the depth the diver is able to descend, usually 200–300 feet. If the material of the case is opaque then these controls will have to be lined up to fit the camera in a definite position each time the case is closed up, and indicators of movement and position placed on the outside of the case. These are additional sources of trouble and cost which can be avoided by placing the whole instrument in a clear plastic case. Strength, beyond that to stand the knocking about that is sure to occur over rocks and when coming ashore or into a boat in wild weather, is not necessary if the case is pressure-compensated by a small demand valve and bottle unit which pressure-balances the inside of the case with the sea outside.

The use of the wide-angle fast lens gives the photographer considerable latitude in focussing, and if the water is clear enough, and the light sufficient, ranging can be done by adjustment of the aperture and shutter speed. This is less satisfactory than adjusting the range itself as an additional control (shutter speed) is required, whereas it might be possible to work with only focussing available as a variable control once the camera is submerged. This is particularly true when flash lighting is being used because the flash lasts for a limited time and no significant additional light is admitted after this time has elapsed so that a fixed shutter can be used.

In murky waters when relatively flat objects have to be viewed, such as dock walls, bridge piers, or ships' hulls, a screen of clear water fitted to the camera and interposed between it and the subject will give a photograph extending over a larger area than could otherwise be obtained using a close-up lens. However, the lighting of such a device is difficult and still requires the water to be sufficiently clear to allow light to penetrate to the centre of the picture from the outside edge. Lighting placed inside the clear-vision screen is always reflected back off the transparent surface in front of the screen sufficiently strongly to hide the dark subject beyond. Thus, because of the clumsiness of this screen, often weighing 450 lb. when full of water, it is sometimes quicker to take a mosaic of a number of close-up shots with simple lighting.

If natural lighting is being depended upon it will pay the photographer to make his adjustments according to the reading of a good quality light meter, unless he is very experienced. The eyes adjust so readily to poor conditions and the diver's awareness has sufficiently deteriorated that detection of changes which will considerably affect the shutter speed or aperture can be missed easily. The meter should be contained in a case with a window of the same transparent material as that in front of the camera lens and should be constructed so that when not being used it can be slung out of the way or put in a convenient pocket or made as an attachment to the camera assembly.

Cine filming underwater gives the photographer the great advantage that he is able to manoeuvre in three dimensions with ease, but it also creates the difficulty of holding the picture steady whilst he is moving in addition to keeping it in focus while at short range. As on the surface if really steady sequences are required it is necessary to secure the whole apparatus to a tripod standing securely on the sea-bed.

For most engineering work the value of the cine camera lies in the very great number of single, still shots that it can take. This is useful when a large area or a long length of work, such as a pipeline, needs to be examined.

When it is possible to station a large boat nearly over the diver, or when he is working close to a platform on the surface, it is sometimes useful to use underwater television. This has the advantage that not only can the diver's view be seen by a large audience, but the view required by the engineer concerned with the work can be got by directing the diver, and photographs then taken of the screen. Furthermore, as the television camera can be made more sensitive to light than the human eye it can be used in comparatively dirty or murky waters where the diver has difficulty in obtaining a visual picture of a situation.

The camera is, however, only a second-hand method of obtaining information. To be of value it has still to be directed by a diver, preferably with knowledge of the engineering involved, while if it is used without direction and only suspended from the surface the results are likely to be disappointing. As the camera swings the view will change rapidly and in the absence of any indication of direction is likely to be meaningless.

A great part of underwater work takes place in murky water, or the data to be recorded are not suitable for film. Under these conditions a tape recorder is invaluable provided the diver is using a breathing system which is silent in the region close to the mouth, and has no mouthpiece. A recorder can be used both as a two-way telephone between the diver and the surface and as a recorder at the same time as required. To be effective the diver must have his mouth clear for enunciation otherwise the noise is unintelligible without considerable previous knowledge of the context of the message.

Finally, the diver's slate is of most use in water where sufficient visibility exists to order the writing on the slate. Otherwise a telephone, or signal line, to the surface where the attendant can write will be necessary to compose a coherent picture. Figures can be transmitted quite successfully on a life-line, but of course comments have to wait until the diver surfaces, whereas a more complete picture is obtained via a telephone or recorder.

When surveying an area or structure, no comment on the work should be omitted, and no measurement left to memory. Too much information is always preferable to too little, while the circumstances under which the diver is labouring and the sudden change from underwater to surface conditions make the diver's memory for all data unreliable.

10

Underwater Work

Labouring underwater involves handling tools for cutting, drilling, or joining wood and metal, digging, and lifting.

Each type of operation will be considered because, although each has its own well-known technique developed for surface use, the techniques are still in an early stage of development underwater.

Cutting wood such as baulks of timber or wooden piles is extremely arduous work if the only tool available is a hand-saw. In every case it saves time, money, and effort to use a machine or some more powerful source than muscles to do the work. There are both compressed-air band-saws and submersible electric motor-driven saws that will do the work. In addition, explosives can be used if the timber is not very thick (up to 12 inches diameter), or very tough, and will be discussed under the heading of explosives.

Cutting metals is usually accomplished by the use of a flame when ferrous structures are the object of the operation. Nowadays oxy-arc is favoured both because the cutting speed is higher, the skill on the part of the operator is less, and the same apparatus can be used for welding. The equipment consists of a welding generator or source of electric power which will give at least 80 volts to strike the arc and a constant supply of 300 amps. The leads from the generator pass through an inductance coil which serves to build up the voltage when striking the arc at the start of a cut, and thence to the electrode holder. The negative lead passes from the generator to an earth clamp secured to the metal which is being worked. As the electrical resistance of even sea-water is high compared with metals there is little danger to the diver holding the insulated electrode holder, nor is there any great loss of efficiency when the electrode tip is close to the work-piece. The diver should be careful not to come in contact with the electrode and the work-piece when the switch is made as he does then complete the circuit and this could be dangerous.

Because an electric current passing through water dissociates or splits up the constituents of the water into oxygen and hydrogen it is important that there should be a free escape for the gases away from the diver. If he is working below a space in which these gases could accumulate then arrangements must be made to release any gas gathering there continuously, either by cutting escape holes or providing a suitable ventilating system. Casualties have resulted through failure to observe these precautions, particularly when using flame cutters in which hot and still burning gas may be ascending from the site.

The cutting effect is obtained by blowing a jet of oxygen down the centre of the hollow electrode when the arc is struck which oxidizes the iron and blows it away in small particles. The electrode is held at an angle of 15° from the plane of the work-piece so that this debris is blown well clear. When welding the electrode is generally held at right angles or just inclined off the perpendicular to the plate and no oxygen is used.

The diver's indication that the cutting is successful is that the colour of the flame is blue, if it is orange then the gas pressure is probably insufficient and the hot oxydized metal is being blown back instead of through the plate.

Where the metal is backed by a solid filling such as might be found behind sheet steel piling, then the debris cannot be blown through the back and the cut will probably have to be completed by the arc itself creating a considerable crater.

The usual welders' darkened window is used to protect the diver's eyes during this work, as on the surface. There are various methods of securing it to the diver's face-glass but all ensure that the shade can be raised and lowered easily.

Although oxy-arc cutting can be carried out in water where there is no visibility, welding requires the operator to be able to see the work if a good weld is to be obtained, and as all underwater welding done surrounded and quenched by water is unreliable, anything that tends to deteriorate the work further should be avoided.

When cutting is done with oxy-hydrogen a special underwater cutting torch is used. Oxy-acetylene should never be used in any more than 10 feet of water as the danger of its exploding in contact with the oxygen as the pressure increases becomes greater, until at a pressure equivalent to depth over 30 feet in water it will detonate spontaneously.

The heat of the burning oxygen and hydrogen is 5,260°F., and is amply sufficient to build up a pool of molten metal. However, unlike the oxy-arc method there is a short time lag for the temperature to grow at a hot spot and during these few seconds the torch must be held steady. Furthermore, if the torch is moved too fast along the metal as the cutting proceeds so the hot spot will be lost and the operation must be begun again. When this hot spot has been established a jet of oxygen is directed at it in order to oxidize and blow the metal away. Cutting by this method is neater and cleaner but more difficult than with the arc, and also requires that there shall be some visibility in the water. The makers of the cutting equipment issue tables of pressure to be used with this equipment, but it is arranged so that the oxygen and hydrogen are supplied for burning in the ratio of 1:2 and additional oxygen is available for the cutting when the cutting lever is depressed, opening a valve to allow this supply to the nozzle. The torch can be lighted underwater by means of an electric spark generated by drawing the nozzle across a serrated plate connected by an insulated lead to one terminal of a battery, the other terminal being similarly connected to the torch.

The gas supply is usually at pressures between 80–150 lb./sq. in., and is led through reinforced rubber hose made in 60 ft. lengths and joined up as required. It is usual to tape the oxygen and hydrogen hoses together to form one line for ease of handling. Similarly the oxygen hose and electric cable are bound together when using oxy-arc.

Cutting can also be accomplished by means of explosive, and it is in this realm that the shaped charge is expected to show marked improvement in performance over other methods. At present, however, only solid charges are used which require a considerable quantity of explosive for a limited effect, and incur the additional disadvantages of a widespread damage.

The cutting power of the shaped charge is achieved by what is known as the Monroe effect. It has been found that when a detonating wave passes from the top end of a cylinder of explosive towards a cone-shaped concavity at the bottom end it gathers momentum, that is, speed and pressure, until it reaches a limiting speed depending upon the type of explosive.

As this wave reaches the top of the concavity it becomes shaped or focussed into a jet of very high velocity and high pressure gas. In order to make use of this gas jet it is necessary to line the concavity with a material which will absorb as much of the energy of the detonating wave as possible and this is usually achieved by the use of a copper lining of suitable thickness. This lining is then molten and formed into a stream of metal particles having the form and velocity of extremely fast bullets which have sufficient energy to drill holes of considerable depth and diameter in any solid target. Several variables are important in the design of shaped charges in order to realize the most efficient use of the explosive charge. These are as follows.

The density and detonating speed of the explosive, the point of initiation of the charge, the physical dimensions and proportions of the charge, and whether it is contained or not, the angle of the conical or paraboloid concavity, the thickness and properties of the metal liner, and the distance away from the target, that is, the stand-off distance, that the charge is held from the target (see *figures 27*).

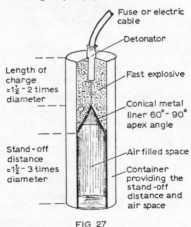

Fuse or electric cable

Detonator

Length of charge =1½ - 2 times diameter

Fast explosive

Conical metal liner 60° - 90° apex angle

Stand-off distance =1½ - 3 times diameter

Air filled space

Container providing the stand-off distance and air space

FIG 27

Shaped charge

Considerable improvement in penetrating power has been claimed for some American charges used in oil wells for perforating the casing and as far into the surrounding rock as possible, by inserting a steel 'wave former' between the liner and the advancing detonating wave. This has the effect of preshaping the wave before it reaches the liner so that more of the wave energy is transferred to the liner with a consequent increase in its effect on the target.

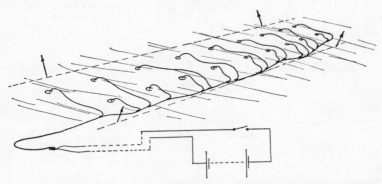

(a) Blasting a trench. Note Cordtex leads to each hole initiated by single detonator fired electrically. All joins made with ends facing detonation wave and sharp bends avoided. Delays if required from one end to another

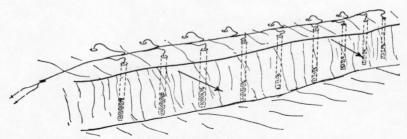

(b) Blasting a face. Cordtex leads as in (a). Delays arranged to fire front row first and remaining rows in succession

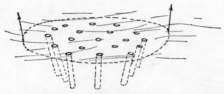

(c) Blasting a hole. Charges laid in hexagonal pattern with holes sloping inwards. Delays arranged to fire from centre outwards

FIG 28 (a) (b) (c)

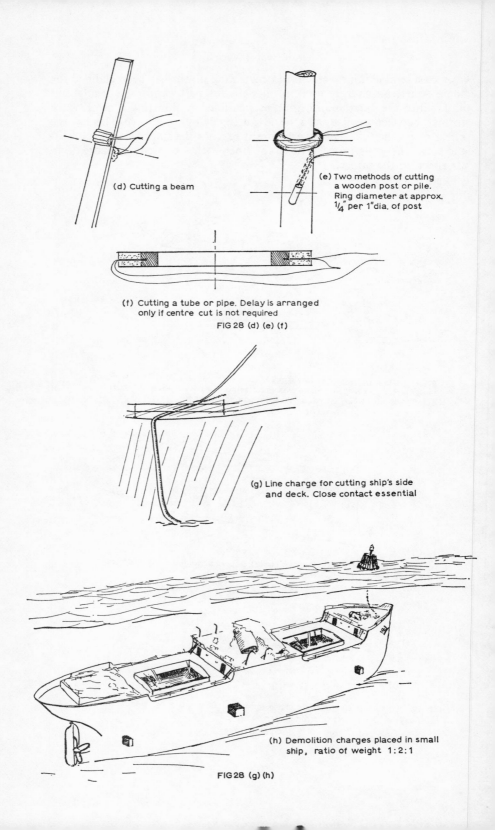

(d) Cutting a beam

(e) Two methods of cutting
a wooden post or pile.
Ring diameter at approx.
$1/4$" per 1"dia. of post

(f) Cutting a tube or pipe. Delay is arranged
only if centre cut is not required

FIG 28 (d) (e) (f)

(g) Line charge for cutting ship's side
and deck. Close contact essential

(h) Demolition charges placed in small
ship, ratio of weight 1 : 2 : 1

FIG 28 (g) (h)

Less work has been done to date on the science of the linear charge than on the conical one although the commercial applications for the former appear to be more promising.

A second method of explosive, or cutting by using chemical energy, is promised with the use of materials that burn very quickly, emitting a large amount of heat. One of these is provided by the well-known thermite of the old incendiary bomb, and there are many others which provide sufficient heat and mechanical disturbance for a short time to serve as cutting instruments against steel plate for example. If these are developed they will no doubt be superior to explosives in that they have a less extensive effect on nearby structures, on the other hand they are not nearly so neat.

Explosives have been used for many years in cutting up wreckage, cutting piles, and other forms of demolition where no comparatively delicate structures exist which might be damaged by the enormous quantity of energy released in a small period of time and which is not absorbed by the target.

The methods are generally rough and brutal, depending for the economy of their effect on the fact that explosive is fairly cheap, very easy to use, and can be used under conditions in which more efficient and sophisticated methods would not produce more efficient overall results (see *figures 28 (g) (h)*).

For cutting sheet steel, such as decks where there may be supporting deck beams below, explosive is made up into sausages at about the rate of 3 lb./ft. run, which will smash the plating of most large merchant ships. The thicker plate of armoured warships will of course require more, while the thin plate of destroyers can be cut with approximately half that amount. Where beams, piles or bars are to be cut and there is access to both sides it is usual to use the shearing effect of two charges displaced opposite to each other. It will be found for example that 1 lb. of explosive on each side of a standard 85 lb. rail will cut it easily.

The use of explosive is a matter mostly of common sense. If it is realized that each type has its own characteristics and is used with attention to these features as well as the old reminder that all explosives are safe while it is remembered how dangerous they are, then the user should experience nothing but success with them.

We come now to methods of drilling underwater and start by examining the types of materials that may require holes in them for various purposes.

Firstly, the ones that immediately spring to mind are piles, sheet steel, and fittings generally, which are necessary in building outfalls, harbours, bridges, and other public works.

The methods used here are extensions of the methods used on land bearing in mind that the diver cannot see as well as his opposite number ashore, is never as stable on his legs, and is frequently subjected to the effect of currents with a similar force of full gales of wind on the diver's body.

Thus, compressed air-driven tools are generally in use for drilling wood, while metals will probably have any holes requiring cutting underwater done by torch or Cox's gun. It is always best to support air tools on a jig secured to the work. This ensures that the operation is as true as the tool will allow and relieves the diver of hours of frustrating and exhausting effort trying to keep poised in the right position while bringing his effective weight to bear on the tool. The jig should leave him with only the starting and stopping of the tool to do, followed by resiting the jig.

Sheet steel can be drilled by similar methods and may have to be, but it is a tedious task and better to use the rougher and more powerful methods of burning or punching if great precision is not required. Burning is carried out as for any other kind of cutting except that the torch is either not moved at all, for holes of approximately $\frac{1}{2}$ inch diameter, or only slightly if a larger hole is required. Punching includes not only use of the Cox's bolt-driving gun, in which a solid cylinder of metal is fired through the plate, but also the cylindrical-shaped charge. Both methods tend to depress the surface of the plate around the hole which itself is usually neat and precise. The other side of the hole tends to be ragged and carries the fringe of metal forced aside by the missile. The Cox's bolt gun fires a punch which makes a hole that will accommodate a $\frac{5}{8}$ inch bolt. The shaped charge can be made to punch a hole from as little as $\frac{1}{10}$ inch diameter upwards and is particularly useful if the hole is required to penetrate other material as well. The usual ratio obtained with most small-shaped charges of the proportions given (see *figure 27*) being $\dfrac{\text{Diameter}}{\text{depth}} = \frac{1}{10}$.

If the material to be drilled is rock then the usual method is as on land using air-driven tools, but sometimes it is not possible to bring a large stable platform near to the work carrying the necessary compressors to work the drills. Under these conditions a thermic boring lance is sometimes of use. This is a tube of standard mild steel gas piping packed with iron wire down which a quantity of oxygen is blown. The end is ignited by means of an underwater cutting torch and burns fiercely at a temperature of about 5,000°F. This is a sufficient temperature to melt the rock while the superfluous oxygen also serves to blow out the slag and molten metal from the hole. The method is restricted to drilling horizontal (actually slightly inclined upwards) or vertical holes; in any other position the oxygen does not blow out the slag and the water solidifies it in place. If this method is used the diver must be prepared to withstand strong steam explosions. These are not harmful provided he keeps at least 3 feet away from the hole being drilled, but can be quite shaking particularly if they take him by surprise. An experienced driller can see when the explosions are about due if he can see the formation of the lava. As the viscosity of rocks is largely dependent upon their acidity it is obvious that it is best to use thermic boring against alkaline or basic rocks as the melt from these will run more easily. The rate of drilling has been found to be at approximately 9 inches per 10 feet of lance per 2 minutes and consumes about 30–40 cubic feet of oxygen. It is the large consumption of oxygen that makes this method unattractive as it is the one factor that militates against its use in isolated places where logistics command the techniques in any operation. If a thermic compound could be found that was suitable for the lance-filling the technique would have wide application. However, despite the disadvantages it can be used from a small boat or inflatable craft and therefore in inaccessible positions. Waggon drills have been used effectively underwater when the requisite compressors can be brought to the area to provide the necessary power (*plate 27*).

Drilling in rock is usually carried out in order to place explosive charges and blast the rock, although it may also be necessary to drill holes to place anchorages for structures, apart from drilling for site investigation work.

When drilling in rock for the purpose of blasting it is usual to drill according to a definite pattern for each type of problem. The principle idea being to use the explosive force so that as much of the explosive energy is transferred to the rock and in the desired direction, as possible.

Thus, if for example there is a circular hole, tunnel face, or shaft, to be excavated the shot-holes are drilled at a slight angle to the axis of the tunnel, in concentric circles around the centre and spaced alternately. The diameter, depth, and spacing of the holes being decided by the nature of the rock, the density of the explosive being used, and the weight of explosive required per unit weight of rock. The charges are then connected up so that a fractional delay is introduced both to reduce the shock wave on the rest of the structure by spreading it out in time and to get the rock moving in a sequence so that each part of the charge will assist the subsequent part to exert its maximum effect.

This is achieved by use of detonators with delays built into them and by using an explosive cord, like Cordtex, which, having a speed of detonation of 23,000 feet per second, can also be used as a useful delay mechanism.

Delays must be designed so that the main detonating wave from each charge reinforces the effect of the next charge on the target. This is most easily shown in *figures 28* (*a*) (*b*) (*c*) The detonating wave in the target consists of a region of very high pressure travelling at the speed of sound through the target, and as it is the aim of the diver to use this wave with every succeeding detonation, so the layout of the charge scheme and the factors effecting the operation must be carefully considered.

For example, in the case of shaft, tunnel, or area excavation, the hole pattern that will be found most satisfactory is that based on the hexagon. The sides of the hexagon, which fix the distance apart of the holes, the diameter of the holes, their depth, the type of explosive, amount, and delay time, are the variables which generally have to be settled by empirical rules adjusted by experience on the site. However, it is always as well to plan the operation theoretically as accurately as possible beforehand in order to reduce the margin of error.

The information that will be available before arriving on the site or working on it will be the rock type, the cost allowed per cubic yard of rock, the drill sizes available, and the types and characteristics of explosives available.

A sophisticated calculation will not only take into account the state of the target rock after each series of detonations, but will attempt to arrange these detonations so that they are in a suitable phase to assist the general purpose. Where the charge lengths are short, or the charge weight/unit volume of rock is high, and the holes closer together, this will not be of practical importance as the wavelengths are shorter than the diameter of the shot-holes.

Generally the excavation is made by blowing out in lines towards the free face, or, in the case of tunnels or shafts, by blowing out a centre core followed by concentric layers one after the other to the full circumference.

Although it is seldom practicable, initiation of the charges should be from the bottom of the charge. However, this is only possible if electric detonation alone is used as Cordtex passing through the charge may partially initiate it while failing to fire the detonator if there is a sharp bend in the cord to point the detonator upwards, or initiating the detonator so that its detonating wave quickly passes out of the bottom of the charge and again a low order, or partial detonation, results.

Safety fuse should only be used for single charges underwater. This is in case the charge fails to explode. If it is only one amongst many, the failure may go unnoticed, thus leaving a charge ready to fire amongst the rubble which may then be initiated by a chance blow from a tool or boot.

We must now turn to consideration of the tools that the diver may direct but which are generally too large for him to operate himself, at least without assistance from machinery at the surface, or his base.

In public works these tools mostly take the form of methods of pumping loose material from the site at which the diver is working. There are two main types of pump in use for removing debris which are the 'air-lift' and the water-ejection lift. Neither of these requires the spoil to pass through a pump and their simplicity is the key to their widespread use.

The air-lift depends upon the difference of density between the mixture in the spoil tube (see *figure 29*) and the density of the external water. This difference of density gives rise to a difference of pressure at the mouth of the tube which increases with the depth of the water, and therefore the length of the tube (assuming that the spoil is always carried to the surface). The lift, or distance above the water level that the spoil can be lifted, therefore increases with the depth of the air-lift, and so does the efficiency of this method. The air is blown into the bottom of the lift through a mesh of small holes in an annular ring round the lowest point. For the best results it must be in a finely divided state so that it mixes well with the entrained water and spoil, and prevents the water slipping back, as it does past large bubbles.

Assuming that the efficiency of the method is approximately 33 per cent the formula for the amount of air (in cu. ft. of free air) required per cubic foot of water pumped is given by Goodman and Purchas (1899) (Trans. I.M.E. 1917) as follows:

$$V = \frac{L}{B \log \left(1 + \dfrac{S}{B}\right)}$$

where V = volume of air pumped, B = barometric pressure in feet of water, S = submergence in feet (i.e. the depth of the air entrance), and L is the lift in feet.

The capacity of the compressor should be twice the figure required by this formula to allow for maintaining a steady flow. The compressor pressure must be sufficient to overcome the water pressure at the level of the bottom of the air pipe. The cross-section area of the water pipe (sq. in.) should be equal to the discharge in gallons/minute divided by 12–15. This will ensure that the pipe is not too large to allow the air to slip away

Compressed
air

Discharge

Mixture of air
bubbles, water
and soil less
dense than
outside water

Annular ring
with fine holes
on inside

Suction

FIG 29

Air Lift

without entraining the water, or so small that it imposes a high frictional loss and does not allow efficient expansion of the air bubbles.

The air-lift is not advised for use in less than 11 feet of water as the distance that it can lift the spoil is practically useless. Otherwise its use is more widespread than the water-ejection method as compressed-air plant is always available on public work sites whereas the high pressure water pumps required by the second method have to be specially obtained and are expensive pieces of machinery.

The water-ejection pump depends upon the transfer of energy from the small stream of high velocity water to the general body of water in the discharge pipe which it entrains as it is directed up the discharge-line. The faster this body of entrained water can be made to move the better the suction, or speed of flow at the intake. The advantage of this type of pump over the air-lift is that the depth of water does not affect its operation, except that when there is a great length of discharge pipe the frictional effects must be taken into account. In a practical rig the lift above the water level may be up to approximately 24 feet, but it depends for its effectiveness upon the pressure of the supply through the driving jet. The calculations required for this pump are simply a matter of equating the momenta of the driving jet and the entrained water, with suitable allowance for frictional losses in the discharge pipe. This method is particularly useful for digging out spoil from one place and, without carrying it to the surface, disposing of it in another way or blowing it into the current to be taken away downstream.

Both types of pump may be very large indeed, and for some types of excavation air-lifts up to 18 inches in diameter have been used. Such pumps will generally be found where it is undesirable to pass the spoil through any pumping mechanism and where the comparatively low efficiencies can be tolerated.

Where the diver simply has to clear sand or mud out of the way he may use a high pressure water hose, sometimes fitted with a reaction jet to prevent his being pushed backwards by the jet or air hose. However, a small diameter water-ejection hose will generally give more effective service, particularly if there is any visibility available. Under these conditions the water-ejection pump will keep the scene clear where the simple hose would swiftly destroy any hope of seeing at all.

Apart from clearing spaces of unwanted spoil the diver may also have to use these methods in order to clear a path so that wires or attachments can be passed or made for lifting or manipulating purposes.

Various forms of lifting devices are used in salvage and public works. For heavy lifts, beyond the capacity of even the largest lifting vessels when lifting over the bow, the lifting pontoon is used. This is often an old hulk suitably fitted to take the 9 inch (circumference) wires used for this work. These wires may be passed under the object to be lifted, which is usually a wreck when of these dimensions, through tunnels dug by the divers using the pumps and jets mentioned above. Having passed the wires they are then secured to the hulk at low water, and as the tide rises the length of each is adjusted until there is an equal strain on all the wires. The lift then begins and is sometimes reinforced by flooding tanks in the hulk beforehand and pumping them out again as the lift begins to give a thousand tons extra buoyancy. The object is then brought to the shore in stages. Often two or more pontoons or barges are used and the whole operation is one calling for great skill and judgment in heavy engineering and seamanship.

For smaller lifts sunken pontoons, called camels, may be used. These are rigid tanks secured to the object on the sea-bed. They are then pumped dry and rise together, if all goes well, with the prize slung between them. In all these operations it is not only necessary to get the strain on all the wires exactly even, but also to trim both the lifting and the lifted craft exactly right. Trimming the lifted craft, of course, can only be done by placing the wires correctly in the first instance, that is, until any pumping operations become possible when it breaks surface.

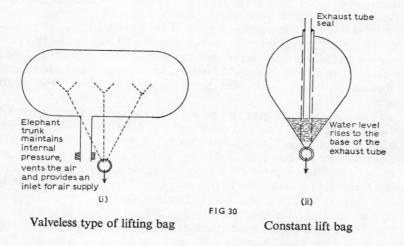

FIG 30

Valveless type of lifting bag   Constant lift bag

Flexible proofed fabric bags may also be used for lifting and have the advantage that, although they are basically expensive, yet they are far more easily transported and stowed than the rigid examples. On the other hand they are also more vulnerable to damage, and furthermore, cannot be only partially emptied as their volume varies with pressure and this changes with depth, therefore they must always be used either full or empty, but never half-way. In this latter condition they provide an unstable, or positive, feed-back means of support. In addition, in order to safeguard them against over-filling by expansion during a rapid ascent it is necessary to fit a large capacity relief-valve such as the elephant trunk shown in *figure 30*.

II

Future Developments

As the achievements of Hannes Keller have recently shown, we are on the verge of a great advance in the techniques that will enable mankind to move with ease and certainty in the underwater environment. Furthermore, as the cost of using the less tractable areas of the land increases, so the harvests to be reaped from under the sea will be won comparatively cheaply. It is with the conviction that mankind will eventually enjoy complete freedom of manœuvre over the submerged land masses that this part is written, and is an endeavour to visualize the form of the techniques that are likely to be employed and the goals to be achieved. Thus, efforts can be directed with some clear idea of the direction in which we hope to progress.

In the shallower margins of the sea, that is, out to the continental shelves and the slopes down to 3,500 feet, mankind must move with the freedom to explore and manipulate that is enjoyed on land. At present this can only be realized from inside the confines of machines, expensive to make, which by virtue of their complexity and expense are limited in number. But before being able to free man from his machines with safety several physiological problems have got to be solved.

Undoubtedly we shall soon see the first descent into the sea by a soft-suited diver to the maximum depth that is physiologically possible, and which is thought to lie between 1,800 to 3,500 feet. This is the point at which, on the molecular weight theory of narcosis, hydrogen becomes narcotic. Thereafter, although record-breaking dives may increase the depth by a few hundred feet, there can be no significant extension of the limit unless totally new chemical or physiological discoveries are made. The real extension of man's present limitations in underwater operations will be seen when the break through is made by learning to extend the diving periods to an unlimited time. Theoretically, provided the apparent narcotic effect of the heavier inert gases can be avoided, then, once the diver's tissues are fully saturated with the dissolved gas, the decompression period will be exactly the same for every dive extending in excess of this saturation time. This is obvious when it is remembered that the mass of any gas dissolved in any solvent (i.e. the tissues) will be the same for each pressure no matter how long the gas and solvent are in contact beyond the saturation time. There is, therefore, only this one mass of gas to be eliminated for each pressure and the safe elimination rate will be the same for each dissolved mass of gas.

Therefore, if the diver can be kept for long periods on the sea-bed the time spent there beyond the saturation time is time gained with no decompression penalty.

The engineering problems must then be solved to enable a man to live under these conditions.

At present the operations are restricted by prevailing conditions at the surface of the sea because the diver's time underwater is so limited. When once this time can be extended so that he can become independent of surface-borne resources for long periods, or even altogether, then it will be necessary to consider the various forms of apparatus and machinery required to support life. Having once established Man living underwater it is then necessary to develop the techniques that will enable him to navigate and work in this new environment before he can exploit the new wealth of resources opened up for him.

As mentioned before the chief physiological problems appear to be those of respiration and effusion of dissolved inert gases.

It has been shown that the lighter gases such as helium and hydrogen may well be effective in preventing narcotic effects altogether at depths down to a few hundred feet. However, as it has been found that nitrogen has a measurable narcotic effect even at very slightly increased pressures so it is unlikely that these other gases do not have the same effects, although scaled appropriately in terms of time and pressure. If this is so then there is likely to be a further limit to underwater endurance but at a considerably greater duration than that in force now. Mixing the number of inert gases used in a breathing mixture may be one method of reducing the narcotic effects as it is for reducing the decompression times required for unsaturated tissue to-day. This will only be so if the partial pressure of each 'inert' gas is the factor responsible, in other words the gases are not in fact chemically inert. If the total density of the mixture is found to be the factor then of course it will be necessary to operate with the lightest possible carrier, such as helium or hydrogen, bearing in mind necessary safety factors. Thus helium would be necessary for all depths from 132 feet. Thereafter there would be no risk using hydrogen provided special precautions were taken during decompression on the ascent to eliminate the possibility of spontaneous combustion when the hydrogen evolving from the tissues forms an explosive mixture in the breathing equipment and lungs. If hydrogen formed the main constituent of the atmosphere in the living quarters then of course this atmosphere must be changed when the quarters are recovered and brought above 132 feet at the conclusion of the operation.

Whether or not the prime factor giving rise to narcosis is found to be the partial pressure of the breathed 'inert' gas or the effect due to impaired diffusion of CO_2 because of the increased density of the atmosphere, there is no doubt that it is linked to the presence of CO_2. Elimination of this gas from the alveoli, and thus from the tissues, is most important and is mostly dependent upon the efficient ventilation of these minute processes of the lungs. Ventilation is obviously assisted if the resistance to the passage of the atmosphere in the lungs is reduced as the total muscular effort of breathing is also reduced. Again this calls not only for low density of breathed mixture but also low resistance to the flow of gas through the breathing apparatus. To some extent it may be possible to overcome this resistance at great pressure by forced breathing but only by incurring the penalty of complex and delicate equipment.

Because of the long periods of time visualized under conditions of high pressure, and probably a certain degree of psychological stress, it will be necessary to keep the O_2 partial pressure as low as possible consistent with efficient saturation of the haemoglobin of the blood at low breathing rates. This is normally accomplished in air and using this as the normal from which deviation should be slight the O_2 partial pressure must be maintained in the breathing apparatus and the living quarters close to 0·2 atmospheres.

At a depth of 627 feet this would call for a metering system with a tolerance of $\pm$ 0·1 per cent volume error to maintain the pressure between 0·18 and 0·22 atmospheres.

CO_2 elimination is also of very great importance. Fortunately the methods of elimination are chemical and thus depend upon the partial pressure of the gas so that the systems will retain their efficiency at all depths provided the resistance due to the flow of an increasingly dense gas mixture is overcome at the greater depths. However, the methods in vogue are not really efficient and limit the diver's exertions long before his muscular capacity is limited. Even the increased resistance to flow in his lungs is sufficient to impede the proper ventilation of the alveoli as they should be ventilated so that in systems working on unassisted open-circuit his muscular power is still not fully exploitable. This limitation can only be dispelled by recourse to lighter breathed atmospheres and eventually forced breathing.

With the descent into greater depths the diver will confront the problem of remaining warm under all conditions of activity. At present during the comparatively short dives that are possible the protective clothing need only be sufficient to prevent too sharp a rate of heat loss. When once long periods of time can be spent submerged then this situation is no longer tolerable and the diver must have it in his control to gain or lose heat from his environment as necessary. It has already been shown that as far as his personal garb is concerned it is only necessary to enclose him in an envelope insulated by $\frac{1}{2}$ inch of CO_2 and heated by 41 watts to enable him to remain warm under the worst possible conditions. The problem of insulating and warming the living quarters is similar although this larger volume, with its smaller surface/volume ratio, will be easier to achieve than keeping the diver warm. It is a problem adequately explored by those concerned with living under Arctic or Antarctic conditions.

Saturation decompression has already been mentioned and is not considered to offer difficulties that approach those stemming from the requirements to cut short decompression times from semi-saturated states. As transferring the diver under pressure to a large decompression chamber would be common practice, and as a few hours' additional time spent decompressing would not be important after some period such as a month spent submerged, so the difficulties and dangers incurred by the modern diver would not be encountered.

A problem that would arise and which has already been found to be very important in nuclear submarines and consideration of long-term space capsule design is that raised by the various organic gases evolved in the process of living arising from metabolism, cooking, painted surfaces, and lubricants. In the submerged living quarters where the atmospheric pressures are so much higher these problems are still acute. Again, chemical methods of absorption coupled with an efficient ventilating system will be necessary.

Each one of the physiological problems mentioned requires apparatus to be designed to cope with it. Considering the diver's personal outfit first we will examine the specifications that we must assume will be the minimum.

Man's normal working rhythm is approximately four-hourly. After four hours he requires a rest, a meal, the opportunity to excrete, and relaxation of concentration. Thus we have the forenoon, afternoon, and early evening, comprising an active day of twelve hours' work with one-hour periods between each working period, and at the beginning and end of the main rest of the day. This is a practicable routine for long periods of time and is followed by the greater part of the working population although the working periods may not all be devoted to the same occupation.

Thus a diving equipment which will include a breathing apparatus and protective clothing must enable the diver to live comfortably for at least four hours, plus a safety margin which we consider should be at least two hours, before having to return to base to restore himself and the equipment.

Each man's oxygen consumption is different as are his working rates and while it is necessary to consider a generalized figure for the main design layout it is also necessary to consider maximum and minimum recorded requirements.

Thus a supply of 2 litres of oxygen per minute is adequate for most work and also matches the present absorption capacities for CO_2 of most breathing apparatuses. But, given the increased efficiency with which CO_2 can be eliminated then a few people are capable of absorption rates between 6–20 litres a minute for short periods and this should be possible if the apparatus is to be safe, efficient, and comfortable. In the other direction the least amount of oxygen required may fall to 0·25 litres a minute at complete rest. Thus the gas supply must be so arranged that while keeping the oxygen partial pressure within 0·02 of an atmosphere around 0·2 atmospheres it can be supplied at rates at least between 6·0 and 0·25 litres per minute. CO_2 absorption must be so efficient that at any of these rates of oxygen consumption the partial pressure does not rise above 0·01 atmospheres in the apparatus throughout the designed period of operation of the equipment.

Finally, the breathing equipment must give the diver the facility to fill his lungs without having to overcome greater than 1 or 2 inches W.G. pressure at any breathing rate. The breathing rate actually achieved at high work rates may rise to 600 litres per minute.

Before considering the details of how these specifications might be met we will next examine the specifications for protective clothing because the two outfits must be welded effectively into one set of equipment which our imagined diver will never wear separately operating as he will be, surrounded by cold water throughout the time of each 'dive' away from the submerged base.

The water at depths of 1,000 feet or more is cold and approaches the steady deep-water temperature of 39°F. In very cold weather this temperature is of course frequently experienced in the sea near the surface.

The diver may find himself immersed in this cold water for long periods while he does a job requiring practically no activity except that of his mind, which must remain sharp and efficient. This it cannot do if he is at all cold or conscious of any discomfort in his environment. The protective clothing must not only keep the diver warm, it should also keep him dry, although this is not so necessary provided the wetness is warmed sufficiently and the breathing apparatus is immune. Thus the outside of the suit must resist abrasion, tearing, and piercing, by the many sharp growths and projections encountered in all submarine work while remaining flexible so that the least resistance is offered to movement of the limbs and body. As the protective suit is also the outer layer in contact with the water it should offer as little frictional resistance to the flow of water as possible so that movement through the water is unimpeded. This is yet another reason why the breathing apparatus and the protective clothing cannot really be considered separately other than as parts of the same set of equipment.

For short distances the diver will probably remain propelled by his legs. This is the most convenient, and therefore overall efficient, method for local movement, although whether boots or fins are used will depend upon the circumstances. As on land, for greater distances recourse would be had to vehicles equipped with power, also it would possibly carry resources to increase the endurance of the diver away from his base.

Unlike the breathing equipment it is difficult to state figures for the specifications of the protective clothing other than those concerned with the conservation of heat. In this case it is simply stated that, disregarding production of body heat, a temperature of 85°F. must be maintained at the skin when the water temperature is at 32°F. Also less than 10 per cent of the diver's output in mechanical work should be involved in moving all parts of the protective clothing at once.

The set of diving equipment visualized to meet the specifications will now be considered.

At depths below 100 feet it is no longer feasible to use open-circuit apparatus which is not supplied from the surface because the method is so wasteful that enormous quantities of gas are used and these quantities increase with the depth. For example a man working moderately hard will require 35 litres of air per minute at the surface which will have increased to four times that volume of free gas at 100 feet. For any prolonged submersion where carefully adjusted mixtures of special gases are necessary obviously this open-circuit system is quite unsuitable and some method of recovering the spent mixture and regenerating it is required. Modern semi-closed circuit apparatus is adequate for depths to 200 feet for short dives of twenty minutes' duration from the surface, or half an hour at 300 feet from a small submerged base-hut. The apparatus is totally inadequate for prolonged exploration particularly as the consumption of valuable gas such as helium is high. Thus it is necessary at these depths to be equipped with a fully closed-circuit regenerative apparatus. Whether this apparatus will be carried by the diver as a self-contained set, or whether he is linked to the apparatus in the base by means of supply and return breathing lines, will presumably be decided by the requirements of the work and the technological development of O_2 partial pressure metering devices and CO_2 absorbents.

Undoubtedly the bulk of the equipment to be carried will be made up of the CO_2 absorbent. It is after all the concern of the greater part of our bodily mechanisms, for the necessary oxygen uptake can be achieved with far less bulk and complication. Whether the absorption remains in its present form of small dry granules packed together to give a large absorbent area, develops into a type of gill with a large closely packed area exposed on one side to the water, or is achieved by the addition of power in a small chemical plant, it is unlikely to be greatly reduced below the size that it is at present. Thus an apparatus required to last six hours at an average oxygen consumption rate of 2 litres/minute will have to carry approximately 12 lb. of absorbent. This can be packed into 450 cubic inches by pouring and better packing, while achieving a smaller bulk for the same weight incurs greater resistance particularly at the higher gas densities to be experienced. The total oxygen required must be sufficient to supply a man at a rate of 2 litres/minute (NTP) for six hours. If CO_2 is to be dissolved into the surrounding water a suitable permeable membrane must be evolved that restricts the passage of the other gases and fluids while allowing free passage to the CO_2. Approximately 45 gallons per minute of sea water would have to circulate past 2,400 sq. ft. of permeable membrane to achieve the same efficiency as the CO_2 absorbent. While it would have the advantage that the endurance would depend only upon the power that gas required during the period, and not on the absorptive capacity of a chemical, the advantage would only become apparent when the weight of CO_2 absorbed exceeded half the weight of the absorptive apparatus. In round figures, 800 litres (NTP) of O_2 must be carried and an approximately similar quantity of CO_2 absorbed or dispersed.

The diluent gas or gases will only be required to make up the volume of a breathing system as though the dive had begun on a mixture of 20 per cent oxygen and 80 per cent diluent gas (by volume) at the surface. Thus if the total volume of the system is 10 litres and the maximum pressure that is to be worked at is 20 atmospheres then the amount of inert gas needed for one descent or dive (with no alteration of depth) would be 198 litres altogether:

$$0.8 \times 10 = 8 \text{ litres required for the surface mixture,}$$
$$10 \times 20 - 2 = 198 \text{ litres required to make up the volume on the descent, or to}$$
make up the volume at the depth.

If any changes of depth are expected that will lead to a change in volume of the breathing system so that some of the inert gas is lost and then requires adding to it will be necessary to increase the total supply carried. As dives to these pressures are unlikely as normal operations from the surface, but will be carried out from a submerged base, it is probably unrealistic to require to carry more than 200 litres of diluent gas for any one dive.

The suit material will necessarily incorporate a tough skin but may have to be of several different types of material for the various purposes for which it may be required. For instance, a suit required to enable the diver to swim long distances with the least possible effort must be stream-lined and use may be made of a thin layer of viscous fluid under a thin, smooth, outer skin to eliminate the wetted area drag and ensure liminar flow over the diver. This dress would obviously be quite unsuited for working in contact with wreckage, rocks, or in any engineering works where high abrasion resistance is important and the diver is not required to be mobile over a large area.

Both suits will have to incorporate the breathing equipment and will also have to be fitted with an insulated layer and a heating system.

Through-the-water and directional hearing equipment will have to be fitted to ensure that constant communication is maintained with the base and to keep the diver orientated with the base.

The problem of safety would be an urgent consideration as the instinctive urge to surface if any trouble occurred would be a powerful and utterly fatal one. It might be found to be most practicable to fit an ultimate emergency equipment which would render the diver unconscious to prevent his surrendering to the instinctive urge to surface, and at the same time reduce his metabolic rate. This would then give any rescuers the time and opportunity to render assistance which a semi-conscious and panic-stricken man might resist.

With these general requirements in mind the equipment visualized might be as shown in *figure 31* below.

Once the diver has been equipped so that he can dive from a base on, or near to, the sea-bed, and the physiological problems of extended submersion have been overcome, the next design that must be evolved in detail

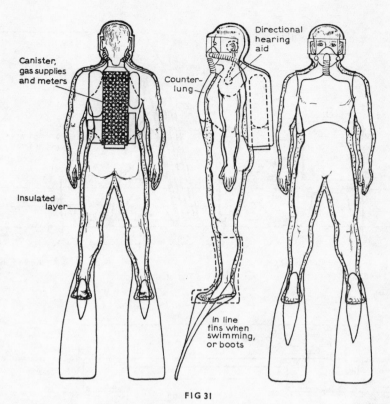

FIG 31

Possible composite diving equipment

is the construction of the base, the methods of transferring men under pressure, and the methods of surface support and decompression (see *figures 32 (i) (ii) (iii) (iv) (v)*).

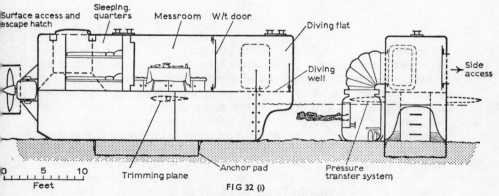

FIG 32 (i)

Submerged bases   (i) Mobile Base

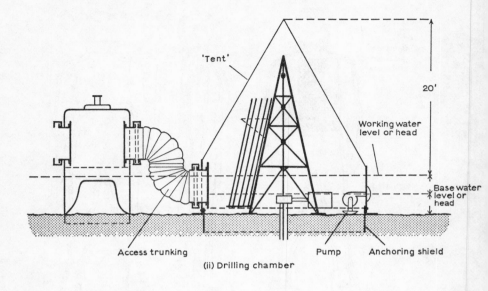

(ii) Drilling chamber

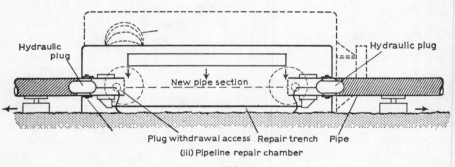

(iii) Pipeline repair chamber

FIG 32
Submerged bases

As the purpose of the diver being kept under pressure for long periods is to eliminate the need for frequent long decompression routines and substitute one routine at the end of a very extended dive, so there is no requirement for the base to be kept at anything other than the ambient pressure at the sea-bed or the depth at which it is submerged. A light structure can therefore be designed open to the sea-water pressure but retaining the atmosphere on the same principle as the diving bell. It would in fact be a diving bell with facilities that might be very extensive in the case of a large base, or similar to that of a yacht for a small expedition.

The specifications for this bell must therefore follow the general lines considered down here. Firstly the bell must be gas-tight from the bottom level, from which it is required to be dry, to the top. Secondly, there must

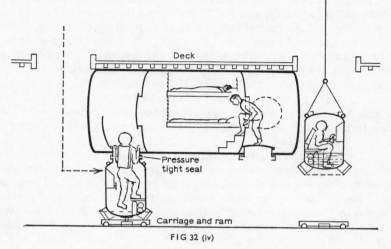

FIG 32 (iv)

Multi-cell decompression chamber

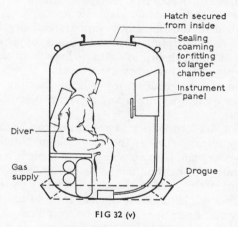

FIG 32 (v)

Honey-pot chamber

be an opening to the sea at the bottom to allow the water pressure to be exerted upon the atmosphere inside and thus balance the pressure at the lowest point of the bell. The pressure elsewhere will always be higher than the water outside depending upon the level, or the distance above the water level showing at the bottom and this pressure will be equal to the head of water over that distance. This positive difference of pressure is already useful in small bells where it is utilized to keep a fabric 'inflated' (*figure 32 (ii)*).

For men to enter, leave, work from, and live in the bell there will have

to be means of transferring them under pressure, facilities enabling them
to enter and leave freely, and finally the apparatus necessary to maintain
an atmosphere of the correct composition free from poisonous concentrations of vapours and gases and at the right partial pressure of oxygen.

Entry and exit can be effected through the bottom of the bell through
a well. Transfer under pressure can be achieved by entering into a mobile
pressure chamber such as the 'honey pot' shown in *figure 32* (*v*), either from
a specially constructed well in the side of the bell or into one separate from
the bell. Alternatively decompression could be carried out in a second bell
rising to the surface in stages under its own buoyancy and anchored by
the main base.

Maintenance of the right atmosphere inside the hull must be achieved
and would require instruments to control it within fine limits. Provided
the sensing devices are sensitive to partial pressure this should not raise
any difficulty. Oxygen can be constantly metered and the partial pressure
adjusted by the supply of additional amounts, reliance on the presence of
man to reduce it, or addition of diluent gas. CO_2 would be removed by
circulating the atmosphere through an absorbent which could well be
the sea water separated from the gas by a thin permeable membrane of
large area, or passed through a column of water in the form of fine bubbles
provided a loss of the other atmospheric gases in solution could be
accepted. Removal of the remaining vapours and organic gases would
require other similar absorption methods. Thus a supply of gases to make
up losses due to solution, absorption, and perhaps leakage, must be carried
as well as a supply of the necessary absorbents.

Power would also be required for lighting, heating, ventilating, and
domestic services quite apart from any demands made by the machinery
required for working.

The most compact form of potted power that can be carried apart from
that supplied by nuclear fuels is the accumulator battery, although if a
surface-based power plant is acceptable carried either in a ship or a moored
float then naturally this method would be chosen, at least to supplement
the battery or maintain it ready charged. Even in its present state of development the fuel cell is the most efficient form of battery and the most
suited to underwater operations. As can be seen from *figure 33* the maximum available capacity would be seldom required, most of the load being
small in comparison with this capacity, and neither weight nor bulk would
be important.

With the advent of cheap and compact nuclear plants already available
for military installations in isolated posts this form of power will become
available for use underwater, and this is the ideal place to use such a
plant as shielding by the water is easy and effective.

Limitation of gas supplies and other essential commodities will necessitate recourse to surface resources for replenishment but at least this can
be arranged to be a relatively infrequent requirement and the weather can
be chosen for such an operation. Under suitable circumstances, where the
bell carries its own source of propulsion then expeditions directly from

land-based facilities could be conducted, the return to shallow water, or the ascent, being adjusted to suit the decompression routine of the crew.

Because the structure of the bell is essentially light, subjected only to forces similar to those experienced by a ship of the same displacement in flat calm water, but acting in the opposite direction, there should be no difficulty experienced in trimming or manœuvring it horizontally or in depth.

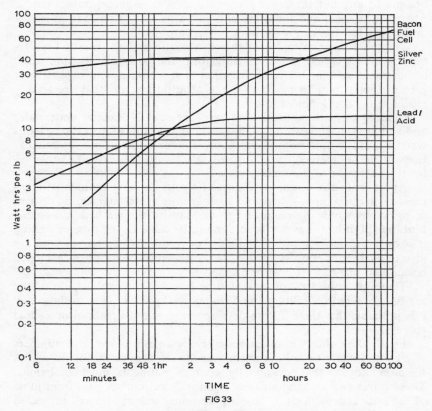

Battery capacity diagram (by courtesy *Engineering*)

By suitable design completely dry and securely anchored working spaces can be constructed on the sea-bed by merely dropping the pressure in the bell below that of the sea outside by a fraction of a pound per square inch. This will then drive the bell securely on to the bottom and hold it there with a force dependent upon the area in contact and excluding the water. This would enable operations that require to be free of water to be conducted in safety and very simply.

The design of a different type of bell for each particular purpose would follow as it does with ships, but as each has to be brought from its place of manufacture to the site of operations, navigation underwater and without reference to celestial aids will become important.

The features of navigation in this medium are that visibility is similar to that in very dense fog, sometimes as a moonless night, and sometimes at midday. Very seldom is vision possible beyond 100 feet and is usually restricted to 4 or 5 feet within a few miles of tidal shores or estuaries and is often nil close to the shores. Secondly water is nearly opaque to any but the lower frequency electro-magnetic transmissions. Therefore wireless and radar are eliminated as aids to navigation except in the very low frequency (or long wavelength) bands.

The most practical aid available is acoustic and the use of low frequency noises would most probably form the basis of any submarine navigational system. Inertial navigation is so complex and expensive at present that it is unlikely to rival the acoustic systems that are readily available for development to-day.

Compasses, both magnetic and gyro, are equally effective underwater and would give the heading of the vessel or bearings of acoustic beacons while currents would not introduce any unknown factor into the calculations of the submerged navigator in contact with the sea-bed as they do for the navigator of the surface vessel.

Apart from the unknown effects of living for long periods in high-pressure artificial atmospheres no basic research into engineering devices or principles would be required to put Man on the sea-bed and enable him to exploit it. It has not been done yet because at the time of writing it is only the curious with a military background of resources who are able to pursue the enquiry further. No commercial interest has developed because no one has yet opened up the field.

Therefore consideration now will be given to the exploitation of the sea-bed from both a military and a commercial point of view to show why it is probable that these 'future developments' may be realized in a short space of time.

Firstly the military implications of being able to move large numbers of men and quantities of materials over the sea-bed, or in 'flights' across the ocean abysses that occasionally separate continents, must be obvious. These forces can be 'camouflaged' against detection, are safe from most of the radioactive effects of modern weapons, and can be well protected against all but the most violent blast. They also have very large areas in which to manœuvre and will not be affected by the state of the 'ground' so that heavy vehicles can pass with the same ease and speed as light ones. As nuclear-powered submarines have shown, no sea is impenetrable and so far no frontiers are patrolled. Under the sea is therefore accessible to large 'motorized' land forces suddenly enabled to move swiftly and secretly over completely new and unpopulated territory in which no obstacles exist.

Surely this is an important factor in considering whether or not any deterrent might retain its deterring force? With the armed forces sheltered and perhaps some shelter available for the civilian population this might be lost. It will deprive the seafaring nations of the superiority they have enjoyed despite smaller populations. Once they were safe against the enemy soldier behind a moat that required a specialist to transport the soldier in a special craft either on the surface of the sea or in the air where they were easily accessible and defenceless; in future the specialist need only be the designer while accessibility will have ceased.

It is true that this sombre picture of the highly civilized nations once again being threatened by hordes, this time rising up out of the waves unaffected by sophisticated defences does depend upon the assumption that large numbers of ordinary soldiers can be successfully ordered to propel themselves into the depths of the seas. There they will hear their own and their companions' voices change so completely it will sound like a different race of beings chattering incomprehensibly; some restrictions may be placed on smoking, food will probably change in taste and, unless they are prepared to venture alone into the foggy dark enclosed in a close-fitting envelope, must be restricted to cramped quarters for long periods. Boredom and psychological stress may well take its toll and provide unexpected defences against this potential threat. The same psychological stresses will operate to some extent in commercial enterprises. It is unlikely that boredom will play so large a part or that the permanent threat of sudden destructive offensive action will tauten the nerves; instead, the hectic round of activity and the possible side effects of overwork and climatic or atmospheric deterioration (analogous to that shown at great heights) may eventually set in and cause trouble. Developing sensitivity or allergy to high gas pressures may also terminate a man's fitness to remain submerged.

Until comparatively unspecialized Man can be worked underwater it will never be a field in which large-scale commercial enterprise can operate economically.

For example, it will become possible to herd, restrain, feed, and contro the breeding of fish, so that fish farming becomes feasible, from a scientific point of view. But in order to do this economically at present one man would have to be able to manage a 300-acre 'farm' by himself and with capital outlay of about £15,000 provided his pay only amounts to that of a factory worker with overtime. At present the skill and force of personality required for such a job would command a far higher wage and so the proposition is not commercially viable.

If, however, the techniques are evolved which make the job easy and completely safe so that it comes within the capacity of the ordinary man, and if the power of his elbow is strengthened, then a balance will be struck and the era of hunting fish instead of domesticating them will have passed. We may then look to an improvement in the quality and quantity of fish which we can only compare to the difference between the unselectively bred and ill-nourished Indian village cattle and the stock carried on the average English farm.

This may sound fanciful to those who imagine all fish as roaming freely over the whole ocean only to be contained by nets slung from the surface to the bottom which are subjected to the wear and tear of tides, storms, and passing ships.

In fact, the majority of fish living near the bottom are creatures restricted to a certain range. They roam like sheep, between strictly defined territorial limits, and will only be driven away by disaster. So, like sheep, while a few will wander, the majority will remain within their home territory and losses will mostly occur from outside causes. Predators also have habits but their range is usually wider than their prey so any well-known stock will require protection. This is likely to prove the greatest difficulty.

Flatfish are even easier to contain. They seldom if ever willingly rise more than a foot or so above the bottom and an inward-sloping fence should be a sufficient boundary, particularly if the 'field' contains an ample supply of food.

Static sea-life such as the shellfish, or those forms that live amongst rocks naturally, like the majority of the crustacea, would of course be amenable to more compact and easily accessible living quarters. Their breeding habits would require isolated breeding tanks if it is to be directed towards producing more suitable varieties of animal and this would be true of the majority of the commercial fish.

Actually herding the fish might be done electrically to a limited extent although sea water is a poor medium in which to practise the method, particularly over large distances, because the ratio of the power required to the effect produced is enormous. Instead, experiments in America seem to indicate that, as on land, the predators can be tamed to become the protectors of their erstwhile prey. The genus cetacea, which includes the dolphins and the porpoises, have a very high level of intelligence, are thought to use a language and have perhaps developed a nomadic, acoustic culture comparable in complexity to our own preliterate societies.

They are also endowed with a sense which we lack entirely, that of echo detection exactly similar to a built-in asdic set which enables them to locate and attack the fish they live on accurately and swiftly. The situation is slightly similar to that in which Man presumably found the Dog vis-à-vis himself and so perhaps Man vis-à-vis the Dolphin may evolved a similar relationship, but quicker and more comprehensive.

Farming on a large scale assumes an intimate knowledge of the particular area, the life it supports already, and the habits and requirements of the animals that will thrive best on that land. It is exactly the same underwater, and before successful cultivation can begin marine ecology, of which we are largely ignorant at present, must be considerably improved. This can only be done by scientific experiments and comprehensive field surveys.

So much for an outline of the developments which will be forced on us eventually in the search for food to support a growing population on a diminishing area of cultivable land. We can foresee the events and could prepare for them now.

In the realm of marine public works, such engineering constructions as pipelines, power cables, tunnels, and bridge-piers, the ability to remain at work quietly immune from the violence of the weather and inconvenience of the tides is a boon most engineers would surely welcome provided someone else had tried it first. Most of these works are carried out in comparatively shallow water, although a few pipelines are projected that would descend to a thousand feet or so.

The mobile base or the lightly constructed specialized bell—perhaps even built of fabric—is a cheap and versatile tool. The crews to man them at present are not cheap as men with diving experience would be required.

However, with extension of the methods it is quite feasible to transfer ordinary caisson or compressed-air workers to the bell and back again without their getting wet or indeed even seeing water, while the work could also be conducted 'under cover' if it was of a static nature. Divers would of course still be required to operate equipment external to the base and also the pressure transfer apparatus.

While this might avoid certain psychological stresses and thus enable numbers of comparatively unskilled men to be used it is unlikely that many men will ever become really suitable for employment in operations that require the individual to leave the base and fend for himself for long periods encased in equipment that is complex. If this should be a correct appreciation then the emphasis will be laid on the development of machinery and power to aid and extend the effect of the lone, highly skilled man.

Other forms of engineering work will call for different detailed designs but will leave the main principle intact, that is, diving from the sea-bed upwards rather than from the surface downwards. Even in shallow water where decompression is unnecessary it may be advisable to be able to operate independent of the surface and largely protected from the weather that may be raging there. In particular both shallow exploratory drilling and salvage work may be conducted on these lines. The drilling rig can be contained within a 'tent' 20 feet high built of fabric except for the bottom five feet which would be made of some rigid material capable of withstanding compression. The pressure in the drilling tent is then adjusted so that it is the same as the water pressure at the top of the rigid section after the lip at the bottom of this section has dug into the ground. The rig will then be anchored more securely in place than if it was on a barge using conventional moorings, it will ride through the tide in the same way as a boat with the same shape, it does not need great masses of weight to keep it on the bottom but it would require a suitable sea-bed that gives the foot a chance to seal. Other types of sea-bed would require the bell to be weighted and would never be quite free of water on the ground itself. The drilling tent would be accessible from a conventional living quarters, through an air-lock if there was any differences of pressure being maintained between the two.

Salvage operations are seldom carried out with a view to recovering the ship. Modern ships are usually so badly damaged by the process of sinking, both when they hit the bottom and by crushing as any trapped air is compressed, that the only purpose of the salvage operation is either to clear the wreckage from a shipping channel or to salvage the cargo if it is valuable and of a kind that is not damaged by salt water. Again these operations depend for their efficiency upon the men doing the work being able to spend long uninterrupted periods at work on the site, and if they are exposed to wind, sea, and tide this is only achieved occasionally. If the work is approached from the sea-bed these problems are eliminated, except for tidal effects which are reduced. But, if the whole operation is viewed in a totally new light, it is no longer a ship-borne operation but a mining job. A valuable cargo to be recovered resembles a rich lode of ore that has to be worked out thoroughly and whose location is known within a certain margin of error once the main deposit has been located. At present the methods used are clumsy and require a large crew to work the surface craft as well as the normal seagoing hazards to restrict their activities. Mining operations on the other hand, where seldom more than a few thousand tons of 'ore' are to be recovered, can, by comparison, be carried out by one man and a boy. In fact the crew required for a typical 'mining' job would require four men in the working craft, and the crew of four in the supply and decompression surface ship. Actual recovery of the cargo would be carried out in one or two big operations planned to take place in favourable weather.

The object of this brief survey of a few of the well-known or actively discussed projects that have their place under the sea is to show that by using new techniques that involve no new principle and require practically no further research man can already penetrate the submerged continents of this planet and for no more resources spent than is required to put one satellite into space can exploit these areas to the great benefit of the people who first do this. After all, we have yet to feel the impact of the benefits said to accrue from the machinery whirling over our heads when under our feet we could transform the fishing industry, ease the burden of the civil engineer, and provide ourselves with a defence against our likely enemies cheaply. One has merely cost us effort and wealth, the other will produce it for us.

If we in Britain are able to appreciate that we cannot profitably engage in any other than productive commercial enterprises then, while pursuing the very limited projects that can be productive in space, we would be well advised to press ahead in the realm matched to our resources and our individual genius, which lies under the sea.

Appendices

Royal Naval Decompression Tables

(By kind permission of the Admiralty)

In the event of an emergency the first step with safety is given by $\frac{1}{2}$ Maximum Absolute Depth of Dive—33 in feet when breathing air, or the deepest stop shown in the table for the depth when breathing oxy-helium. Both these depths should be known before the dive begins. There is then time to consult the tables for the correct routine and the stand-by diver can be rendering assistance if required.

Surface decompression is normally restricted to military operations and should not be practised unless absolutely necessary, and certainly not unless the following conditions are fulfilled and limits observed:

(a) The recompression chamber is held immediately ready and close to the diving ladder.

(b) The air supply to the chamber is from a bank of fully charged cylinders capable of pressurizing the chamber to the full working pressure at not less than 45 p.s.i. per minute.

(c) A well drilled and experienced team of attendants is available and waiting at the surface.

(d) The drill for getting the diver undressed and into the chamber must be so good that no more than 5 minutes at the most must elapse between the diver leaving the sea-bed and being repressurized in the chamber to the equivalent pressure. *Note:* The length of time 'on the bottom' is calculated to include the elapsed time between leaving the surface originally and 5 minutes after repressurization in the chamber.

The depth and time limitations on the technique are as follows:

Depth (feet)	Duration (min.)	
Under 130	50	(Leaving the surface to
130–150	40	starting the ascent
150–170	30	from the sea-bed).
170–190	20	
190–200	10	

Therapeutic Decompression

The following conditions must be fulfilled when carrying out therapeutic decompression in a chamber:

(a) A high pressure air supply must be available in addition to any compressor that is supplied, which is sufficient to keep the chamber ventilated, and pressurize the chamber, for the whole length of a decompression routine.

(b) The chamber should be fitted with an air-lock for passing small objects through and it is better if this air-lock is large enough to accommodate a man.

(c) The chamber should be large enough to accommodate the patient and an attendant.

(d) No highly inflammable materials, such as lighters or matches, must be allowed in the chamber. No smoking is possible inside as the high partial pressure of oxygen renders all things such as cigarettes, paper, etc., highly inflammable.

(e) Electric lights must be contained inside pressure-tight fittings.

(f) Fire extinguishing materials such as water and sand, but not foam or chemical extinguishers, must be to hand inside the chamber.

(g) A doctor should be in attendance with the patient in the chamber.

(h) A qualified and experienced person in charge of the chamber must be in constant attendance outside.

(i) All chamber controls must be on the outside.

(j) A method of communication must be available which will remain clear despite high background noise or power failures. A spanner tapping out the single life-line code is the most reliable for routine operations.

(k) Oxygen should be available for use in the chamber.

It has been found that once a diver has contracted decompression sickness he must be decompressed at a slower rate than normally. This is probably because centres around which bubbles can form have been established and remain in the tissues for some time. It is probably also the reason why a higher incidence of decompression sickness may be experienced after breathing oxy-helium mixtures and changing over to air.

Oxygen should be used as indicated in the tables but should not be allowed to shorten the decompression time. Any hint of oxygen poisoning symptoms should terminate the use of oxygen.

If the diver has to be treated in the absence of a chamber the following routine should be observed:

Depth (feet)	Maximum rate of ascent
100–70	2 feet in 3 minutes
70–35	2 feet in 5 minutes
35–0	2 feet in 8 minutes

For maximum control of the diver's depth and rate of ascent at sea in the absence of a chamber he should be seated comfortably on a small staging rigged on a marked shot-line and with as heavy a weight as can be handled slung below it. The whole should be hung from amidships where the total movement of the ship is the least possible.

Should the diver not be in any condition to be re-submerged and no chamber is immediately available he must be sent as quickly as possible to a chamber, or revived so that he can be re-submerged as recompression is the only proper treatment. He should meanwhile be kept warm, be given oxygen to breathe, and be kept relaxed and motionless.

Transport to the chamber should only be by air if any other route is significantly longer and the aircraft can remain below 1,000 feet. Otherwise the lowered barometric pressure can make the patient worse.

The procedure for Therapeutic Decompression in a chamber is as follows:

(a) As soon as the patient is in the chamber increase the pressure at the depth equivalent of 25 feet per minute.

(b) Note the depth at which pain is relieved and enter the table below with this figure.

(c) Never hesitate to treat the diver. Early treatment of slight symptoms may save the patient from serious and permanent injury while recompression will not harm him if he was not in fact suffering from decompression sickness.

If symptoms return during treatment recompress the patient to a depth where he is relieved, but never less than 30 feet, and complete the treatment according to column 4. If relief occurs at a greater depth than 30 feet following this recurrence of symptoms then the patient should be kept at this depth for 30 minutes and then decompress according to column 3 and on air throughout.

TABLE ONE

Showing Ordinary Time Limits in Deep Water and Stoppages During Ascent

Depth in Feet	Duration	Ascent to 1st Stop in Minutes	Stoppages in Minutes at Different Depths			Total Time for Ascent in Minutes
			30 ft.	20 ft.	10 ft.	
0–30	No limit	1	—	—	—	1
30–40	0–2¼ hrs.	1	—	—	—	1
	2¼–2¾ hrs.	1	—	—	4	5
	2¾–3¼ hrs.	1	—	—	9	10
	3¼–3¾ hrs.	1	—	—	14	15
	3¾–4¼ hrs.	1	—	—	19	20
	4¼–5½ hrs.	1	—	—	24	25
	5½–6½ hrs.	1	—	—	29	30
	6½–11 hrs.	1	—	—	34	35
40–50	0–85 min.	1	—	—	—	1
	85–105 min.	1	—	—	4	5
	105–120 min.	1	—	—	9	10
	120–135 min.	1	—	—	14	15
	135–145 min.	1	—	—	19	20
	145–160 min.	1	—	—	24	25
	160–170 min.	1	—	4	25	30
	170–190 min.	1	—	4	30	35
50–60	0–60 min.	1	—	—	—	1
	60–70 min.	1	—	—	4	5
	70–80 min.	1	—	4	5	10
	80–90 min.	1	—	4	10	15
	90–100 min.	1	—	4	15	20
	100–110 min.	1	—	4	20	25
	110–120 min.	1	—	4	25	30
	120–130 min.	1	—	4	30	35
60–70	0–40 min.	2	—	—	—	2
	40–55 min.	1	—	—	4	5
	55–60 min.	1	—	4	5	10
	60–70 min.	1	—	4	10	15
	70–75 min.	1	—	4	15	20
	75–85 min.	1	—	4	20	25
	85–90 min.	1	—	4	25	30
	90–95 min.	1	4	5	25	35

Appendix I

Depth in Feet	Duration	Ascent to 1st Stop in Minutes	Stoppages in Minutes at Different Depths			Total Time for Ascent in Minutes
			30 ft.	20 ft.	10 ft.	
70–70	0–30 min.	2	—	—	—	2
	30–40 min.	2	—	—	3	5
	40–50 min.	1	—	4	5	10
	50–55 min.	1	—	4	10	15
	55–60 min.	1	—	4	15	20
	60–70 min.	1	—	4	20	25
	70–75 min.	1	—	4	25	30
80–90	0–25 min.	2	—	—	—	2
	25–30 min.	2	—	—	3	5
	30–40 min.	2	—	3	5	10
	40–45 min.	2	—	3	10	15
	45–50 min.	2	—	3	15	20
	50–55 min.	2	—	3	20	25
	55–60 min.	1	4	5	20	30
	60–65 min.	1	4	5	25	35
90–100	0–20 min.	2	—	—	—	2
	20–25 min.	2	—	—	3	5
	25–30 min.	2	—	3	5	10
	30–35 min.	2	—	3	10	15
	35–40 min.	2	—	3	15	20
	40–45 min.	2	—	3	20	25
	45–50 min.	2	3	5	20	30
	50–55 min.	2	3	5	25	35
100–110	0–17 min.	2	—	—	—	2
	17–20 min.	2	—	—	3	5
	20–25 min.	2	—	3	5	10
	25–30 min.	2	—	3	10	15
	30–35 min.	2	—	3	15	20
	35–40 min.	2	—	3	20	25
	40–45 min.	2	3	5	20	30
110–120	0–14 min.	2	—	—	—	2
	14–20 min.	2	—	—	3	5
	20–25 min.	2	—	3	5	10
	25–30 min.	2	—	3	15	20
	30–35 min.	2	—″	3	20	25
	35–40 min.	2	3	5	25	35
120–130	0–11 min.	3	—	—	—	3
	11–15 min.	2	—	—	3	5
	15–20 min.	2	—	3	5	10
	20–25 min.	2	—	3	10	15
	25–30 min.	2	—	3	20	25
	30–35 min.	2	3	5	20	30

Depth in Feet	Duration	Ascent to 1st Stop in Minutes	Stoppages in Minutes at Different Depths			Total Time for Ascent in Minutes
			30 ft.	20 ft.	10 ft.	
130–140	0–9 min.	3	—	—	—	3
	9–10 min.	3	—	—	2	5
	10–15 min.	2	—	3	5	10
	15–20 min.	2	—	3	10	15
	20–25 min.	2	—	3	15	20
	25–30 min.	2	3	5.	20	30
140–150	0–8 min.	3	—	—	—	3
	8–10 min.	3	—	—	2	5
	10–15 min.	3	—	2	5	10
	15–20 min.	3	—	2	15	20
	20–25 min.	2	3	5	20	30
150–160	0–10 min.	3	—	2	5	10
	10–15 min.	3	—	2	10	15
	15–20 min.	3	2	5	15	25
	20–25 min.	3	2	10	20	35
160–170	0–10 min.	3	—	2	5	10
	10–15 min.	3	—	2	10	15
	15–20 min.	3	2	5	15	25
170–180	0–10 min.	3	—	2	5	10
	10–15 min.	3	2	5	10	20
	15–20 min.	3	2	10	15	30
180–190	0–10 min.	3	—	2	5	10
	10–15 min.	3	2	5	15	25
	15–20 min.	3	2	10	20	35
190–200	0–10 min.	3	—	2	10	15
	10–15 min.	3	2	5	15	25

Showing Stoppages During Ascent after exceeding the Ordinary Limits of Time
on the bottom given in Table I

Depth in Feet	Duration	Ascent to 1st Stop in Mins.	Stoppages in Minutes at Different Depths								Total Time or Ascent in Mins.
			80 ft.	70 ft.	60 ft.	50 ft.	40 ft.	30 ft.	20 ft.	10 ft.	
30–40	Over 11 hrs.	1	—	—	—	—	—	—	—	39	40
40–50	190–240 min.	1	—	—	—	—	—	—	9	40	50
	240–360 min.	1	—	—	—	—	—	—	29	40	70
	360–450 min.	1	—	—	—	—	—	—	34	40	75
	Over 450 min.	1	—	—	—	—	—	—	34	45	80
50–60	130–140 min.	1	—	—	—	—	—	—	9	30	40
	140–150 min.	1	—	—	—	—	—	—	9	40	50
	150–160 min.	1	—	—	—	—	—	—	14	40	55
	160–180 min.	1	—	—	—	—	—	—	19	40	60
	180–200 min.	1	—	—	—	—	—	4	30	40	75
	200–255 min.	1	—	—	—	—	—	9	35	45	90
	255–325 min.	1	—	—	—	—	—	19	40	45	105
	325–495 min.	1	—	—	—	—	—	34	40	45	120
	Over 495 min.	1	—	—	—	—	—	34	40	50	125
60–70	95–105 min.	1	—	—	—	—	—	4	5	35	45
	105–120 min.	1	—	—	—	—	—	4	10	40	55
	120–135 min.	1	—	—	—	—	—	4	20	45	65
	135–150 min.	1	—	—	—	—	—	4	30	45	80
	150–165 min.	1	—	—	—	—	—	9	30	50	90
	165–180 min.	1	—	—	—	—	—	14	35	50	100
	180–210 min.	1	—	—	—	—	—	24	40	50	115
	210–240 min.	1	—	—	—	—	4	30	40	50	125
70–80	75–80 min.	1	—	—	—	—	—	4	5	30	40
	80–90 min.	1	—	—	—	—	—	4	10	35	50
	90–105 min.	1	—	—	—	—	—	4	20	40	65
	105–120 min.	1	—	—	—	—	4	5	30	45	85
	120–140 min.	1	—	—	—	—	4	10	35	50	100
	140–160 min.	1	—	—	—	—	9	30	40	50	130
80–90	65–70 min.	1	—	—	—	—	—	4	10	30	45
	70–75 min.	1	—	—	—	—	—	4	15	30	50
	75–80 min.	1	—	—	—	—	—	4	20	35	60
	80–90 min.	1	—	—	—	—	—	4	25	40	70
	90–100 min.	1	—	—	—	—	—	4	30	45	80
	100–110 min.	1	—	—	—	—	4	15	35	45	95
	110–120 min.	1	—	—	—	—	4	20	35	50	110
	120–135 min.	1	—	—	—	—	5	25	40	50	125
	135–150 min.	1	—	—	—	4	10	35	40	50	140

Depth in Feet	Duration	Ascent to 1st Stop in Mins.	Stoppages in Minutes at Different Depths								Total Time for Ascent in Mins.
			80 ft.	70 ft.	60 ft.	50 ft.	40 ft.	30 ft.	20 ft.	10 ft.	
90–100	55–60 min.	2	—	—	—	—	—	3	10	30	45
	60–70 min.	2	—	—	—	—	—	3	20	35	60
	70–75 min.	1	—	—	—	—	4	5	20	40	70
	75–80 min.	1	—	—	—	—	4	5	30	40	80
	80–90 min.	1	—	—	—	—	4	15	30	45	95
	90–105 min.	1	—	—	—	—	4	25	35	50	115
	105–120 min.	1	—	—	—	4	10	30	40	50	135
100–110	45–50 min.	2	—	—	—	—	—	3	10	25	40
	50–55 min.	2	—	—	—	—	—	3	15	30	50
	55–60 min.	2	—	—	—	—	—	3	20	35	60
	60–65 min.	2	—	—	—	—	3	5	20	40	70
	65–70 min.	2	—	—	—	—	3	10	20	45	80
	70–75 min.	2	—	—	—	—	3	15	25	45	90
	75–80 min.	2	—	—	—	—	3	20	30	45	100
	80–90 min.	1	—	—	—	4	5	20	40	45	115
	90–100 min.	1	—	—	—	4	10	25	40	50	130
	100–110 min.	1	—	—	—	4	20	30	45	50	150
	110–120 min.	1	—	—	4	5	25	40	45	50	170
110–120	40–45 min.	2	—	—	—	—	—	3	10	25	40
	45–50 min.	2	—	—	—	—	—	3	15	30	50
	50–55 min.	2	—	—	—	—	3	5	20	35	65
	55–60 min.	2	—	—	—	—	3	10	25	40	85
	60–70 min.	2	—	—	—	—	3	20	30	45	100
	70–75 min.	2	—	—	—	3	5	20	35	45	110
	75–80 min.	2	—	—	—	3	10	25	35	45	120
	80–90 min.	2	—	—	—	3	15	30	40	50	140
	90–100 min.	1	—	—	4	5	20	35	45	50	160
	100–110 min.	1	—	—	4	15	25	40	45	50	180
	110–120 min.	1	—	—	4	20	35	40	45	50	195
120–130	35–40 min.	2	—	—	—	—	—	3	10	25	40
	40–45 min.	2	—	—	—	—	3	5	15	30	55
	45–50 min.	2	—	—	—	—	3	5	20	35	65
	50–55 min.	2	—	—	—	—	3	10	25	40	80
	55–60 min.	2	—	—	—	—	3	15	30	45	95
	60–70 min.	2	—	—	—	3	10	20	30	50	115
	70–75 min.	2	—	—	—	3	15	25	40	50	135
	75–80 min.	2	—	—	—	3	20	30	45	50	150
	80–90 min.	2	—	—	3	5	25	40	45	50	170
	90–100 min.	2	—	3	5	15	30	40	45	50	190
	100–110 min.	2	—	3	10	25	30	45	45	50	210
	110–120 min.	2	—	3	15	30	40	45	45	50	230

Appendix I

TABLE TWO—*Continued*

Depth in Feet	Duration	Ascent to 1st Stop in Mins.	Stoppages in Minutes at Different Depths								Total Time for Ascent in Mins.
			80 ft.	70 ft.	60 ft.	50 ft.	40 ft.	30 ft.	20 ft.	10 ft.	
130–140	30–35 min.	2	—	—	—	—	—	3	10	25	40
	35–40 min.	2	—	—	—	—	3	5	15	30	55
	40–45 min.	2	—	—	—	—	3	10	15	35	65
	45–50 min.	2	—	—	—	—	3	15	20	40	80
	50–55 min.	2	—	—	—	3	5	15	25	45	95
	55–60 min.	2	—	—	—	3	5	20	35	45	110
	60–65 min.	2	—	—	—	3	10	25	40	45	125
	65–70 min.	2	—	—	—	3	15	30	40	50	140
	70–75 min.	2	—	—	3	5	20	30	45	50	155
	75–80 min.	2	—	—	3	10	20	35	45	50	165
	80–85 min.	2	—	—	3	15	25	40	45	50	180
	85–95 min.	2	—	3	5	20	35	40	45	50	200
	95–105 min.	2	—	3	15	25	35	45	45	50	220
	105–115 min.	2	—	3	20	35	40	45	45	50	240
140–150	25–30 min.	2	—	—	—	—	—	3	10	25	40
	30–35 min.	2	—	—	—	—	3	5	10	30	50
	35–40 min.	2	—	—	—	—	3	10	15	35	65
	40–45 min.	2	—	—	—	—	3	15	20	40	80
	45–50 min.	2	—	—	—	3	5	15	25	45	95
	50–55 min.	2	—	—	—	3	10	20	30	50	115
	55–60 min.	2	—	—	—	3	15	25	35	50	130
	60–65 min.	2	—	—	3	5	15	30	40	50	145
	65–70 min.	2	—	—	3	10	20	30	45	50	160
	70–75 min.	2	—	—	3	15	25	35	45	50	175
	75–80 min.	2	—	3	5	20	30	40	45	50	195
	80–85 min.	2	—	3	10	25	35	40	45	50	210
	85–90 min.	2	—	3	15	30	40	45	45	50	230
150–160	25–30 min.	2	—	—	—	—	3	5	10	25	45
	30–35 min.	2	—	—	—	—	3	10	15	30	60
	35–40 min.	2	—	—	—	—	3	10	20	40	75
	40–45 min.	2	—	—	—	3	5	15	25	45	95
	45–50 min.	2	—	—	—	3	10	20	30	45	110
	50–55 min.	2	—	—	—	3	15	25	40	45	130
	55–60 min.	2	—	—	3	5	20	25	40	50	145
	60–65 min.	2	—	—	3	10	20	35	45	50	165
	65–70 min.	2	—	—	3	15	25	40	45	50	180
	70–75 min.	2	—	3	5	20	30	40	45	50	195
	75–80 min.	2	—	3	10	25	35	40	45	50	210
	80–85 min.	2	—	3	15	30	40	45	45	50	230

Depth in Feet	Duration	Ascent to 1st Stop in Mins.	Stoppages in Minutes at Different Depths								Total Time for Ascent in Mins.
			80 ft.	70 ft.	60 ft.	50 ft.	40 ft.	30 ft.	20 ft.	10 ft.	
160–170	20–25 min.	3	—	—	—	—	—	2	10	25	40
	25–30 min.	3	—	—	—	—	2	5	15	30	55
	30–35 min.	3	—	—	—	—	2	10	20	35	70
	35–40 min.	2	—	—	—	3	5	15	25	35	85
	40–45 min.	2	—	—	—	3	10	20	30	40	105
	45–50 min.	2	—	—	3	5	10	25	35	45	125
	50–55 min.	2	—	—	3	5	15	30	40	50	145
	55–60 min.	2	—	—	3	10	20	35	45	50	165
	60–65 min.	2	—	3	5	15	25	35	45	50	180
	65–70 min.	2	—	3	10	15	30	40	45	50	195
	70–75 min.	2	—	3	15	20	35	45	45	50	215
	75–80 min.	2	3	5	20	25	40	45	45	50	235
170–180	20–25 min.	3	—	—	—	—	2	5	10	25	45
	25–30 min.	3	—	—	—	—	2	10	15	35	65
	30–35 min.	3	—	—	—	2	5	15	20	40	85
	35–40 min.	3	—	—	—	2	10	20	25	45	105
	40–45 min.	2	—	—	3	5	10	25	35	45	125
	45–50 min.	2	—	—	3	5	15	30	40	50	145
	50–55 min.	2	—	—	3	10	20	35	45	50	165
	55–60 min.	2	—	3	5	15	25	40	45	50	185
	60–65 min.	2	—	3	10	20	30	40	45	50	200
	65–70 min.	2	—	3	15	25	35	45	45	50	220
	70–75 min.	2	3	5	20	30	40	45	45	50	240
180–190	20–25 min.	3	—	—	—	—	2	5	15	25	50
	25–30 min.	3	—	—	—	2	5	10	20	35	75
	30–35 min.	3	—	—	—	2	5	15	30	45	100
	35–40 min.	3	—	—	2	5	10	20	35	45	120
	40–45 min.	3	—	—	2	5	15	25	40	50	140
	45–50 min.	3	—	—	2	10	20	30	45	50	160
	50–55 min.	2	—	3	5	15	25	35	45	50	180
	55–60 min.	2	—	3	10	20	30	40	45	50	200
	60–65 min.	2	3	5	10	25	35	45	45	50	220
	65–70 min.	2	3	10	15	30	40	45	45	50	240
190–200	15–20 min.	3	—	—	—	—	2	5	10	20	40
	20–25 min.	3	—	—	—	—	2	10	15	30	60
	25–30 min.	3	—	—	—	2	5	15	20	40	85
	30–35 min.	3	—	—	—	2	10	20	30	45	110
	35–40 min.	3	—	—	2	5	15	25	40	45	135
	40–45 min.	3	—	—	2	10	20	30	45	50	160
	45–50 min.	3	—	2	5	15	25	35	45	50	180
	50–55 min.	3	—	2	10	20	30	40	45	50	200
	55–60 min.	2	3	5	10	25	35	45	45	50	220
	60–65 min.	2	3	10	15	30	40	45	45	50	240

Descend 25 ft./min.   Ascend 1 min. between stops

		'Bends'—Pain Only		Serious Symptoms	
		Pain relieved at depths *less* than 66 ft.	Pain relieved at depths *greater* than 66 ft. If pain does not improve within 30 mins. at 165 ft. the case is probably not bends.	1. Spinal 'bends'—weakness or numbness of limbs. 2. 'Staggers'—staggering, vomiting, dizziness, vertigo, nystagmus. 3. 'Chokes'—pain in chest with shortness of breath, cyanosis, collapse, unconsciousness.	
				Symptoms *relieved* within 30 min. at 165 ft.	Symptoms not *relieved* within 30 min. at 165 ft.
Stops		*Table 1*	*Table 2*	*Table 3*	*Table 4*
Lb./in.^{2}	Ft.	Time in minutes unless otherwise indicated			
73·4	165		30 (Air)	30 (Air)	30–120 (Air)
62·3	140		12 (Air)	12 (Air)	30 (Air)
53·4	120		12 (Air)	12 (Air)	30 (Air)
44·5	100	30 (Air)	12 (Air)	12 (Air)	30 (Air)
35·6	80	12 (Air)	12 (Air)	12 (Air)	30 (Air)
26·7	60	30 (Air)	30 (Air)	30 (Air)	6 hrs. (Air)
22·3	50	30 (Air)	30 (Air)	30 (Air)	6 hrs. (Air)
17·8	40	30 (Air)	30 (Air)	30 (Air)	6 hrs. (Air)
13·4	30	60 (Air)	2 hrs. (Air)	12 hrs. (Air)	First 11 hrs. (Air). Then 1 hr. (O$_2$ or Air)
8·9	20	60 (Air)	2 hrs. (Air)	2 hrs. (Air)	First 1 hr. (Air). Then 1 hr. (O$_2$ or Air)
4·5	10	2 hrs. (O$_2$ or Air)	2 hrs. (O$_2$ or Air)	2 hrs. (O$_2$ or Air)	First 1 hr. (Air). Then 1 hr. (O$_2$ or Air)
Surface		1 minute (O$_2$ or Air)	1 minute (O$_2$ or Air)	1 minute (O$_2$ or Air)	1 minute (O$_2$ or Air)

By Dr. A. S. Jarrett

Medical Selection of Divers

When a doctor is asked to examine a man for fitness to dive he should consider first of all whether he is fit for physical work. The slowness of movements underwater makes diving look relaxed and languid, but those slow movements are slow because of the resistance water provides to movement. Although work against gravity is reduced underwater the muscular work demanded is high, both because of the frictional resistance already mentioned and the stability brought about by buoyancy which makes movement which is simple on land inefficient underwater. The doctor should take the essential medical history and carry out his usual full clinical examination. Ancillary investigations, such as electro-cardiography, are no more, or less, indicated for a diver than, for example, a docker.

'Physical work' is vague, but it is difficult to think of a satisfactory alternative definition. The decision must be that of the doctor concerned and will depend upon his experience. Rules for age, weight, blood pressure, and exercise tolerance are based on the average man and while carefully weighing up all these factors the doctor should not use arbitrary figures blindly. An abnormality in any system which endangers the candidate if called on to undertake hard physical work must eliminate the candidate in the doctor's opinion. In the following paragraphs it is assumed that no such abnormality has been found, so certain systems can be examined more closely for their ability to function safely in the special conditions underwater.

Ear, Nose and Throat

The pressure of water increases roughly one half a pound per square inch for each foot in depth. Since the product of pressure and volume remains constant for a gas at constant temperature, gas in the body will contract and to prevent cavities such as air sinuses and middle ear collapsing during descent more air must pass into them. As far as sinuses are concerned this will happen automatically *provided that the ostia have not been blocked by infection*, so that the doctor must check that the nasal mucosa is healthy. But even the healthiest middle ear cavity will not equalize its pressure automatically and requires conscious effort to open the Eustachian tubes. This can be done variously by protruding the jaw, swallowing, or both, but the most efficient method, and the only one effective in really rapid descents, is to blow against closed nostrils. It is important to blow down the *nose* and not into the mouth, for it is into the back of the former that the Eustachians open, and bulging cheeks merely indicate misapplied and wasted effort. In every aspiring diver the doctor must confirm auroscopically that both drums move freely during these Valsalva manœuvres correctly performed. The drum will not move if there is a perforation present, which is usually a bar to diving. Not because of any difficulty in clearing the ears, for this is automatic, but because the immediate access to the middle ear makes water-borne infection a constant probability. It should be pointed out to anyone with a perforation who is very anxious to dive that plastic repair is often a very simple operation, and more surgeons in Great Britain are now ready to undertake it.

Chronic otitis externa is usually considerably worsened if the candidate is to be exposed to the constant wetting involved by diving with equipment that does not keep his head dry. Attempts at cure are not always successful unless the patient can be persuaded to stop the local scratching which frequently accompanies the condition. Hay fever also debars from diving unless it can be completely controlled by drugs. As attacks are always intermittent sufferers may be able to demonstrate adequate ear clearing when examined, but during an attack are most likely to find this impossible. Repeated jamming of the ears under these conditions can not only be very painful but can lead to secondary infection. A doctor should always discourage anyone from diving when suffering from a cold. The attempt to force air past inflamed or oedematous mucosa merely aggravates its condition and a few days' suspension should be imposed.

Lungs

When ascending from depth a diver's lungs are full of high pressure air which must expand and escape as the surface is approached. If this is prevented a positive pressure passively dilating the lungs may cause alveolar rupture at a differential of only 58 mm. Hg. Very much higher pressures are produced in coughing and straining but here there is little danger of alveolar rupture because compression of the chest wall protects the fragile alveolar membrane from stretching and tearing. *Any condition which could interfere with the free ventilation of any part of a lung is unacceptable in a diver.* A poorly ventilating bulla, or local emphysema, could provide just such a danger spot; unfortunately they are very difficult to detect before the damage is done. Clinical examination cannot be expected to reveal them unless they are unusually large. If radiological aid is available it is insufficient to take only posterior and anterior views as these do not demonstrate abnormalities lying posterior to the heart. As small local areas of emphysema can arise after acute respiratory infections it would be desirable to repeat X-rays throughout a diver's career. It is difficult to say how frequent these should be; twice each year is an arbitrary figure often stated as expedient.

If a man's history and examination indicate a normal capacity for physical work, then no weight should be attached to the vital capacity of his lungs; it bears no relation to diving ability, though the ability to dive deeply on a held breath is determined by the ratio of total lung capacity to residual volume. Vital capacity nearly always increases as a diver becomes more proficient.

Mental State

Every diver must be a volunteer; this is the most effective screen of all. Even this is not fully reliable, for it is impossible for anyone to predict exactly how they will feel in a strange environment which they have not yet experienced. Only when the temperamentally unsuited have started to dive or have been diving for some time can they be reliably discovered. Some selection tests have been devised, based on retrospective surveys, but without success. These selection tests cannot be adequately tested unless all candidates, failures and successes, be allowed to dive. The highly nervous man is unlikely to want to dive, but should he want to do so the doctor will try to dissuade him, as he would if he wanted to undertake any activity which might endanger himself or others.

At some stage or other every candidate must learn not to dive if he feels unhappy at the prospect. In no other field can pride or courage lead so easily to disaster, and it would be right for the doctor to make sure that this was understood at the initial examination. It may save face to dive rather than risk ridicule but the risk may then become a mortal one.

Overweight

Weight is an important consideration for a diver simply because he must be physically fit. The doctor will not be concerned by the vexed question of weight and bend susceptibility because the subject's fitness or otherwise to dive will have been already determined by this other simpler criterion.

Age

There is no limiting age for diving provided the candidate is fit and the diving required lies within his competence. It should be made quite clear to the candidate over 50, however, that because of his age greater allowance must be made for these effects which are dependent upon respiratory or circulatory efficiency, such as treatment for decompression. Thus decompression routines should be increased by a factor of two as a general rule.

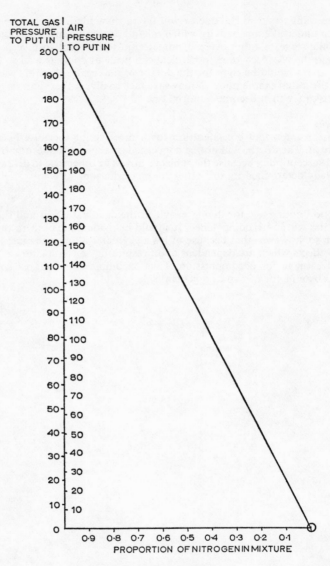

Air/Oxygen Mixture diagram

Air/oxygen Mixture Diagram

This diagram is an aid to finding, or checking, the correct air pressure to add to cylinders when making up a mixture.

If the cylinders are empty then the pressure already there is one atmosphere.

The diagram assumes that the previous mixture is the same as the one to be made up if any more gas than the one atmosphere is held in them.

If this is not so then either the cylinders must be drained off, or the expression:

$1.265 \ (P_F M_{N2} - P_C M_{N1}) = A$, must be worked out, where:

P_F = Final cylinder pressure.
P_C = Pressure already in the cylinders before any gas is added.
M_{N1} = Proportion of nitrogen in the mixture already in the cylinders.
M_{N2} = Proportion of nitrogen in the final mixture.

To use the diagram look down the *left-hand vertical scale* to the total pressure that has to be added to that already in the cylinders to bring them up to the desired working pressure.

Line up a ruler between this value and 0, which is ringed, on the right-hand side of the horizontal scale.

Follow along the ruler until it crosses the vertical line coming up from the proportion of nitrogen in the final mixture shown on the bottom scale.

Follow the horizontal line at this crossed position to where it cuts the right-hand vertical scale and read off the pressure of air to be added to the cylinders on this *right-hand scale*.

The remaining pressure up to the final cylinder pressure is then made up with oxygen.

Index